CW00351457

IN YOUR RIGHT MIND

In Your Right Mind

Everyday Psychological Problems and Psychiatric
Conditions Explored and Explained

Dr Thomas Stuttaford
in association with Dr Tonmoy Sharma

faber and faber

First published in 1999
by Faber and Faber Limited
3 Queen Square London WC1N 3AU

Photoset by RefineCatch Ltd., Bungay, Suffolk
Printed in England by Clays Ltd, St Ives PLC

Thomas Stuttaford is hereby identified as author
of this work in accordance with Section 77
of the Copyright, Designs and Patents Act 1988

A CIP record for this book
is available from the British Library

ISBN 0–571–19416–8

2 4 6 8 10 9 7 5 3 1

Contents

Acknowledgements   vii
Introduction   ix

1   Depression   1
2   Anxiety Disorders and Phobias   52
3   Personality Disorders   82
4   Schizophrenia   126
5   Alzheimer's Disease   180
6   Eating Disorders   202
7   Somatoform Disorders   220
8   Orgasmic Disorders   234
9   Paraphilia   248
10   Drugs   271
11   Children's Disorders   284
12   Suicide   307

Select Bibliography   325
Glossary   327
Glossary of Drugs   336
Resources   340
Index   348

Acknowledgements

Thanks are due to the many hundreds of patients who, knowingly or unknowingly, have contributed to this book. It is a medical truism that doctors learn as much from their patients as patients learn from them, and in no medical disciplines does this apply more than psychiatry and general practice.

Particular thanks to Dr Tonmoy Sharma, my associate in writing *In Your Right Mind*, who remained as good humoured and entertaining as he was knowledgeable. The book would not have been possible without his contribution, and his power of veto.

Over the years my mentors, especially Dr Arthur Spencer-Paterson, Dr Kingsley Jones and a host of other doctors, have given unstintingly of their time as they educated me in the mysteries of psychiatry. I am also grateful to Jenny Beddington of the British Association of Psychotherapists, who has tempered my pharmacological approach to psychiatric problems.

Faber and Faber have been wonderfully tolerant, and special thanks are due to my editor, Belinda Matthews, who was ever-encouraging, and to my copy editor Dominique Enright.

I am very grateful to my research assistant, Camilla Ballinger, whose thoroughness and hard work were a necessary balance to my own rather more optimistic approach. Her literary knowledge was invaluable.

Finally, apologies and thanks to my family, whose domestic life, even meals, has been disturbed by endless discussion of psychiatric subjects ranging from anxiety to zoophilia.

Introduction

Few families are without members who have not at some point suffered from some form of psychiatric illness. In the past this was often kept as a dark secret, but today mental disease no longer has to be hidden, for patients have every likelihood of receiving effective treatment, and many will make a full recovery.

Late in the 1950s the one person in twenty who had moderate or severe depression, and the one in a hundred with schizophrenia, were suddenly offered hope. New forms of treatment had just become available. Revolutionary antidepressant drugs and antipsychotic medication restored many patients' personalities to the extent that they could return to normal life, in many cases resuming their previous jobs. The face of psychiatry had been changed for ever. And it continues to change, as medication becomes increasingly refined, precise – and gentle.

The number of cases of psychiatric disease hasn't fallen since the 1950s, but the mental hospitals are now empty, and many of those who could only have expected a lifetime of incarceration can now hope to live a comparatively normal life, provided that they are offered – and accept – the skilled treatment available. The misfortune is that in this new age of psychiatry the enthusiasm of some psychiatrists, supported by an alliance of well-meaning social reformers and asset-realizing politicians keen to sell the prime sites on which hospitals had been built, led to the closure of an excessive number of hospitals. The medical services, encouraged by a cost-cutting Treasury, therefore co-operated in the emptying of the mental institutions. This originated from an overestimate of the resources and capacity of community care workers to look after the minority of seriously disturbed – and very unhappy – patients who might have thrived if offered suitable asylum.

The study of psychiatry was at its most exciting in the late 1950s. I discovered this when I spent six months working in an acute psychiatric unit, attached to a general hospital, under the late Dr Arthur Spencer-Paterson. At this time, the mental hospitals were bulging with swarms of patients suffering from severe depression and various schizophrenia-type illnesses, for whom there was little hope of effective treatment. So hopeless was the outlook that families blotted out their relatives' very existence once they had gone through the hospital gates. They were visited infrequently, if at all, and not talked about – the very mention of them was a reminder of a family susceptibility. Illnesses for which there is no cure have always been the subject of taboo: in my youth even TB wasn't discussed.

My mentor Dr Spencer-Paterson had graduated in classics at Oxford before reading medicine at Edinburgh. He was by nature an academic and possessed of an immense intellect. He was one of the pioneers of the psychiatric revolution. He had become fascinated by physical treatment of psychiatric disease, whether by the newly discovered innovative drugs or by the dreaded, but sometimes miraculously effective, electro-convulsive therapy (ECT); however, neither did he scorn non-organic treatments, and he was equally interested in hypnosis and abreaction – the process by which patients relived an earlier disagreeable experience which could have affected their whole lives.

Dr Spencer-Paterson was also a natural historian, but his interest was the study of human behaviour, rather than that of birds and animals. He was therefore intrigued by the influence of a patient's parentage, early background and subsequent life on his or her present condition. He always wrote down the more personal details of a patient's life in French so that the ward notes would not be the subject of idle gossip: descriptions of patients' fears, hopes, delusions, and sometimes bizarre love-lives, stretched the schoolboy French of junior doctors to its limit.

Although born into a general practice, I had, so far as I remember, the same prejudices about psychiatric disease as had both the general public and the medical profession. Psychiatrists were seen either as hard-pressed doctors who looked after the physical needs of the tens of thousands of patients locked up in mental hospitals, or as mysterious Viennese-trained doctors who reached perplexing conclusions after their patients had spent hours upon the couch. For me, watching the effect of the new drugs on patients who had been disturbed, unhappy and unable to enjoy normal relationships, opened up a whole new vista. The diseases which strike the mind, I realized, are not so very different from those that afflict the body: many have an organic cause and accordingly respond to physical treatment. And of course physical and mental diseases are intrinsically connected because of the unity of mind and body.

Armed with a basic knowledge of psychiatry gained from Dr Spencer-Paterson, and excitedly clutching cardboard cartons filled with newly minted antidepressant and antipsychotic tablets, I joined my family's practice in Norfolk. The practice was untilled psychiatric territory, with cases undisturbed by searching questions, or by any pharmacological intervention other than the then acceptable prescription by my predecessor of bromides, paraldehyde, barbiturates or amphetamines. These drugs, the staple psychiatric remedies during the first third of the twentieth century, were generally unsatisfactory. Bromides and paraldehyde were unpleasant to take or administer, and frequently ineffective. Barbiturates and amphetamines did have an effect on the psyche, but they were also potentially addictive; larger and larger doses were needed to achieve the same effect. Little wonder that drug therapy for mental disease acquired a bad reputation, a reputation based on obsolete preparations and one which, although now long unjustified, is still current.

The behaviour of disturbed patients, at the time probably more common in isolated Norfolk villages than in some other parts of the country, had a free rein. The doctor's drugs were, people thought, useless, and in any case the patients so feared addiction that, even if drugs were offered, they would have been refused. The depressed people sat around in their cottages withdrawn from their families and village life, no longer working, eating adequately or sleeping, until eventually they either shot themselves, jumped into the river or spontaneously recovered.

A typical case was that of Mrs Adamson, an elderly woman suffering unexplained and distressing gynaecological symptoms. She had not left her house for twenty-eight years and was adamant that she would not visit a consultant, or be examined. Soon after I started work in Norfolk I was asked to call upon her. It soon became obvious as I chatted to her that she was severely depressed, and had been for years. We struck a bargain. Mrs Adamson would swallow the new magic pills and if after three weeks she felt happier she would agree to be taken to Norwich by the hospital car service.

Within a comparatively short time after starting on the medication, the hopelessness which had weighed her down seemed to be lifting. Then, one day, well before the end of the three-week trial period, I went to see her at her house, but found it empty. Had Mrs Adamson, like some other depressed patients, found that having started to get better she now had enough energy to commit suicide? The recovery phase is always a time when doctors and family must be alert to the danger of self-harm. With some trepidation I went next door to see if the neighbour knew what had happened – and there was Mrs Adamson, who had crossed the threshold of her house for the first time in a generation, sitting and drinking tea, at the kitchen table. She had become a different person, comparatively cheerful and outgoing, and as interested in her grandchildren as any other woman of her age. She had even begun to look forward to her next meal and, despite her physical problems, was putting on weight; and for the first time in all these years she was sleeping through the night.

Mrs Adamson was as good as her word, and not only eventually agreed to go into hospital for the necessary surgery, but made a complete physical recovery from cancer of the womb. The story of her recovery spread throughout the practice and I was soon being asked to see sons who only crept out at night, daughters who spent their days chatting to the Almighty, husbands who were preoccupied with keeping the Russians or Chinese at bay, and hordes of people who were overwhelmed by depression. The district now realized that mental disease was not just an affliction which has to be borne.

Mrs Adamson's recovery also demonstrated that when mental illness strikes it is not only the patient who suffers – its consequences reverberate among family and friends, and they too can benefit from the most up-to-date treatment.

Mr Adamson, a hardworking farmworker, red-faced and snowy-haired, found that his life had suddenly been transformed. He was able to go out and about without suffering terrible anxieties about his wife left alone at home. He could visit friends and members of his family and was again able to take part in village affairs. At home, life was not only less uneasy, but considerably more comfortable, as Mrs Adamson was able to keep the house clean and bright, rather than lying in bed or sitting listlessly by the fire.

I felt rather ashamed that my reputation for treating mental disease had become absurdly exaggerated, for it was all based on no more than the prescription of a few standard drugs such as Tofranil, the first of the tricyclic antidepressants readily available to general practitioners. I was fortunate to have started in general practice at a time when the pharmaceutical revolution at last enabled doctors to alter the course of mental disease and often even restore someone's personality to what it had been before it was overwhelmed by misery and hopelessness. Mrs Adamson had suffered from the classic symptoms which together constitute the syndrome of clinical depression, but so amazing was her recovery in the eyes of the community, that the local parson told me that some of the local people even thought I had mystical powers. In fact, Mrs Adamson's recovery was not quite as complete as that of many other patients – she was one of the 14 per cent or so of depressed patients who now, as then, need to take regular treatment to keep their depression at bay, as the underlying biochemical cause of their troubles is still present. Many of those patients who do not make a full recovery and need to continue taking medication also benefit from psychotherapy in its various forms, or they may gain from complementary medicine, which, like psychotherapy, aims to treat the underlying causes of mental illness. (As the name implies, complementary medicine can work very effectively with a traditional therapeutic approach.)

The concept of psychiatric disease still conjures up in many people's minds images of deranged, crazed patients, shrieking in Bedlam. In fact, mental disease is far more likely to take the form of depression in a kindly, tea-brewing Mrs Adamson than manifest itself as the dangerous ravings of some wild axe-man on the London Underground. Whether the patient is waving an axe or pouring tea, however, help is in theory available to restore them to their rightful place in their families, or local communities. What is more, today the great majority are treated at home, while those who do have to stay in hospital are cared for with a degree of kindliness which would surprise those who worked in the psychiatric services forty years ago. However, there is the ever-present tragedy of patients suffering from schizophrenia and allied diseases who are neither welcome in their own home communities, nor yet in hospital, and are therefore abandoned to live as well as they can on the streets, or in mean hostels.

" SORRY MATE - THERE'S A WAITING LIST FOR BOXES"

It is an irony that general practitioners are encouraged to take an ever-increasing part in the treatment of patients with surgical, medical and gynaecological problems, and in the full range of the minor specialities such as dermatology – but not in psychiatry, where their greater familiarity with their patients' lives and their training in the vagaries of family life and human behaviour would be so useful. Psychiatry is treated as a discipline apart. It is not surprising, if the care of mental and that of physical illness are so completely separated in this way by doctors, that the general public should continue to regard mental disease as a taboo subject.

If even medical leaders regard psychiatric disease as a mysterious and crippling affliction which is better not talked about, can they blame the public for following them? This taboo even extends to the press. Although it is considered constructive, even praiseworthy, to write about lung cancer or cervical screening, and acceptable to discuss, for instance, Linda McCartney's breast cancer, writing about mental problems, however physical their origins, can be considered of questionable taste. (All credit, then, to John Bayley and Nancy Reagan in helping to break this taboo in the cases of the novelist Iris Murdoch, wife of John Bayley, and of former President Ronald Reagan.) The problem is made more complex by the lack of general comprehension of the terminology of psychiatry. While the aim must be for psychiatric disease to be as clearly understood as physical disease, it is yet to be achieved.

Patients with psychiatric problems have for generations disappeared into an unknown world, one, until recently, hidden behind dour walls and thick shrubberies. Furthermore, the complexity of the symptoms in psychiatric disease has resulted in a language which is little understood in the bar of the George and Dragon and is not even always clear to those sitting in a university common room, or in a discussion between doctors. Psychiatrists themselves are all too well aware of the problem. In *Troublesome Disguises*, a series of papers written by sixteen eminent psychiatrists and edited by Dr Dinesh Bhugra and Dr Alistair Munro, the introduction comments upon 'the enormous variety of interpretations of mental illness and its causative factors' and quotes the well-known psychiatrist Professor Antony Clare, who notes that 'this bewildering array often leads the clinician and layman in completely different directions. This can lead to acrimonious debate as to whether psychiatric diagnosis has any inherent legitimacy.'

There has been no better, or worse, example of the variety of interpretations of abnormal behaviour – and its treatment – which can occur than the case of Michael Stone, who was found guilty of murdering a mother and daughter, together with their dog, and grievously injuring a second daughter (he, however, lodged an appeal against the verdict, on the grounds of unsafe evidence). The motive appeared to be trivial robbery and the crime was committed by a man with a long history of violent acts. He had previously been imprisoned and, before this crime, had pleaded to be admitted to a mental hospital. The psychiatrists agreed that he was suffering from an antisocial personality disorder – in the old terminology, that he was a psychopath. As, in many doctors' opinion, no amount of treatment would help, his was seen as a case for the police, the courts and the prisons. The general public, thinking of psychiatric hospitals as places of safety rather than necessarily of therapy, tend to believe that any system which allowed Michael Stone to stay loose must be fatally flawed.

Perhaps this book will help layman and clinician to speak the same language. The purpose of *In Your Right Mind* is partly to demystify psychiatry: to open up its highways and byways to the general public, so that when they read case histories in the newspapers, or are told that their nearest and dearest is depressed, but not suffering from 'clinical depression as the result of an affective disorder', they may not be completely baffled. The book deals – in, it is hoped, straightforward language – with common psychiatric conditions such as depression, schizophrenia and anxiety states; it describes the eating disorders, anorexia and bulimia, and such personality disorders as narcissism or antisocial and borderline personality disorders. While the whole of psychiatry cannot by any means be covered in this book, and neither can all the complexities of psychiatry's terminology, it will serve as an introduction, and it is intended to improve the likelihood of early diagnosis, at the same time giving some reassurance to patients and their families. Once people know about a subject it becomes less alarming; the Princess of Wales's frank discussion about her own personality, for instance, has proved a considerable support to many who suffer as she did. This book is intended therefore to make information about psychiatric conditions accessible and thus make it easier to discuss such matters with family and doctors.

Another objective of *In Your Right Mind* is to introduce modern psychiatry to the general public, and I hope it may dispel the fear of the medication used in the treatment of psychiatric disease, now so much more effective than fifty years ago, and so very much less unpleasant to take than were drugs used even ten years ago. Stage by stage, molecule by molecule, the medications used in the treatment of psychiatric disease improve. They are more potent, more efficacious and have fewer side-effects. Just as in the 1950s the introduction of Tofranil (imipramine) and Tryptizol (amitriptyline) revolutionized the treatment of depression in many of its forms, so in the 1990s the advent of atypical neuroleptics, such as Risperdal (risperidone) or Zyprexa (olanzapine), is set to transform the treatment of schizophrenia and its allied conditions. But in each instance government enthusiasm has been extinguished by worries about immediate cost.

Finally, if this book succeeds in persuading people to talk as openly about their depressed minds, or their anorexia, as they might exchange accounts of irritable bowel syndrome or thrush, life might become happier for patients and easier for doctors. This is likely to remain a utopian dream, but it is now becoming possible to talk about being severely depressed, although unacceptable to mention suicide (albeit the two go together), to admit to being hypomanic (wildly exuberant), although not manic (irresponsibly exuberant). People may be rather proud of their eccentricities but shun discussion of any symptoms which could label them as having schizophrenia. The difference is in the question of reason. As humans we value an intact personality, together with our reason, which not only distinguishes human beings from the rest of the animal kingdom, but for those who are religious, is a divine gift giving us kinship with God. Thank God we now have pills which in many cases will restore a disordered reason. How disastrous it is that anxiety over the NHS bills prevents their optimum use in keeping people in their right mind.

1

Depression

To a depressed person life is hopeless. Overwhelmed by feelings of misery and despair, with no way out, and with no relief, as all the pleasures of life have lost their savour, the person longs to retreat from the treadmill of daily existence. The depressed individual's mood is a sustained one – there may be variations in it during the course of the day and there may even be good days, but the overall pattern is one of irremediable pessimism.

There are between five and six million people in Great Britain who suffer from severe, disabling depression. At any one moment one person in twenty in the country is actually being treated, or should be being treated, for a depressive illness. Statistically, this means that most of us meet a depressed person every day of our lives.

These five to six million people should take some comfort from knowing that there is nothing new in their condition. Depression has been recognized for two thousand years, since it was described by the Greek physician Aretaeus. The difference now is that the majority of cases of depression can be diagnosed and treated. In Britain, in the seventeenth and eighteenth centuries, depression was known as melancholia, and while it was frequently diagnosed, it was, however, not always distinguished from other forms of what was considered insanity. Robert Burton's book, *The Anatomy of Melancholy*, first published in 1621, for instance, despite its title, was a general treatise on mental illness.

By the late nineteenth century the concept of a melancholic temperament had become firmly established, and with it even the acceptance of the 'melancholic facies', the facial expression – or lack of expression – which can so often be seen in those who are

1

perpetually miserable. Treatment was rudimentary, but as depression is nearly always associated with some degree of anxiety, it was possible to make some inroads into the sufferers' overall condition. While nothing was known which would alleviate the melancholic mood, various devices – suggestions as to daily routine and diet, together with long hot baths, for instance, and drugs, including herbal ones such as valerian, and laudanum – were used to calm the patient's anxieties.

A hundred years ago a German doctor, Emil Kraepelin, named the illness first described by Aretaeus, and Kraepelin's description, 'the manic-depressive psychosis', proposed in 1899, held. Kraepelin, whose classification of mental diseases is the basis of today's, divided his depressed patients into different groups. While his Austrian contemporary, Sigmund Freud, looked at mental disease from a psychological viewpoint, Kraepelin believed that mental illness had its roots in the physiology of the brain, and was therefore a disease like any physical illness.

In the early part of this century the psychoanalytical approach to treatment, developed by Sigmund Freud, held sway. This attempted to explain the patient's present condition by analysing their past and their subconscious, but Freud himself always insisted that psychoanalysis was only suitable for those people who were not seriously disturbed. He did not treat patients who suffered from any psychotic symptoms, including schizophrenia. He recognized the increasing complexity of modern life and its influence on the psyche, emphasizing the importance of the First World War as an example of this. The First World War also accustomed people to the effect of stress on the mind, and made some forms of mental illness respectable if their onset could be attributable to war service. Society allowed any soldier who had survived the trenches to suffer from what was then called 'shell shock'.

In the 1930s, particularly in Britain, the psychoanalytical movement found itself under attack from competing disciplines. Unfortunately, some of the psychiatric treatments that followed, such as lobotomy and insulin coma (the induction of unconsciousness by giving an unnecessary dose of insulin), which were initially prescribed by those who saw psychiatry in terms of physical disease within the brain, were certainly no more successful than psychoanalysis had been, and rather more destructive. Electro-convulsive therapy (ECT), used in the treatment of depressed patients, is one 'advance' from this period which still has a limited use today.

In the 1950s the psychoanalyst's couch, lobotomy and insulin coma were largely replaced by the pharmacist's medicines. By chance, it had been found that at least two drugs affected the patient's mood. Patients with tuberculosis who were treated with the drug iproniazid became happier in themselves, even before they lost their infecting tubercle. Conversely, those patients whose blood pressure was being treated with reserpine some-times became seriously depressed. These changes in mood could have had nothing to do with nursery traumas thirty or sixty years earlier, yet such symptoms of depression were often the very symptoms which psychiatrists and psychoanalysts had spent fifty years probing and debating. Psychiatry had successfully moved into the realms of science. It confirmed that some patients' abnormal moods, and psychiatric diseases such as depression and schizophrenia, had a physical, biological, origin – for they had responded to physical treatment.

The scope of psychiatry now extends beyond the treatment of specific mental diseases ranging from Alzheimer's to such rare conditions as Wernicke's encephalopathy. Psychiatrists also look after patients with a wide range of personality problems, some of which may have stemmed from these mental diseases. However, although the pharmacological approach to mental conditions has revolutionized the treatment of many of them and thereby society, most psychiatrists believe there is still room for psychotherapy. Doctors are becoming increasingly interested in the role of cognitive therapy, a form of psychotherapy which helps people to understand their problems and their own worth, thereby transforming their approach to the everyday difficulties which are threatening to overwhelm them. Research has shown that cognitive therapy is, like antidepressive medication, effective by itself and can produce a long remission, but if only one of these two treatments is to be used, medication is likely to be slightly more effective. However, if the two are combined the power of the whole is greater than the sum of the parts.

Ironically, many of the five million people or so suffering from depression in the United Kingdom are unaware that they are ill. They continue to suffer, if not in silence, without the support and help which is available. Patients will often say that they are 'fed-up', that they feel sad or miserable, or they just remark, deprecatingly, that they are 'down in the dumps'. They know that they are not on top form, they may admit to feeling sad, but they don't realize that over 60 per cent of the people like them, who are in fact depressed, are suffering from an eminently treatable disease. The majority will need the doctor's pills rather than bracing advice to pull themselves together.

Despondency and, more seriously, feelings of hopelessness are arguably the most significant symptoms of depression and they are as much part of the depressive syndrome as high blood sugar is indicative of diabetes. Furthermore, in both cases, the fundamental cause is an alteration in the body's biochemistry. The central nervous system, including the brain, relies upon neurotransmitters; these are chemicals which are essential parts

" THAT BOOK HAS REALLY CHEERED YOU UP"

of the mechanism by which a message is transmitted from one nerve cell – neurone – to another. Each neurone has a thousand contacts with other neurones and so, not surprisingly, any fault in the transmitters can wreak considerable havoc. Depression is associated with changes in the levels of two important neuro-transmitters: serotonin, and noradrenaline.

Medical treatment restores the normal level of the neuro-transmitters and with this the patient's former sense of content-ment and even joie de vivre. These biochemical abnormalities in the brain can no more be altered by 'snapping out of it', 'pulling yourself together' or 'jumping up and grinning and bearing it' than a diabetic person can alter their blood sugar by not thinking about insulin and food. Likewise, just as diabetes can be triggered by lifestyle and life events, so may depression be influenced by circumstances and, furthermore, just as there is a genetic predis-position to diabetes, so there is to many of the depressive ill-nesses. The misfortune is that while there is no stigma attached to having one set of biochemical disorders – the physical ones, like diabetes, for instance – if someone suffers from psychiatric symp-toms as a result of a biochemical disorder they may be socially ostracized. As a fault in the patient's biochemistry is becoming accepted by the vast majority of doctors as the immediate cause of many types of depression, it is becoming apparent that more patients will need long-term medication than was previously believed.

It is the imprecise use of the term 'depression' which causes much misunderstanding amongst patients and may possibly even confuse some doctors. Depression has to be distinguished from feelings of being 'fed-up' or 'rather unhappy'. When patients say to doctors, 'I am suffering from depression', or 'I think my wife is depressed', they frequently use the term as if it were the beginning and end of the diagnosis. In fact, all that they are doing is describing a symptom which may occur in a multi-tude of diseases. To a doctor, the term 'depression' sums up a number of symptoms which may be caused by many different psychological or physical conditions, even though lay people almost universally think of these symptoms collectively as depression.

Although the patients might not know the term, many of them are suffering from an 'affective disorder', a disorder of the mood. Mania and depression are the hallmarks of an affective disorder, the abnormalities in the mind which cause either deep gloom or irresponsible gaiety. An affective disorder is simply a prolonged disturbance of someone's mood, so that the patient is either absurdly over-elated (manic or hypomanic), or unreasonably cast down and depressed; as a result they are withdrawn, apathetic and plagued by feelings of hopelessness (depressed). This type of moderate to severe depression is popularly described as 'clinical depression' – commonly abbreviated by patients, the broadcasting media and most doctors simply to 'depression'. There is an anomaly here, as doctors tend to use the term 'clinical depression' in a much more restrictive way, which can be confusing for the general public.

Describing such an intense response as depression as a 'disorder of mood' sounds as if the problems of depressed people are being belittled, for nobody is likely to be pleased if they hear themselves being described as 'moody'. This description conjures up the image of a tiresome, self-absorbed person, who grumbles their way through life and is so upset by the minor changes and chances of life that others are infected by their dissatisfaction.

Doctors, however, are taught to think of depression as an abnormality in the patient's mood. The term 'mood' to them is far more than a description of the state of mind of, for instance, Sid Perks when the bar takings of The Bull at Ambridge are disappointing. We all continually have a mood, just as there is always weather. Mood varies. Most people have a standard mood, their equilibrium, which is normal for themselves, but this may become elevated or depressed. Everybody experiences mood swings, especially as a person's mood is easily influenced by external events, and even when we sometimes think that there is no apparent cause in a change in our mood, we might later remember that we slept badly the night before, had received an upsetting letter from the bank manager, or had been subconsciously troubled by something at work.

The lesser changes in mood are also classified as affective disorders, whether they are cyclothymia (a mood which swings from happiness to sadness more readily than usual), hypomania, a milder form of mania, or dysthymia (prolonged deep sadness). Some people suffer from mood swings which are greater than average, but not ones that are so disproportionate or long-lasting that they cause serious inconvenience. Even if their mood swings are more pronounced than most, they are no more than the variations which are found in many people, who are described as cyclothymic. However, the cyclothymic, volatile, character may when pushed too far become either over-jolly (hypomanic or manic) or depressed. Hypomania is a lesser state of over-exuberance than mania, for by the time a patient can be said to be suffering from mania there is usually a problem everywhere he or she goes.

Sometimes, people are particularly unhappy for a spell; the cause may be obvious, and there may be every reason why they should be feeling sad. They are just that – sad and miserable, but not clinically depressed. The severe sadness in these cases is described as dysthymia and refers to a perfectly explicable emotion. The dysthymic episode is usually thought of as a reaction to events which have rendered a person downcast without making them clinically depressed.

Affective disorder, however, is only one of a myriad of psychiatric problems which has depression as one of its features. Thus patients who have 'depression' are depressed, but not all patients who are depressed are suffering from 'depression' as the term is widely used in the newspapers, on television and in daily conversation.

The symptoms of depression may be part of the picture of many different conditions, including schizophrenia. In so far as schizophrenia is concerned, in 75 per cent of patients who have it, or have had it, depression is or was one of its important

symptoms. Indeed, some measure of this depressed state frequently persists after they have lost other symptoms of the
disease. Such physical diseases as hypothyroidism (too little
thyroid), or Addison's disease (steroid deficiency from failure of
the adrenal glands) may cause depression. Both are treatable. It
may also be an early sign of cancer, or other psychiatric disease,
including Parkinson's disease, or certain personality disorders,
where a person may find friendships difficult, and love and
approval hard to come by. Without these, they may cease to like
themselves, and become depressed.

Nonetheless, many people who have depression as a symptom
of these conditions are not suffering from an affective disorder,
which is a distinct syndrome. They may be suffering from a psychiatric condition, and be depressed, but not all have what is
popularly referred to as clinical depression – a clearly definable
disorder of mood.

On one occasion I totally failed to persuade Esther Rantzen's
television studio audience that not every person who is depressed
is suffering from 'clinical depression', because depression can be
a symptom of so many different diseases. Depression may indeed
be part of the picture of chronic fatigue syndrome. As well as
personality disorders, toxic psychoses (such as alcoholism or
drug addiction), physical causes (e.g. cerebral tumours), central
nervous system diseases like Parkinson's, Alzheimer's, or other
dementias, multiple sclerosis, vasculitis, disorders of the endocrine system, and a host of other conditions all give rise to depression, as mentioned earlier.

Would that all depressed patients were suffering from clinical
depression – for although when untreated this form of depression
can create enormous misery, the patient's future, when the condition is properly dealt with, is much brighter than when there is
some other cause, whether physical or mental. Thus the many
depressed patients who had thought that to be told they were
depressed was the beginning and end of the diagnosis are rather
cross when the doctor says, 'Ah, yes, you *are* depressed, but we
have to find out why.' These patients would have assumed that

all they needed was, according to their beliefs, the latest anti-depressant, or the smartest psychotherapist. Thereafter, recovery would be guaranteed. This is not the case. Not only can these patients be cross, they also become confused, if they are, as they see it, depressed, and yet are told that they are not suffering from clinical depression. It may be suggested instead that they are merely very sad, or have a personality problem, or may be experiencing symptoms from some other psychiatric disease, such as schizophrenia or some physical complaint.

The depressed state is therefore not a distinct disease in its own right, and depression is not a diagnosis in itself, but may be induced by a whole collection of physical diseases, psychological problems, personality disorders, or psychiatric diseases. Depression is no more a complete diagnosis than are the terms 'sore throat', 'headache' or 'lumbago': they are descriptions of symptoms and, to be useful, the underlying cause of the symptom has to be determined. The doctor will have to sort out the cause – a patient's depression may be the result of an affective disorder, or it may be symptomatic of some other diagnosis.

In the past a patient with backache was happy to be told that he had lumbago – not a diagnosis but merely a Latinized term for backache, a problem which the patient knew he or she had already. Now they will want further tests so as to know why they have backache, and will not be fobbed off with some bowdlerized Latin. As medicine and the general public become more sophisticated, patients will soon demand that a more precise diagnosis is reached after suitable tests, in psychiatric as well as general, medicine. The result could, for instance, show that they have thyroid disease, a tumour (not always in the brain), or indeed an affective disorder (mania, hypomania or clinical depression). In summary, symptoms of 'feeling depressed' may be induced by many different psychological or physical conditions.

There are various predisposing factors in the development of mood disorders. Some jobs are naturally gloom-inducing ones: not everybody would find it very cheering to work at an undertaker's or in the post-mortem room, although examples of very happy people in both are not uncommon. Illness, too, may have an effect – struggling with some chronic ailment or with a severe infection is not conducive to an easy life, and certain physical disorders are themselves particularly likely to be associated with depression.

Sometimes depression may be the first symptom of a malignant growth, or the return of one which it had been hoped had been banished. Multiple sclerosis is frequently accompanied by severe depression, as is Parkinson's disease. Cancer is not the only terminal illness which can induce feelings of unworthiness and regret for past perceived misdeeds. Dying is for many reasons associated with depression, and this association needs specific treatment. It may be difficult for doctors so used to death to remember that a patient who has lived with relative security within their body now finds that their physical decline has become a source of anxiety, fear, even terror. Impending death, one's own or that of a family member or friend, is often a great source of dread.

A family history of depression is in many cases also a pre-disposing factor. Although depression and mania, like other psychiatric disorders, run in families, their pattern of inheritance is very ill-defined. It is likely that no single gene is solely respon-sible, and more probable that many genes contribute to the way in which a personality is passed on from one generation to another. It is also likely that the foundations of a character are laid down genetically, but what is built on these foundations is profoundly influenced by the way in which a child is brought up. This may be seen in animals too: in those domestic animals, for instance, where the environment is uniform, clearly defined personality traits are nevertheless evident and obviously inherited. But, how-ever carefully bred, an animal can have its temperament des-troyed if it is treated roughly, or insensitively, by those looking after it.

Conversely, in humans natural selection tends to hold sway – mates are not chosen by some provident cattle breeder but for much more complex reasons, and physical beauty may eclipse worries about temperament. Unfortunately, in humans the appearance of any undesirable aspect of temperament in generation after generation is also fostered because the mother or father of the difficult child may be a poor parent as he or she has perforce the same genes as the unfortunate child. These genes not only make them difficult people, but of course the flaws in their character may create an unsuitable environment for their genetically difficult child to develop in. Nature and nurture conspire together, so that, as the Bible tells us, to those who have shall be given, and from those who have not shall be taken away.

The idea that the genetic inheritance of personality plays a part in the development of psychological disorders is unpalatable to many people but clearly demonstrable genetic links can be shown by twin and adoption studies. The upbringing provided to a child may, however, have the power to modify the pattern of psychiatric disease just as it may influence the emerging temperament. External factors, too, can have a profound effect – a particularly damaging blow, possibly with long-term consequences, would be the loss, from whatever cause, of a mother in a person's early childhood.

As in every branch of medicine, discussion of psychiatry is laced with technical terms; in this respect doctors make frequent reference to the *DSM*. The *Diagnostic and Statistical Manual of Mental Disorders* is a guide to the diagnosis of psychological and psychiatric problems, and a classification of their symptoms, regularly updated by the American Psychiatric Press in a series of editions. The fourth, *DSM-IV*, is the latest one. It has enabled an international uniformity of diagnosis to be established. It is hoped, for instance, that with the help of the *DSM* the Danish patient hearing voices will be given the same diagnosis whether at home in Copenhagen, or on holiday in Capetown. The *DSM* is as important to a doctor as Notcutts gardening catalogue, the *RHS Plant Finder*, or a Hillier's guide, would be for a gardener. The *DSM*, for instance, stipulates that before a mood syndrome (affective disorder), whether it is mania or depression or a combination of the two, may be diagnosed, the symptoms should be present for a minimum period of two weeks.

Ted Smith's story illustrates two other terms constantly used when talking about disorders of mood. Ted has a bipolar affective disorder. Sometimes he is manic, sometimes he is depressed, and every now and again, to the relief of his colleagues, family and friends, the pendulum of Ted's mood is stabilized in the middle. It is helpful to understand the terms 'bipolar' and 'unipolar'. The bipolar group of patients with affective disorders have, like Ted, both depressive and manic-depressive episodes. The unipolar group contains those who are simply depressed. To confuse the general public further, psychiatrists tend, illogically, to refer to patients who are only manic as having a bipolar disorder. The bipolar group therefore contains those who are at varying times either manic or depressed and also those who are just manic, but never those who are just depressed. Whereas depressive illnesses are diagnosed at least four times more commonly in women, bipolar affective disorder involves both sexes equally. This may be the effect of lifestyle or, some think, a consequence of hormones.

Ted Smith was usually the over-exuberant life and soul of the party. He was always noisily active, always joking, managing with little sleep, but even so a ball of fire when he was in the office the following day – a life-enhancing leader. His condition on these occasions could have been described as hypomanic, but his slightly unnatural elation and bouncing enthusiasm could become a trial to those around him. As his is a bipolar affective disorder, Ted is at other times cast down for weeks at a time. Some little time ago he came to see me at the suggestion of one of his colleagues as it was thought that on this occasion his miserable mood had gone beyond an acceptable level.

Even as Ted came into my consulting room, I was shocked to see that his collar was loose and his jacket hung limply on his huge frame. He was no longer beaming from ear to ear and he told me that he found it hard to keep tears at bay. He told me that he had lost something over a stone in weight, for he now had no enthusiasm for food and had to force himself to eat. As well as his appetite for food, Ted had also lost his appetite for sex. He had the classic depressive sleeping pattern – off to sleep the moment his head hit the pillow, awake in the early hours, only to drop off again when it was time to get up. The next morning he would feel unrested and be in the depths of despair until later in the day when he would feel slightly more cheerful.

Everything an unsmiling Ted did seemed pointless and hopeless to him; there was no enjoyment in life, and previous pleasures had become a both bore and an effort. Ted was treated with an antidepressant and given every opportunity to talk over his problems.

Although he always had a greater mood swing than most people, his excessive depression had been induced by an unhappy love affair. With treatment he was back at work within three weeks, returned to playing the accordion, and was back on the party circuit. Because Ted's problem was such a classic case of a depressive phase in someone with bipolar affective disorder, it was easy to diagnose and easy to treat.

Ted had almost a full house of standard depressive symptoms, the type of symptoms noticed by a doctor in a busy surgery. As mentioned above, he had the depressive sleep pattern known as 'early morning waking'; he had lost normal appetites and weight; he had diurnal variation – that is to say he became progressively more cheerful as the day went on. He had feelings of hopelessness, guilt, loss of self-esteem and a sense of personal failure. He felt that everyone was talking about him – they probably were, but even so, his anxiety was exaggerated and there could have been some paranoid element to his worry. What he didn't complain of, but his senior colleague from his firm had told me, was that he looked miserable and his once very sharp brain was now much slower. His anxiety showed itself in the firm as irritability and agitation so that he no longer seemed to be as fired with the enthusiasm for making money his boss expected of him. In fact he was suffering from psychomotor retardation, a term which means no more than a lack of structure to a patient's usual thought processes so that they no longer proceed in an orderly manner from A to B to C and so on to a reasonable conclusion. On the contrary, they go round and round in circles and jump from one miserable thought to the next, a disordered process which naturally disrupts their ability to perform ordinary daily tasks. As one patient said to me, 'Forward planning turns the mind into a torture chamber.'

Ted was also a bit of a hypochondriac. When he was depressed his great bulk made him fear that he had early-onset heart disease. His breathlessness when climbing the stairs was bound to be a symptom of serious lung disease, his indigestion was, in his opinion, the sure symptom of inadequate coronary arteries. It is interesting that the hypochondriacal symptoms which depressed patients complain of are usually remarkably similar. When these are only vague troubles, for instance tiredness, weakness and headaches, the problem of excluding serious disease is usually easily solved. But when they are more specific, such as Ted's indigestion and chest pain, it is difficult to avoid ordering detailed investigations.

Devastating feelings of hopelessness and failure permeate depressed people's whole beings. In general, their lives seem quite worthless, and they believe that their future has been undermined by a character riddled with inadequacy and even vice. Their consequent guilt adds to their misery, while they marvel at their own worthlessness. Little wonder that for many depressed patients everything seems so pointless and without hope that they have constantly to fend off the desire to commit suicide and leave the field of battle which has been their life.

Life for the despondent seems to be one long regret, regret for the past, present regret that the momentum of life has gone, and with it the human relationships which were part of it, so that socially the sufferer becomes marginalized and progressively alienated. There is further regret, combined with fear, that the future, however it may improve, will always be marked, and impaired, by some earlier failure, real or imagined, whether dating from the time when depression was at its nadir or from its onset.

Given this wretched scenario, it would be surprising if the depressed person's thoughts were not permeated by feelings of self-doubt, lack of self-esteem and even self-loathing. If this radical change in mood and loss of self-respect is not enough, patients who are depressed also develop further anxieties, as described, about their own health, or the opinions of others of their general ineptitude – one of the misfortunes of the world is that depressed patients do become rather inefficient. Whether anxious or depressed, the patient is so weighed down by their feelings of dejection and rejection that they are unable to believe that the future can offer any hope of a better life.

With the problems of life, and the blows it can inflict, it is surprising that depression is not even more common than it is. Fortunately, for most people life's onslaughts are not continuous and there is respite and happiness in between. However, in peace as in war, the bravest can be worn down eventually. Sir Winston Churchill's famous doctor, Lord Moran, himself a First World War veteran, coined the aphorism that courage is finite. Even so the individual resistance to the horrors which life throws at people varies enormously, although in general the reserves of most are far greater than is usually supposed, and never fail to surprise me as a doctor. The reaction of an army, or a nation, during war is a good example of this resilience. When someone endures solitary suffering, without the support of a group, these reserves are taxed to a greater extent but even then, as the history of the post-war hostage phenomenon has shown, the response is individualistic, determined probably by a combination of genetic inheritance and early upbringing. We should all be grateful to our grandparents, or regretful about them.

Having established the nature of the affective disorders, their unipolar or bipolar character and the symptoms of depression, it is helpful to be able to classify the degree of depression. Through an accepted system of classification, baselines may be agreed, and any change in condition noted by the doctor or, if the doctor hasn't seen the patient previously, brought to their attention, and thereafter the patient's progress is monitored.

Complex criteria have been established over the years but many doctors now adopt an uncomplicated approach to the classification of depression, once it has been diagnosed. They rank it as either mild, moderate or severe (profound), in accordance with the recommendations of the *DSM*.

There are many sophisticated ways in which someone's depression can be assessed, but in general those patients who have mild depression are able to keep working. Mild depression is characterized by sadness, gloominess, unhappiness and dejection – which are the normal reactions to the let-downs in life together with the emotions they induce, such as disappointment, frustration and despair. This degree of depression is classified in a different way by some other doctors. It can also be called 'normal depression' and, as the term implies, doctors do not consider the symptoms abnormal, although they recognize that the patient is depressed and may even need medication or other treatment.

In moderate depression work becomes impossible for the patient. There is a limit to the tolerance displayed by the most paternalistic of firms and many depressed patients exceed this limit. Having to concentrate on what to a depressed person may have become irksome and futile work accentuates his or her dejected mood. Likewise, at home, the moderately depressed patient becomes isolated from family activities, takes little interest in the household performance and becomes unusually irritable if provoked out of the refuge of their gloomy reverie.

In severe or profound depression, there is no question of the sufferer working, or being a reasonable spouse and parent. The only question to be settled is whether it is safe to treat the patient at home or whether the risk of suicide is too great to warrant this. There are advantages to treating the severely depressed but non-suicidal patient in their own surroundings – it not only avoids any possible, inappropriate but lingering stigma with neighbours, friends and family, but also eliminates the need for the person to become deinstitutionalized as they recover. Moreover, being removed from familiar, and therefore 'safe' surroundings could have a deleterious effect. In Norfolk, in the late 1950s, my family practice was one of the first general practices to treat severely depressed patients in their own homes, even those who were so severely depressed that they expressed suicidal intentions. This was possible because of the careful selection and the outreach services provided by the local psychiatrist Dr Kingsley Jones, who took endless trouble with his patients. It proved a very successful policy and was unmarred by any disasters. Nevertheless, there are cases where separation from family has to be part of the treatment. In today's urban world with everyone out at work during the day and worn-out by the evening, the home might not be the ideal environment for someone who is deeply depressed.

The degrees of depression which cause the greatest anxiety are those which can be classified as major depressive disorders. In these cases there may be a causal factor, but it is often not very obvious and is out of accord with the precipitating event. The degree of major depression can also vary, but may be so profound that the patient is frequently a suicide risk. In other cases they may become deluded and their depression is therefore so severe that their condition could be described as psychotic. Psychotic symptoms are those which are characteristic of a severe mental disorder, usually manifested by a gross impairment of perception of reality, contrary to the evidence as it appears to others. In particular, the patient may suffer delusions, hallucinations, and thought disorders.

It is not only patients with schizophrenia or its related conditions, or those with a toxic psychosis who have psychotic symptoms. Both depressed or manic patients may also exhibit them. As depression is better treated, fewer patients reach the stage where they become psychotic but these symptoms may still be encountered in people who are severely depressed or very manic, and in consequence they will suffer marked impairment of their personal and social lives.

In people who are depressed, rather than schizophrenic, the delusions, hallucinations and other psychotic symptoms are 'mood congruent' – the doctor's way of saying that their disturbed thought bears a direct relationship to the degree of depression from which the patient is suffering, and that the nature of the delusions and hallucinations have been coloured by the patient's mood. Extreme guilt is also characteristic of the psychotically depressed patient, whereas it may well be absent when the symptoms are related to schizophrenia.

The *DSM* lists a further, special, category of depression, which they label 'grief' (uncomplicated bereavement). Grief is the appropriate response to the loss of something that had been treasured, and is not confined to bereavement following a death but also bereavement caused by such losses as that of status, income, possessions (possibly from a fire or theft), and the end of a close relationship, particularly with a spouse or partner. Grief is a perfectly appropriate way to react and in time it subsides. It should not leave someone with a serious mental disorder and goes through well-described and well-marked phases. The first stage of grief is numbness, a difficulty in coming to terms with the loss and a refusal to accept it. Numbness gives way to anger, followed by depression and, all being well, recovery. The reaction to the loss usually comes on within hours or days, but may be delayed for some months.

Grief can become a serious problem if the grieving process becomes arrested at any stage. Some people's grief is fixed in the numbness stage and they are unable to admit that a loved one is dead; this is frequently seen after sudden death. Rudyard Kipling, for instance, was for many years unable to accept, despite all the evidence, that his son had been killed in action. More frequently, grief doesn't progress beyond the aggressive stage when the grieving person blames him- or herself or others for the death. A quick perusal of the papers shows that almost every day there are examples where a parent or spouse has failed to come to terms with a death and still seeks a scapegoat for what may well have been an inevitable outcome. For instance, families may seek to blame, without always good reason, police, doctors or social services, following a death. Doctors are in particular constantly blamed, usually unfairly, for a late diagnosis.

The most common time for the grief process to become stuck is during the depressive phase. Fortunately these are the symptoms which are easiest to alleviate. These patients are treated like any other depressed person and make an excellent recovery. Their loss is not forgotten, but they are no longer so grief-stricken that they cannot cope with everyday life.

Other terms used in the discussion of depression need explanation. The description 'atypical depression' is still frequently used although it is not defined in *DSM-IV*. It is used of those people who might once have been described in lay terms as being 'very neurotic'. Some doctors in the past, driven by a desire to be polite to their patients, would refer to their condition as a 'neurotic depression', a description which today would cause even greater offence. These patients tend to be cast down by transient and apparently trivial troubles which would leave their contemporaries unmoved, and suffer from varying degrees of depression, usually out of proportion to the problems facing them. The depression is described as atypical because it is not associated with the typical classic depressive symptoms such as early-morning waking, loss of appetite, feelings of hopelessness and diurnal variation (a mood which lightens as the day progresses). Those who suffer from it are loaded with anxiety, often have phobias and panic attacks, tend to sleep too much rather than too little, are tired and dispirited by evening, and eat to excess. It is not a reassuring diagnosis as patients with atypical depression often find that their symptoms are persistent and do not respond well to pharmacological treatment. Treatment is with cognitive therapy and – as medication is worth a try, though the results are very variable – with 5HT-reuptake inhibitors, a group of recently introduced antidepressant drugs.

Regular listeners to radio programmes will recognize atypical depression in many of the contributors to the interviews with people who suffer from irremediable and persistent depressive diseases which have defeated the best psychiatric brains of our teaching hospitals and Harley Street. It is unfortunate that these sufferers are given so much air time as it detracts from the enormous advances which have been made in treating the more classic forms of depression, whatever their cause. Patients would be encouraged to approach their doctors for treatment if producers found time to interview people who had been near-suicidal but six weeks later were back at their work, after appropriate medical help.

Two classifications of depression now rejected by some psychiatrists but useful concepts in general practice are those described as 'endogenous' and 'exogenous' depression. In my medical youth great play was made of the differences between these two categories of depression, whereas now it is the severity of the depression which is considered of paramount importance. In endogenous depression, it was considered that the precipitating cause, if one was present at all, was out of all proportion to the patient's mood. Endogenous means 'from within': the reason for the depression was entirely or almost entirely the result of the person's disordered psyche. Conversely, in exogenous depression, the cause is from without – the patient has reacted excessively to some external trigger.

Patients with endogenous depression have a very clearly defined group of symptoms, which could start at any age, sometimes not until later adult life, after many years in which they had always seemed to have had a good, well-rounded personality. Among the symptoms they suffer from, early-morning waking is particularly characteristic. Not only does the patient find it hard to get to sleep again after they have woken but they find that it is difficult to feel active during the early mornings. More significantly, they experience self-dislike, even loathing, shame and self-blame. Patients with a depressed mood remember with terrible clarity all the criticisms levelled at them, rightly or wrongly, over the years and accept them so completely that they not only believe them but build on them. These patients, the classic depressives, usually do exceptionally well with antidepressant drugs.

It is a mistake to think that there are not precipitating, trigger factors in patients with endogenous non-reactive depression,

notwithstanding the strong evidence there usually is of a genetically inherited depressive strain in the family. Even in cases
where the symptoms are characteristic of those found in patients
with typical endogenous depression there is often some external
factor which has caused it. Unless this is uncovered, and if possible rectified, drugs, however they improve the situation, may
not restore the patient's equanimity. These stressful factors may
be any of the major life events, the four terrible 'D's – death, debt,
divorce or disease – and those problems associated with these
conditions. The wrong spouse, or the wrong career, can cause
lasting tensions and the acceptance of adversity, like courage, is
finite. Everybody has a breaking point. In other cases, it can
be some comparatively minor incident which has prevented
someone from regaining their former joie de vivre.

Attempts have been made to define endogenous depression,
and a list of characteristics has been drawn up which can be
checked against a patient's symptoms when compared to other
forms of depression. They show:

A less marked family history of depression
Less likelihood of a family history of alcoholism
A lesser likelihood of a family history of antisocial personality
   disorder
Older age time of onset of symptoms
Symptoms are likely to be more severe than in exogenous
   depression
Less frequent suicidal gestures
Less likely to have suffered divorce or marital separation than
   an exogenous sufferer
Fewer major incidents of death, divorce or debt etc.
Fewer personality disorders
Better social support
Less intellectual loss and failure to concentrate
A higher frequency of physical disease
Better response to physical treatment
Poorer response to psychotherapy

In contrast to those with endogenous depression, there are the 'reactive' or 'exogenous' depressives, in whom, as with the atypical depressives, even the minor trials of ordinary life can induce a disproportionately depressed response. Unlike the atypical depressives, however, the reactive depressives have many of the classical symptoms of depression, albeit not so well-defined. Patients with a reactive depression may not always respond to drug therapy, although the comparatively new 5HT-reuptake inhibitors are proving to be more effective than the earlier tricyclic antidepressants.

Mania – the reverse of depression – can be even more trying to the patient, and their family, than severe melancholy. Since the sixties, pop and modern culture has given a whole new meaning to the term 'manic' and not one which would be recognized by psychiatrists in out-patients, although the younger members of the staff might understand it. A manic person in clubbers' parlance is someone who is wildly 'out of it' or 'excessive'; others of the same age group may use 'manic' to describe obsessive behaviour – as for instance in the phrase: 'Chris is manic about computers'. To a doctor, a manic patient is someone who is inappropriately over-jolly and over-exuberant. They are often indifferent to other people's sensibilities as they take life at a gallop, spending without thought, drinking with disregard, and sexually abandoned. To an adolescent clubber the patient described by the psychiatrists as manic or hypomanic, would be 'hyper'. This slang term 'hyper' increases the general confusion: the description 'hypo' in medical parlance means 'too little' whereas 'hyper' means 'too much'. Someone who is hypomanic therefore has the milder symptoms of mania – just like Ted in his buoyant moods, for, like him, such a person is suffering from a bipolar affective disorder.

As mentioned earlier, in affective (mood) disorders, the patient's mood may be either elevated, manic or hypomanic, or characterized by varying degrees of depression. Although depression is well recognized, mania not only frequently escapes diagnosis by family and friends, but also by medical advisers.

"SEE - I'VE CALMED DOWN QUITE A BIT"

Hypomania, even mania, evades recognition because it is too easily dismissed as exuberance; in small doses it may even be rather fun. Those people who have to live with a hypomanic person would not use this description – it can make their lives a wild, and not always happy, merry-go-round. Those who spend too much time with someone who is genuinely manic know what hell it can be. The families of many patients who are bipolar have told me how they find their husbands or fathers – less often wives or mothers – much easier to cope with when they are depressed than when they are manic.

Sir William Osler, a Canadian, who became the father of modern British medicine, once said that if a doctor didn't make many of his diagnoses while the patient was walking from the consulting room door to the chair, he would starve. Osler was a great teacher, and like everybody making a point he exaggerated, but in so far as mania is concerned, he may have been right. Manic patients can even be diagnosed before the door is opened. There is a loud, quick-talking voice, the sound of uproarious laughter and a general noise of commotion in the corridor. When

23

the patient finally comes in their greeting is over-boisterous, or sometimes they launch into a stream of invective because of some minor incident en route. His, or less often her, clothes can be remarkable. The subdued pinstripe, the clerical grey – these are not for the manic patient; they are more likely to wear vivid colours with bright, clashing patterns. Their idea of quiet dressing would be loud bookie's-checks. Once conversation starts it becomes obvious that the patient is euphoric (exuberantly ecstatic): they are restless, pacing around, not listening but cutting across everybody else's conversation with rapid talk. They will tell a story of sleepless hyperactive nights, inappropriate sexual adventures, financial extravagance, gargantuan meals and too much to drink. Ideas will flow from them faster than bullets from a machine-gun. And woe betide the doctor if he interrupts – good humour will vanish to be replaced by irritability, even anger.

The fate which befell one large company illustrates some of the aspects of mania. The company was delighted to recruit a very distinguished financier to head its most important division. The normal routine of medical examinations was waived and the great man settled into his new job. Within a few weeks the new recruit had proved quite unreliable; he was overbearing, antagonistic, loquacious, he was never still, his public appearances were chaotic and his interpersonal relationships had broken down. The failure of this former city genius was attributed to his habit of enjoying a drink or two. This was perhaps an unfair assumption as no one could ever recall seeing him drinking excessively, but his behaviour was bizarre and tricky, and his colleagues assumed he was a secret drinker. Eventually he was retired early, at huge expense, on health grounds.

Some months later, I was at a public dinner, and way down the other end of the table, I could hear an obviously manic person dominating conversation, causing a mixture of embarrassment and distaste all around him. I asked my neighbour the name of the noisy guest. He was, it transpired, the same financier who had caused such chaos in his last company. This man was not a drunk; he was suffering from an easily treatable form of mental disease.

If he had had a medical examination before he joined the company he could have been treated; his firm would have saved a great deal of money, and would have still had a useful adviser, and the man himself would not have had the embarrassment of being eased out.

Another public figure suffers from a classic bipolar affective disorder; unusually, the hypomanic rather than the depressed side of his temperament has come more to the fore as he has grown older. As a younger man he would sit for hours at a time, his head in his hands, divorced from the world and too apathetic to carry out his duties. In later life his public appearances can prove equally embarrassing. He is determined to achieve his goals, he does not allow tiredness or other people to interfere with his aim, he is never still, never rests. When talking, his speech is so fast, his patter so all-pervasive, that nobody else can slide a word in edgeways as his ideas race from one subject to the next. His overbearing mood stops him from paying due attention to the feelings of those around him, which are trampled underfoot in his headlong drive for whatever is the enthusiasm of the moment.

This man's love of activity, and pleasure, have inevitably involved him in some fearful scrapes, but none so embarrassing, expensive or scandalous as to blight his career. Hypomania may not always be a disadvantage. Some of our best salesmen, for instance, suffer from hypomania, but, as in the case of the public figure, their over-elation and expansive mood have been harnessed to achieve their success. Irritability, also a dominant feature of this syndrome, is tolerated by others as just part of an acceptable 'eccentricity'. Treatment isn't always as straightforward as the doctor and those around the patient might hope. These patients lack insight into their own condition and often quite enjoy the feeling of hypomania: it is as if the Almighty had already provided them with two or three whiskys. They are reluctant to take treatment until the world starts to fall around them; before this stage is reached, they can point to their social and business success to defend their stand. The paradox is that, not unnaturally, their family would rather have a quieter more amenable person even if he or she wasn't so dynamic and such a good wage earner.

Very often hypomania can become mania and then the love of luxury combined with an irresponsible, expansive nature can lead to disaster. One patient, an immensely charming, but hypomanic twenty-year-old, without the knowledge of his family, bought enough Jermyn Street shirts to last him a lifetime, hired a Rolls-Royce and headed north. He lived in some considerable luxury in a five-star hotel where he ran up an immense bill. This led to his being restored to his family, who, delighted to have found their prodigal son, readily – if not happily – paid the hotel, returned the car, assuaged the wrath of the shirtmakers, and took him to see a psychiatrist who treated him with a long-term course of lithium. He made a good recovery and was later able to pursue a successful career.

Along with the many other symptoms – the feelings of hopelessness, loss of pleasure, loss of self-esteem coupled with extreme guilt, tiredness and lethargy, and difficulty in concentration – the depressed state is usually associated with weight loss and insomnia.

So commonplace is the loss of appetite in depression that it has sometimes erroneously been said that unless it is present and there has been a corresponding weight loss, usually arbitrarily estimated as at least half a stone, the diagnosis cannot be made. However, the converse may be true and a small number of depressed patients eat more even when seriously depressed. Anorexia may be a symptom of depression, or vice-versa, and others may suffer from bulimia. Similar changes can affect someone's alcohol consumption. Many depressed patients drink more in an attempt to lighten their moods, albeit momentarily, whereas others find that their alcohol intake is markedly reduced. Alcohol to them has always been associated with jollity and celebration, and in their present state of mind they do not think that there is anything to be joyful about.

Changes in the sleep pattern are as common as changes in appetite. The standard depressive pattern is to go off to sleep immediately, then waking within a few hours and lying awake for hours before falling asleep again just when it is time to get up and face another day. On the other hand, this so-called early-morning waking is not universal. Some depressed people are also very anxious and may find it hard to get off to sleep initially. Others, particularly patients who are very young or who have atypical depression, sleep for too long. I had one depressed patient, a late-middle-aged farmer's wife, who never got out of bed at all and seemed to sleep most of the time whilst she was in bed. As she began to improve we struck bargains: initially she would get up to have tea with me, later I joined her for coffee after lunch. As she continued to progress we moved ever forwards into the day and a gin and tonic before lunch became mid-morning biscuits, as our meeting time was earlier and earlier. Before treatment this woman had for a couple of years virtually been confined to her bed, only getting up in the evenings to greet her husband.

Other symptoms include psychomotor retardation and psychomotor agitation – two terms much used to describe the psychological changes met in depression but which are not always fully understood. In psychomotor retardation a patient has monotonous, slow speech, gives only monosyllabic replies, cutting words to a minimum, and is unable to think and act in a constructive way. Associated with this are slow movements and an immobile, unsmiling expression. The eyes tend to droop and have a persistent look of world-weariness.

In psychomotor agitation, on the other hand, the patients are restless and jumpy, may walk around the room, pull at their skin, play with their hair or watch strap, fidget with things, and are thoroughly distracting. Both agitated and retarded patients find that their thought processes are slowed down, which, coupled with a loss of memory, makes it difficult for them to pursue a logical argument or constructive sequence of thought. It is a lack of concentration and preoccupation with anxieties which produce memory loss and because the patient is unable to summon up all the facts immediately they appear indecisive and jittery. The same symptoms are seen in cases of early Alzheimer's disease. The lovers of the programme *Dad's Army* will always remember Corporal Jones, 'Jonesy', the old soldier who had lost the power of consecutive thought and was always agitated and constantly repeating 'Don't panic! Don't panic! Don't panic!' when none of his colleagues had any intention of panicking. Whether in Corporal Jones's case this was the result of early Alzheimer's, or of depression, it is, however, hard to say.

Time is in short supply for the average busy doctor, and dealing with psychiatric patients is nothing if not time-consuming. The diagnosis of depression or, for that matter, hypomania or mania, is often missed by a doctor for, although its signs and symptoms are clearly defined and its consequences serious, they may be ambiguous and inadvertently concealed by the patient. Of all patients consulting the doctor, 5 per cent have symptoms which are the result of a major depressive episode, 5 per cent are suffering from minor depression and 10 per cent have symptoms which could be indicative of a depressive illness. Despite this, over half will leave the surgery without these important changes in mood and behaviour being discussed.

Doctors must therefore keep at the back of their mind the possibility that depressed patients may visit them with 101 seemingly unrelated troubles; they should always be on the look-out for the persistent, all-pervasive depression of mood which saps the patient's drive and initiative, cripples them with tiredness and sleeplessness, undermines their ability to concentrate and makes the future seem hopeless. Likewise, the symptoms of hypomania and mania, if asked about, will be revealing, but to an even greater extent so will the signs of it which the patient does not repress even while in the surgery – the loud clothes, the over-ebullient manner. A depressed patient goes to the doctor and seeks help with the expectancy of being saved, they hope their treatment will be a life belt to keep them afloat in a dangerous sea.

A lifeguard may sum up a situation immediately and throw them a life belt, but too often the time constraints of a busy practice lead to depressed patients drowning in the stormy waters around them.

There are, however, many doctors who claim to be able to diagnose patients with depression, just as Sir William Osler would wish, as they come into the surgery. The lack of animation in their expression, the hunched shoulders, unsmiling gaze and flat tone of voice in conversation betray their mood long before they have started to talk about their troubles. Equally, it is possible to detect an improvement in mood as soon as the patient is glimpsed, even before they have volunteered the information – particularly if their voice reveals a new, more animated approach to life.

All doctors are aware of the symptoms which they should be seeking, but lacking the complex medical jargon, how would the patient describe how they feel? They will not say, 'Doctor, I suffer from diurnal variation,' but they may well say that they are fed up, feel depressed every day, especially in the mornings, and think of themselves as leading sad, empty lives. So many of the changes in their attitude to life are only a question of degree. The cheerfulness of a loved one, once so uplifting, now merely grates, the chatter of children, once so delightful, now sounds as unappealing as the din in a school playground. Office politics become unbearable and office jokes banal. An invitation which would have been greeted with pleasure now provokes a premonition of gloom. Even as other people seem less engaging, the longed-for solitude becomes a rebuke: 'Does no one want to be with me?'

It is difficult for a person's family and colleagues to gauge how depressed they are. Many people have the capacity to continue with their jobs, less efficiently perhaps, but, with an effort, they cope. It is more difficult to maintain the appearance of reasonable cheerfulness when at home. There, a patient's ability to be a kindly, loving or understanding wife or husband, mother or father or flatmate is tested to destruction. The patient with mild depression may be irritable, withdrawn, and lack vitality but they can still take the children to their classes and make love to partners, husbands or wives. Some single, mildly depressed, people find living by themselves emotionally easier as when dispirited they don't have to affect an unfelt cheerfulness.

The depressed patient's parents, friends and partners may find that they are not so much fun as they were; or of course, hardly fail to notice that they are easily reduced to tears. However, a busy doctor who has spent a day dealing with crippling arthritis, wheezing children, cancers and elderly patients with heart failure may miss the clues of depression and the gravity of the situation to which they point. Too easy to condemn the symptoms as trivial and self-pitying – but hardly trivial if they contribute to the ten million attempted suicides worldwide every year.

The interest of a doctor quickens if, when they question the patient in such a way that they reveal the full story, the resulting accounts of their emotional troubles, and the physical symptoms associated with them, start to add up. A bell rings. The collection of symptoms the patient is describing may perhaps point to a depressive syndrome, or suggest that they are not only feeling depressed but could also be suffering from a well-defined psychiatric disease, which is more than likely to respond to treatment.

Research has shown that when a depressed patient visits his doctor primarily complaining of physical rather than mental symptoms, the underlying depressive state is more easily missed. It is a myth that medical students receive little education in psychiatry. The formal psychiatric course may be short, but whenever a case history is discussed on a ward round, the general physician, and even – usually – the general surgeon, will assess the patient's psychiatric state and needs. In hospital departments like that of genito-urinary medicine, which has marked psychological components, psychiatry is an integral part of the daily routine. But, even so, in students' education there is a much greater emphasis on physical disease, and, as a result, it is not surprising that when a patient comes with an apparently physical problem an over-worked doctor will seize on it and may not always enquire too deeply about what it may represent in emotional or psychological terms.

As so many patients who are depressed see their doctor about physical symptoms and discount their psychological worries, it is worthwhile analysing them in some detail. Some patients play down any psychological symptoms and instead emphasize ill-defined physical symptoms, such as headaches, sore throat, constipation, diarrhoea, indigestion, weakness and excessive tiredness. At any particular time most people, when they think about it, have pain from some part of their body. The normal person subconsciously blanks out this pain if it is not too severe; they may shift a bit, stretch, but in general they disregard it. Conversely, the anxious, depressed patient takes note of every ache and pain, dwells on them, and attributes sinister causes to them – much as did Ted, described earlier in this chapter. Some depressed patients seek help from their doctor about these pains, rather than for any underlying change in mood.

One variation of hypochondria when it is a depressive symptom is found in those patients who are described as 'smiling depressives'. These people talk dismissively, but still talk, about the aches and pains that are worrying them and wave aside some symptom of a would-be disastrous illness with a nonchalant smile and brave shrug of the shoulders. Smiling depression is one form of 'masked' depression. Although masked depression frequently presents with physical conditions, prompted by fears about heart disease, tuberculosis, cancer and sexually transmitted diseases, its influence on symptoms extends way beyond those of a hypochondriacal nature. These patients also complain of loss of weight and appetite and of sleeplessness, even as they deny that they are depressed. People with masked depression have, like many others, a very simplistic view of their condition and if they are not weepy they dismiss depression as a possible diagnosis.

Many depressed patients find it impossible to believe that their physical symptoms are the result of their state of mind. Those who are accustomed to complementary medicine understand the concept of the indivisibility of mind and body. This indivisibility is nowhere better illustrated than in depressed patients. Their indigestion is worse, their bowels are disorganized, some will suffer constipation, others diarrhoea, and in both wind will become trapped in the four corners of the abdomen, causing anxieties which range from appendicitis to liver failure. Depression can play havoc with periods, can produce sighing respirations, and a thudding heart. As knowledge of depression increases more patients and their families are beginning to accept that weight loss, muscle tiredness, headaches and, above all, sleeplessness are part of the picture.

One successful farmer suffered, like many of his family, from mild but unacknowledged depression, and had been seeing me for many years to discuss his latest, usually serious, self-made diagnosis. 'I know that when I thought I had TB two years ago it transpired that my chest was perfectly normal, but this time it is different, this time I really am ill. I have heart disease.' His symptoms were investigated – for depressed patients are not immune to physical diseases – but nothing was ever found. They always stemmed from being depressed.

Many years after the farmer retired, he really was ill and eventually went to see his own GP. His complaints were dismissed as being caused by tiredness, or, the doctor thought, the result of his psychological problems, as they had been in the past. It was conceded that they might perhaps be related to high blood pressure and he was thereafter treated for this. In fact, this time his symptoms were the consequence of widespread cancer. His case demonstrates the difficulty of treating patients who have somatic symptoms as part of a depressive syndrome. A fine balance has to be struck, for the symptoms have to be taken seriously, but they must also be dealt with in such a way that the investigations don't accidentally reinforce the patient's own anxieties.

Depression occurs in all age groups. It needs to be remembered that some groups do not complain or even show characteristic symptoms. Children can become depressed but their symptoms may be different from those found in adults. Small children are rebellious, tearful, or sometimes abnormally quiet and with-drawn when depressed. Their growth may be affected and their intellectual advance is slowed. Adolescents when depressed become antisocial and defiant. It is often very difficult to dis-tinguish between the natural rebellion of youth and adolescent depression; the difference is often more apparent to a stranger, like a doctor to whom the person will chat openly, than to a parent.

In old age depression is again common, but, confusingly, very elderly patients may also not complain of all the standard symp-toms of depression. Since the elderly are spared the test-bed of the office or factory, depression is more easily overlooked. The man whose work is hopelessly behind schedule because he is depressed will be spotted, but if it just takes a pensioner rather longer to buy his milk and morning paper, no one will notice. Likewise, any increased irritability is too often considered a nor-mal feature of ageing – after all, isn't it the old bull who is the irascible bull? Even so, the elderly represent a very important suicide risk, especially as they may lose any continuing sense of purpose because of what they interpret as the sheer futility of their lives.

As well as the usual symptoms with which depression may present, there is often a disturbed sleep pattern which dominates their thoughts: like all people suffering from depression they suffer from early morning waking par excellence, and they also have difficulty in getting off to sleep: the worst of both nocturnal worlds. Women, in particular, are disturbed by sleeplessness. Elderly patients very frequently suffer from hypochondriasis and when they are not worrying about their physical health, they are often worrying about the health of their bank balance. A fear of poverty is very great and very common. A few years ago, I was asked to dinner by a patient who told me that he wanted my advice about the cheapest way of running his car: should it be diesel or petrol? Would his present car last him out or should he buy a new one now and hope that it was his last one? I felt guilty when he paid the dinner bill – could he afford it? Two years later he died suddenly, leaving nearly three million pounds.

Depression in elderly people may also show as pseudo-dementia. Their face becomes blank, they lose their powers of rational thought, memory goes and conversation is blunted – just the same facial expression and symptoms as a patient with any form of dementia, including Alzheimer's disease, the most common type of senile depression confronting the world. Doctors must be wary of making assumptions, though: the best-known case in which the depression of old age was misdiagnosed as Alzheimer's disease is that of Mr Ernest Saunders of Guinness, described in the chapter on Alzheimer's.

There is a myth that depression in old age cannot be treated: it can be, even if some of the antidepressant drugs are not entirely suitable for the elderly. The older antidepressants may sometimes affect the heart and some of these may also induce unsteadiness, dizziness and problems with constipation and passing water, side-effects that are especially troublesome in the elderly. The emergence of the new generation of antidepressants, especially the 5HT-reuptake inhibitors like Prozac, has, however, removed many of these disadvantages and makes treatment easier.

Younger women suffering from depression also need special consideration. They are more likely to be depressed than men of the same age, even if not so many young women as young men commit suicide. This is possibly because women are much more dependent on their home surroundings, where they may spend so much of their day. Even if they are working outside their homes, they have a sense of responsibility to them which men do not always have to the same extent. Young mothers may suffer from a superfluity of children – more than three around the house is a risk factor for depressive disease. An unsympathetic husband, who may be physically or emotionally distant even if never violent or abusive, doesn't help a woman overcome any incipient depression, and may be an obvious possible cause of psychiatric problems.

Research from Scotland reported in the *British Medical Journal* in 1998 showed that although women are still more likely than men to suffer from significant depression, there has been a shift in the balance between the sexes: men are catching up. This has been attributed to problems at work rather than in the home, as more women are taking positions of command in industry and commerce. Male pride and supremacy has been challenged, and this, together with the increasing insecurity in the labour market, is disturbing to the male ego. The once dominant male may not only lose promotion to a woman, but may even lose his job to her.

One interesting feature reported in the *BMJ* review was that while women when depressed often seek the company of other women, who are supportive, men tend to keep their troubles to themselves, and their colleagues or friends are alienated by their gloomy approach to life and by their reticence. Interpreting the withdrawn behaviour of the depressed person as an insult rather than as a symptom of trouble, those around him (less often, her) make no effort to bridge the gap and are even dismissive, if not reproachful, thus compounding the problem.

In the case of some women, extremes of mood might be hormone-dependent and they may be either unusually depressed or even manic for a while, though obviously much more frequently the former. In a standard textbook, *Gynaecology*, edited by Professor Robert Shaw, Mr Patrick Soutter and Professor Stuart Stanton, over ninety signs and symptoms have been shown to be related to the premenstrual syndrome. Depression is one of the most common and, with it, its associated symptoms of irritability, loss of confidence, aggression and tearfulness. There is also an association between suicide and PMS. PMS is discussed in greater detail in the chapter on personality disorders – its official designation, not mine!

While pregnancy is not without its psychiatric problems, the more classic forms of depression are seen after delivery. Two-thirds of all women have a transient emotional upset three or four days after they have had their baby. Third-day blues, or 'baby blues', are traditionally associated with alterations of mood, accompanied by tears, doubts, irritability and depression. This mood usually passes without treatment, other than the offer of an understanding shoulder to cry on. Its causes are unknown but are thought to be either hormonal, or arising from anxieties about her capabilities as a mother, or deriving from a sense of anticlimax after the excitement of the delivery and the pleasure of being the centre of attention.

Depressive disorders after delivery are much more common than psychoses. They usually start about a fortnight after the baby has arrived and the degree of depression may be mild or moderate. Depression is particularly likely to occur in women who have had psychiatric problems previously or who have had an unsatisfactory early life, particularly if their family has been uncaring in their adolescence. Women who are only children and have lacked the experience gained from having younger siblings, have an increased rate of psychiatric disease in pregnancy. A distant or aggressive husband or the absence of a close friend at the crucial time could also be trigger factors. Even an uncommunicative doctor, or an unsympathetic, tough midwife met during an antenatal visit, may cause psychological problems later. Social isolation from whatever cause can be risky. Finally, one of the most important factors predisposing to psychiatric breakdown after delivery is the nature of the delivery. If the labour was long, or if it was complicated by possibly life-threatening events, trouble is more likely.

It may be very difficult for family and friends to understand why a woman who has just had a baby is depressed. Many are deeply envious of her: they may be childless themselves or their children may have grown up and they look back with fondness on the time when they had young children. Depressive states after childbirth are an illness like any other and not a subject for reproof. One of the underlying causes of unhappiness after childbirth in women having their first baby is that they may subconsciously have thought that their newborn baby would look like the one from an advertisement for nappies or tinned milk – instead they discover to their horror, which they are reluctant to express, that a newborn baby is an extra-uterine embryo which demands food, cleaning, care and only rewards the mother by crying. The apparent vulnerability of this floppy-headed creature is perhaps unnerving, and the feeling of helplessness of a mother unable to stop a wailing baby that refuses to feed, together with the constant work required of her and the lack of freedom and of sleep, can all come as a terrible shock.

Psychotic breakdown, although rarer, is also a danger. It usually starts about ten days after delivery but can be earlier or very much later. One in five hundred women are affected and the psychosis may or may not be associated with severe depression. Any schizophrenic symptoms may also appear for the first time and a woman may become suspicious, paranoid; her thoughts become bizarre and irrational, frequently including delusional ideas about her child or husband. In any subsequent pregnancy the woman has about a 20 per cent chance of the trouble recurring. The symptoms respond to atypical antipsychotic medication.

As with severe depression after delivery, a psychotic break-down is more likely to occur if the patient has a history of psychiatric disease, or if close family members have been similarly affected. The same factors which predispose to depression may also induce a psychotic breakdown. When there is a cause for concern, the doctors and nursing staff will watch carefully for sleeplessness and any bizarre remarks or behaviour.

Suicide is a risk when a newly delivered mother becomes severely depressed or psychotic. There is also the danger that she may harm the baby, particularly if she has delusional ideas about its health or appearance. This seems a remarkable aberration but in fact can be a misconceived attempt at kindness – an attempt to spare it the trauma of living with its imagined disability.

Certain characteristics mark out the person who might become clinically depressed if life became problematic. The depressed patient often has a serious, pessimistic, even gloomy, personality. Very often when someone who is obviously suffering from an affective disorder is asked about his or her family, they will, for instance, deny that any of their forebears were similarly afflicted but then go on to tell you how their father and grandfather plus a few aunts and uncles were all notorious for their pessimism. The obsessional person whose accounts always add up faultlessly, and whose kitchen floor can be eaten off, is also at risk. They may have escaped the bacteria on the grubby dishcloth, but they will fall prey to despondency when they are overwhelmed by their own standards.

It is the experience of everyone who has suffered from depression that depressive episodes vary in intensity and may well come and go. There may be no apparent precipitating cause. The depressive phase is usually of a reasonably slow onset, but may occasionally come on suddenly. Left untreated, the majority, but not all, will in time improve but, even so, over 50 per cent of people who have a major depressive episode will suffer a recurrence.

After the first attack, 15 per cent of patients will develop a chronic depressive illness if they do not receive treatment. It is a common observation, confirmed by various surveys, that depressive attacks tend to become more frequent, and the interval between them shorter, as the patient grows older. The majority of patients in whom the depression is part of an affective disorder – in this instance a despondent mood – will respond to treatment. With modern treatment an attack which used to last many months, even a year or two, has usually lifted within a matter of weeks – and with certain of the latest antidepressants, there is even some improvement within a matter of days.

One of the trials of medicine is that many patients who are quite seriously depressed refuse treatment because they are unwilling to 'admit' that they could be suffering from psychiatric disease. Patients are reluctant to take treatment for a variety of reasons. Many have a fear of 'drugs'; this is not surprising as they will have been brought up with the beliefs of their grandparents that all drugs which act on the mind are dangerous and most of them addictive. As mentioned in the introduction, in their grandparents' day very few drugs were available which were mind-altering. Opium and morphia, available for centuries, certainly produce pain relief and euphoria, but equally they can very readily become addictive. Bromides were popular tranquillizers but they had very unpleasant side-effects; and barbiturates, introduced before the Second World War, can also be habit-forming.

Patients, when given medication, are very open about the fear that they may be 'turned into a zombie'. Many psychiatric patients are creative, if over-sensitive; they fear that, when taking medication, not only may they be half asleep all the time, but they may lose the ability to enjoy the glories of nature, the pleasures of close human relationships, even possibly the ability, for instance, to write, act or paint. The present-day depressed patient finds it hard to believe that antidepressants have no 'kick' and do not give rise to a 'rush'; that they are not addictive, that the side-effects of tiredness and emotional blunting are now very much less, and that nowadays most patients when treated with anti-depressants will find themselves more alert and less blunted than they would have been by their illness.

Antidepressants are not addictive and everyone who starts taking them should continue to do so for at least six months, and even then the biochemical abnormality which made it necessary to take them in the first place may persist, so that one in six depressed patients will need them indefinitely. This is a difficult decision for someone to make, even if the choice seems obvious to the doctor – better to swallow a couple of pills a day than to be laid low by despondency.

Patients rightly complain that any medication which is likely to be effective is also likely to have side-effects. They are absolutely right. The nature of the side-effects may vary but nearly everyone will suffer in some way even if it is only in a very minor way. The side-effects have to be balanced against the misery of suffering the depressed state. Most people would feel there is no comparison. One of the paradoxes is that some of the people who would be most helped by mood-altering drugs are also some of the most sensitive: a side-effect which might hardly be noticed by an 18-stone Norfolk farmworker might lay some other psychiatric patient low, for, because of their very nature, their body is highly tuned to feel and suffer from what, to others, is an almost imperceptible discomfort.

The doctor can minimize patients' anxieties by taking time to talk to them about side-effects and their underlying fears over treatment, as well as the fears they discuss openly. It is important to explain to patients that their mind isn't going to be remoulded, in some Orwellian fashion, to suit society and its agent, the wicked doctor. The medication will not give them a new personality but will only restore their old character, and/or allow it to develop, unencumbered by a thousand unnecessary worries. Relatives are very useful allies in persuading patients to take their medication, but co-operation is best engendered through the establishment of a trusting rapport between the patient and the doctor, nurtured, if at all possible, by many and leisured visits.

When autumn comes most people feel cast down by the cold and damp and mourn the passing of the summer sun. A small number of such people have always been aware that the most distressing aspect of approaching winter is not the change in temperature, but the dark early evenings and the lack of sunlight. These feelings can be severe enough to warrant the description of a major depressive episode.

Over the past few years the recurrent pattern of a major depressive episode or the onset of bipolar affective disorder occurring during the sixty-day period when the daylight is at its least, has been named Seasonal Affective Disorder (SAD). In order to fit the criteria laid down by the *DSM*, the symptoms have to come on at the same time on at least three different occasions and the symptoms must all disappear once the darkest days of winter are over. Some experts believe that occasional patients who have suffered SAD in the autumn and winter may become hypomanic in the spring in an over-enthusiastic response to the joys of spring.

It is claimed that those who suffer from SAD not only show the expected signs of depression but that they are more likely to

" GEORGE IS ASLEEP AT THE MOMENT –
COULD HE PHONE YOU BACK IN MARCH ? "

suffer from hypersomnia, unlike most depressives (other than those who suffer from atypical depression) and they want to sleep far more than is usual. They also want to eat more. The combination of these two symptoms has produced comparisons with hibernation, in which the animal stores up fat in the form of a high-energy food intake before the onset of winter, and then hides away. Other prominent features of this kind of depression are a reluctance to move outside the house, a loss of sexual drive and rapid mood swings.

If the pattern of shortening days and lengthening nights is interrupted and the patient spends several hours a day sitting in front of a very strong light, it is claimed that in some cases no other treatment may be needed. In most, however, it is a variant of an affective disorder and antidepressant treatment will be needed as well.

There is a belief that other factors, as well as dwindling light, may contribute to depressed feelings in the darkest months. Many people's professional, or domestic, work is made more difficult by the shorter days; in other cases where there is poverty the increased costs brought on by winter may contribute to a general sense of misery. Many patients with an affective disorder need only a small change in their environment, which would be shrugged off by those who are more phlegmatic, to induce a relapse.

Although not recognized as a disorder by the *DSM* – it is indeed more of a symptom – it is most doctors' experience that some of their patients in fact look forward to long, dark evenings and the opportunity to sit, without any feelings of inadequacy, by their own firesides. Those people who have a dislike of a social life, but feel that they should be taking part in it, dread summer dresses, bathing-pool parties, barbecues, tennis and, consciously or otherwise, envy their socially more adept, and seemingly more alluring contemporaries. Those who put on their summer clothes and are able to shine in the summer months may be some of the 5 per cent of people who suffer in the winter. Conversely those who have had to 'screw their courage to the sticking point' in the summer sometimes come into their own when they can walk out confidently into the stygian darkness of the winter night, protected from the view of and therefore any criticism from their neighbours.

Depression is treatable. Like many doctors, I find one of the greatest rewards of a medical life is to be able to treat people successfully. I am pleased when I see a depressed patient – here is a challenge, and a challenge which not only do I have every intention of winning, but where the statistics tell me I have a 70 per cent chance of victory. Of those patients who come to their doctor for treatment for depression, 70 per cent will respond to antidepressants prescribed in the correct dose for long enough. 30 per cent will need other forms of treatment, and there is a considerable likelihood that their symptoms, although they could be indicative of an affective disorder, may be a sign of some other, underlying condition.

If the patient shows no improvement whatsoever within two or three weeks, patient and doctor have to think again. Have they settled on the wrong diagnosis? Are they taking the wrong drug?

Or, if the right drug, is it the right dose? A rather disturbing survey showed that 72 per cent of patients treated with the old-style tricyclic antidepressants were given them in inadequate doses. Even when the safer SSRIs (selective serotonin reuptake inhibitors, also known as the 5HT reuptake inhibitors – the newer antidepressant drugs) – the best-known of which is Prozac – are prescribed, 8 per cent of depressed patients were initially given sub-therapeutic doses.

Over half the patients who start and benefit from a course of antidepressants stop taking them too soon. Some of this is medical error: many doctors are just not aware that patients, once started on a course of antidepressants, should, provided there are not serious side-effects, stay on them for at least six months, and that at the end of this time they should be tailed off. The accepted advice is that the patient should continue to take the medication for four or six months after their mood has returned to normal.

For many years, I told patients who responded well to treatment that only about 8–10 per cent would need long-term therapy with medication. This is now thought to be too optimistic. The numbers may be twice as high. Just as patients who suffer persistent physical ills because of some biochemical dysfunction in the body – such as diabetes or thyroid disease – need long-term medication, so may some depressed patients. Long-term care should often be a combination of antidepressants and psychological support, including cognitive therapy.

In many other cases, it is the patients who stop taking their medication once they feel better. This can have disastrous results. Sudden cessation of treatment may bring back the symptoms and patients don't always do quite as well when treated a second time as they did initially. As discussed in the introduction, too many patients have fears about antidepressant drugs, which they think might be addictive – they are not. Other patients don't care for the side-effects, and one in five gives up within a fortnight, before they have had time to discover that side-effects often become less after three weeks or so. Perseverance is to be recommended.

It is true that the older antidepressants did have some troublesome side-effects, ranging from the socially inconvenient to the medically worrying. Unfortunately, changing medication can have tragic consequences: in November 1997 the press carried the story of Janet Thomas, a forty-four-year-old patient who been treated for SAD for the previous five years. Mrs Thomas normally responded to a combination of antidepressants and light therapy over the appropriate months, coupled with a trip to some sunny clime during the worst of the winter weather. In that year, because of adverse side-effects, it was decided to change the antidepressant pill upon which she had previously relied. During the changeover Mrs Thomas hanged herself.

Such occurrences are rare, and the newer antidepressants are free of most of the unpleasant side-effects of the older kinds. Many people, however, have allowed themselves to be swept along by the great wave of popular enthusiasm for 'counselling', to the exclusion of medication and well-structured cognitive therapy. These forms of psychotherapy have a role but, even ardent psychotherapists agree, not in severe depression.

Cognitive therapy, in all its varied forms, has an important role in the treatment of depression, particularly when combined with medication. It is intended to help patients become conscious of disordered thought processes, which can lead to depression. A depressed person may, when they have failed to achieve some object, misinterpret this as being their own fault, and that they are therefore useless. As a result, their self-esteem takes a battering. Cognitive therapists endeavour to persuade the patient to see both the original objective and their, probably praiseworthy, efforts at achieving it, in a new light. In controlled studies cognitive therapy has been shown to be efficacious by itself, and its results in some trials have been shown to be almost as effective, and remission may be longer once treatment has stopped. A combination of medication and cognitive therapy is the best option – but only by a factor of 5 per cent. This is not to say that emotional support, and time spent in conversation, whether formal counselling or not, isn't an essential part of anyone's recovery programme.

Antidepressant drugs, too often vilified in the trendier sections of society, can be divided into at least three groups. The oldest group are the tricyclic antidepressants, the drugs which revolutionized the treatment of depression. Such preparations as Tofranil (imipramine) and Tryptizol (amitriptyline) opened up a whole new world for some sufferers who had lived in their own secluded hell for years. On the other hand, they do have side-effects. Few patients are prepared to accept that their shake, if they pick up a cup and saucer, will produce a rattle audible across the room. They have to learn not to fill their glasses too full, and to keep their hands in their pockets. A very dry mouth, and a smacking noise as they endeavour to find some saliva is rather more trying. Constipation can be uncomfortable, and in older men urine retention can precipitate a crisis so that they cannot pass urine at all. But most people don't suffer enough to persuade them to give up, and many don't notice the side-effects at all. Fortunately, those who persevere find that side-effects tend to become less as time goes by. Rather more important are those which cause serious disease. In elderly people tricyclic anti-depressants can lower the blood pressure if someone leaps to their feet, particularly if they have been in a warm bed and have to make a nocturnal trip to the bathroom, a journey which can result in a stumble or fall. Occasionally, the tricyclics upset the rhythm of the heart.

Tricyclic antidepressants not only have an important place in psychiatry, but also have a significant role in treating various neurological complaints, including the pain from shingles. Although they are still, sometimes, the drug of first choice in depressed patients, the improved safety profile of the SSRIs (the Prozac group) have led to these becoming the initial treatment for someone who needs medication, despite their cost.

Another well-established group of antidepressants are the monoamine oxidase inhibitors (MAOIs) – such drugs as Nardil (phenelzine), Parnate and Parstelin (both tranylcypromine). These preparations were a great standby in the past, in particular for the treatment of people with so-called atypical depression in which there is a large element of anxiety, hypochondria and somatic symptoms. Their depression is often manifest by anxieties over the body's normal aches and pains. Unfortunately the use of these drugs has always been limited by the restrictions it places on diet. Patients taking the MAOIs must avoid cheese, and have to forswear their Oxo and Bovril and other meat extracts – this might not sound too great a handicap but it can be embarrassing to ask one's hostess just how she made the gravy. Yeasts are not allowed and therefore Marmite sandwiches are out, broad beans are forbidden, and pickled herrings are a thing of the past. These constraints would be bad enough if it wasn't that the MAOIs also react with alcohol – no more half-bottles of claret – and with many other drugs, including some of those used to treat conditions ranging from runny noses to blood pressure problems. Recently, a new kind of MAOI, Manerix moclobemide (an RIMA – reversible inhibitor of monoamine oxidase), has been marketed; this has fewer and less severe side-effects and doesn't react with quite such a long list of other everyday substances.

Some years ago, I went to a reception at the Royal Society and was astounded to see one of the world's better-known scientists going from plate to plate and opening up the sandwiches before finally selecting one. He caught my inquisitive eye and with a smile explained that he was taking Nardil and was just making certain that the sandwich he was about to eat didn't contain Marmite or cheese. With Nardil his mood had apparently settled and now, once again, streams of papers written by his students were flooding into the editors' offices of the scientific journals.

Patients are understandably suspicious of the doctor who is already writing out a prescription before they have finished giving their case history. It belittles the art of medicine to assume that a comprehensive knowledge of the drugs listed in the *British National Formulary*, *MIMS* (*Monthly Index of Medical Specialities*) and *Martindale's Pharmacopoeia* can replace a sympathetic ear and the ability to assess a patient's condition. In treating a depressed patient it is particularly important that in the early stages of treatment a person should be assessed very regularly, notwithstanding constraints of time, so that the doctor is fully aware of any signs of suicidal intent. It is equally important that the patient should always know when their next appointment is and it shouldn't be too far in the future; the thought that a visit to a supportive doctor is imminent has deterred many a patient from committing suicide.

Not all patients will be treated immediately with drugs. Some patients with relatively mild depression may be treated with cognitive therapy, or some other form of psychotherapy may be used in conjunction with antidepressants. Conversely, in very severe acute depression in which there is an obvious acute risk of self-harm, ECT may be called for. Even so, most clinically depressed patients will need antidepressant medication.

There is still a role for the tricyclic antidepressants and amitriptyline, of which Tryptizol is the best known, is still widely prescribed. The problem with the tricyclics (TCAs) is that they cause more adverse side-effects than the SSRIs (selective serotonin reuptake inhibitors), which inhibit the reuptake of 5HT – hence they are often referred to as 5HT reuptake inhibitors. The best known of the SSRIs is Prozac fluoxetine. Whereas some side effects of the TCAs are inconvenient, even mildly distressing, such as a dry mouth, a fine tremor and a tendency to sweat, others may cause medical problems. The same pharmacological action which causes a dry mouth may make it difficult for someone to pass urine, which can be important in an older person with an enlarged prostate. Patients on tricyclics may also have nausea and constipation, a blurred vision and feelings of faintness.

The side-effects which are most dreaded are those which affect the rhythm and rate of the heart. These are particularly important in overdose, which is why an overdose of tricyclics is more likely to have a fatal outcome than an overdose of an SSRI. SSRIs are not, however, free of side-effects, although these have been exaggerated by the tabloid presss.

SSRIs can only be used with considerable caution in patients who are suffering from epilepsy and are not recommended for patients having ECT. Care must be taken, too, if there is a history of heart, liver or kidney disease, and since some patients taking SSRIs become hypomanic, signs of this must be looked out for. SSRIs can make patients rather sleepy by day and wakeful by night; they also give rise to gastrointestinal ill effects, including nausea, abdominal pain, diarrhoea or constipation. There are established regimes for swapping from one antidepressant to another, and the rules must be strictly adhered to.

Each of the SSRIs has a slightly different profile, both as regards its benefits and its side effects. Prozac (fluoxetine) is the best known of this group. As the effect of these drugs on physical co-ordination varies from person to person, and drug to drug, patients should be made aware that driving may be impaired, as it can be with the tricyclic antidepressants Sexual prowess may occasionally be lessened and some of this group of drugs will, in a minority of patients, reduce or even eliminate libido – but not permanently. Use can be made of a variant of this side-effect in paroxetine (Seroxat), and it has been much prescribed, although not officially licensed, for use as a treatment for premature ejaculation. As both it and Faverin (fluvoxamine) are licensed also for the treatment of obsessive compulsive disorders, they have also both been prescribed for the same condition.

In the United States Faverin is, for instance, thought of primarily as a treatment for obsessive compulsive disorders, albeit that it is a very efficient antidepressant. Similarly SSRIs, like tricyclic antidepressants, have proved useful in the treatment of several different personality disorders and even pathological crying and laughing (the uncontrollable and inappropriate crying and laughing which can be a symptom of various neurological diseases).

As illustrated by the story of the scientist and the sandwich, another group of antidepressants, now less commonly used, are the monoamine oxidase inhibitors (MAOIs). These over the years have been particularly useful in treating patients in whom depression is associated with marked degrees of hypochondria, anxiety, and other features of atypical depression. Unfortunately they interact with many common foodstuffs, including such everyday items as Bovril and some cheeses – which is why the scientist had to be so careful about his sandwiches. It is hoped that the new antidepressant with a novel action, a reversible MOAI, moclobemide (Manerix), which has fewer side-effects than such drugs as phenelzine (Nardil), will have a wider use. It is licensed for the treatment of major depression and social phobias. Another recent introduction is venlafaxine (Efexor), which is both a 5HT and noradrenaline reuptake inhibitor; it and reboxetine (Edronax), which is a noradrenaline reuptake inhibitor, not only treat depression but, it is claimed, also are likely to elevate the patient's mood more rapidly to the point where they have enough enthusiasm to return to work and their previous social commitments.

Mania in its acute phase needs to be treated with an anti-psychotic drug in order that the patient's mood may be rapidly damped down. Lithium, which is still the most commonly prescribed drug in the treatment of mania and bipolar disorder (manic depression), can be given at the same time, and takes several days to exert an effect. Lithium is also used prophylactically but care must be taken to check blood levels and to make certain that thyroid, renal function and blood-cell count remain normal. Recently, drugs more often used in the treatment of epilepsy, including carbamazepine (Tegretol), have been used in preference to lithium or as a substitute for it if the patient has failed to respond.

Having a wide variety of different antidepressants – and there are many more than those described here – is useful, as patients are very idiosyncratic in their reaction to them, and the first or even second prescribed is not always the answer to the problem. An essential aspect of the treatment regime is that an adequate therapeutic dose should be prescribed from the start, and that the patient should continue to take it for not less than six months, or, in the case of the elderly, some doctors would say two years.

Cognitive therapy, already described, is the form of psycho-therapy most frequently recommended by doctors in the treatment of depression. As its beneficial effects have been statistically verified, doctors are by nature and training drawn to it. However, other forms of psychotherapy, whose proponents would argue are deeper acting and historically based on the psycho-analytical movement, have a great following. Psychotherapists would argue that the concept of trained counselling and similar psychotherapeutic disciplines are based on the unconscious, and therefore psychoanalysis as practised by Freud and by modern exponents.

Although cognitive therapy may be the treatment of choice for many doctors, in reality a patient is more likely to be referred by their GP to a practice counsellor. They may, in their turn, refer a patient for more specific psychotherapy.

The aim of the psychotherapist is to help patients to understand any underlying cause to their depression. This is often influenced by loss, whether the loss is the result of separation, bereavement, divorce or death. Loss in adult life may trigger the sadness of a loss experienced in the past, which has remained unconscious until it is triggered by the later event. The therapists suggest that loss in childhood is sometimes too painful to bear at the time but may rise to the surface after some adult crisis. The oft-quoted example of this is Queen Victoria, who grieved terribly and lengthily over her husband as a result, the psychotherapists believe, of her father dying when she was very young. She then had a remote, isolated, lonely childhood with a domineering mother and absentee, much older, half-siblings. Early emotionally traumatic experiences, other than loss, may also have a profound effect later on.

Therapy helps patients to understand that feelings not only stem from the present but are linked to experiences in childhood. Further understanding of their emotions is elicited by the relationship they make with their therapist, onto whom they unconsciously transfer their feelings from the past. Psychotherapists offer short-term focused therapy or a longer-term relationship, depending on the problem. Patients need to be carefully assessed. Most psychotherapists don't treat depression when it is complicated by psychotic symptoms (a loss of contact with reality), in particular schizophrenia or very severe manic depression. Patients must be motivated to want therapy. Generally speaking, therefore, those with a mental handicap, anti-social personality disorders, or people who have obsessive-compulsive disorders are, most psychotherapists believe, unlikely to benefit from their skills.

2

Anxiety Disorders and Phobias

Mothers often bring their sensitive children to the doctor: 'He is so timid that he is afraid of his own shadow.' The doctor's first task is to make certain that Colin is only showing his true character, and that any excessive anxiety he is displaying has not been induced by tensions at home or by bullying at school. Many timid children are merely highly intelligent – they learn to reason very quickly, and as they come to recognize the hazards of life soon learn to take avoiding action. This is interpreted by adults as a cowardly timorousness though, ironically, their timidity has often all too obviously been inherited from one or both parents.

If the mother, however sensitive she is herself, looks unconvinced by reassurance and is still obviously hoping for her child (usually it is a son) to be as brave as St George or David, slayer of Goliath, I then tell her that one of the few classic early-warning signs of a potential psychopath is foolhardy courage in extreme youth. Better to have a nervous, intelligent child, who grows up to be an Oxford lecturer, than a little 'toughie', who may, if lucky, grow up to drive Formula One cars, or captain an international bobsleigh team, but is far more likely to become an ill-disciplined delinquent.

Anxiety and fear are emotions familiar to everybody, but the difference between them in ordinary everyday life is hard to define. In medical terminology, fear is the normal response to some real danger, and for the emotion to be entirely normal, the degree of fear should be proportional to the menace. Fear always has to be distinguished from abnormal anxiety. Small children are not the only people to be fearful; normal, well-orientated, productive people have justified fears. People devoid of fear are often antisocial and fail to conform to the cultural rules of the society in which they live, as very often their fearlessness does not only apply to physical danger, but also to the consequences of their behaviour, so they are unafraid of the effect of their actions on other people's feelings.

Anxiety may, like fear, involve all the symptoms of alarm, but unlike fear the level of apprehension is disproportionate to the danger, and indeed bystanders may find it hard to understand why the patient is upset at all.

Panic attacks are peaks of fear and apprehension associated with a huge variety of physical symptoms and signs. The attacks are very similar to those of fear, or acute anxiety disorders, but usually pass off. *The Diagnostic and Statistical Manual of Mental Disorders-IV* (*DSM-IV*) stipulates that panic attacks are characterized by feelings of extreme tension, fear and impending doom, and that at least four of thirteen different symptoms should be present and should occur within ten minutes of the patient's being exposed to whatever has brought on the panic attack. These symptoms include a racing heart, sweating, trembling, shortness of breath, feelings of choking, dizziness or vertigo. Many patients have a fear of dying and, because they overbreathe, they have chest pains and tingling sensations in the limbs.

Phobias are the persistent and irrational fear of some specific object, activity or situation. The phobia is so intense that the patient who has it will go to considerable lengths to avoid confronting the subject of their phobia – they in fact indulge in avoidant behaviour.

A generalized anxiety disorder (GAD for short) is associated with at least six months of excessive anxiety and worry. It is not necessarily precipitated by some particular incident, although it may be; and it may also be associated with many other psychiatric conditions, especially major depression, schizophrenia and various personality disorders. The disorder is chronic, and the level of anxiety is abnormal and out of accord with its cause.

About 5 per cent of the general public are thought by their doctors to be chronically anxious, a condition which affects women twice as often as men. Interestingly, it is one of the neurotic states which is more common in younger than in older people, and, as is commonly observed, it is a personality trait which runs in families. Although the textbooks describe the typical patient as a twenty-five to forty-five-year-old woman, living alone in a city and without the benefits of a sustained education, the disorder is also found in the over-sensitive university graduate, even after they are established in a profession or have hit the headlines as media stars. Whether star or shop assistant, their acquaintances will probably describe them as 'highly strung'.

When a person is in a state of anxiety their response to danger, imagined or otherwise, is excessive. People respond to anxiety and fear in the same way, and the physical and psychological symptoms they have are the consequences of too much noradrenaline, one of the stimulative hormones secreted by the adrenal glands, which affects a wide variety of tissues all over the body.

In a traditional acute anxiety state – a panic attack – the person feels terrified, has a sense of doom, the heart races and can be felt thudding away in the chest, which seems in imminent danger of bursting. Frequently, the heartbeat becomes irregular, but even without this happening, the person may experience chest pain and a sense of gripping and constriction of the neck, and not unnaturally he or she starts to breathe more rapidly. This hyperventilation not only exacerbates the pain, but creates tingling and spasm in the hands and feet, and numbs the lips; the legs feel weak and the sufferer sweats and trembles. If there are other people about, the sufferer feels distanced from them; the voices of those talking to him or her seem to be coming from afar. If the sensitive person is aware that other people have noticed their state, this can make the situation even worse, as they then self-consciously feel that they are the centre of everybody's attention.

As said, problems arise when the fear or anxiety is out of all proportion to the threat. Very often sufferers are not even aware of the cause of their apprehension; they only know that they are experiencing the disagreeable symptoms normally associated with fear. People, like the mother of the little boy Colin described earlier, often do not distinguish between fear and anxiety. She would have been wise to be concerned about unreasonable apprehension, but did not need to be concerned about a fear, however trivial by adult standards. In fear, the source of the worry is apparent and real, even if, as often in the case of children, it is an imaginary fear – a tiger under the bed, for instance. Anxiety, on the other hand, produces an unpleasant feeling of apprehension, often associated with physical symptoms, present for much of the time, for which a cause cannot be readily identified.

Children are not the only people to experience ill-defined fears. Life in a new and alien environment, where there could be concealed hostility, may induce feelings of apprehension in anyone who is sensitive – that first-day-at-school feeling is an emotion which recurs throughout life, and is a common response which can only be described as an anxiety state if it is disproportionate.

There is no better example of the acute anxiety state than the state of mind which afflicts a public speaker who, before he mounts his rostrum, is flushed, sweating, nauseous and sometimes even incontinent before a speech. During my brief spell as an MP it fell to me and my agent to organize a huge party rally for the east of England. One of the most prominent Cabinet Ministers of the day was to address the party faithful, who had gathered in their hundreds. Just before the meeting my agent, George Howard, came to me to tell me that the speaker was missing.

Experience had taught me that on these occasions the first place to look was the lavatory, which we proceeded to do. There, we could hear terrible retching and vomiting noises through the door and, shortly afterwards, the massive figure of the speaker emerged. George Howard was brave enough to ask the great man if he was well. 'Of course I am, you bloody fool. I am just nervous, as anyone else would be.' He went on to make an excellent speech, showing no signs of his earlier terror, and everyone thought he was as relaxed as he was captivating. Terror at appearing before a crowd of thousands would be normal – a reasonable fear – in most people, but is unusual in a man who has spent a lifetime under the public gaze, and in him can therefore be classified as an anxiety.

Anxiety is no more than an exaggerated reaction to a perceived threat. Most anxiety states are not acute, like the speaker's, but chronic. The reactions of the chronically anxious are similar to, but less marked than, those which characterize the response in an acute anxiety state. Chronic anxiety may show itself in an easily recognized form, or it may be hidden. However Dickens represented him, Scrooge was not so much an evil man as a man who was suffering from a chronic anxiety state. He was terrified of poverty. It had induced in him a state of anxiety which coloured the whole of his professional and domestic life and destroyed his relations within society. How many people realize that the city miser, who devotes his whole life to making money and keeping it, is in fact suffering from an anxiety disorder? He has perceived a threat – poverty – and his miserly behaviour is a symptom of his excessive and unreasonable fear of it.

The outward symptoms of chronic anxiety, although all of them may be said to be exaggerated reactions to a perceived threat, vary from the very long-term, such as those which affect the miser who hoards his cash, to the medium-term symptoms, in which the underlying tensions may produce nothing more specific than ill-defined headaches, unexplained indigestion, gut disturbances and genito-urinary symptoms – the physical symptoms of a badly balanced autonomic nervous system, the self-controlling system which looks after our routine bodily processes and responses. Quite apart from the physical manifestation of the chronic anxiety state, there is always a constant, even if unreasonable, anxiety about what the future may hold. Many who suffer from chronic anxiety find that their symptoms, whether physical or behavioural, are a cause of anxiety to their families – which exacerbates the situation.

Dad's Army – such a rich source of the psychologically colourful – featured the 'boy Pike', who was perpetually anxious. Regrettably, as in poor Pike's case, periods of chronic anxiety are also interspersed with acute episodes. Depending upon the

severity of the patient's conditions, these will be of varying intensity and the gap between each acute attack also varies. During a
bad period the patient may feel that they are merely living from
one acute anxiety state to the next, and they may sometimes
wonder if life is worth living. Not unnaturally such a state of
mind may provoke depression. But diagnosis in medicine is
never simple and in other cases it may be that it is the depressive
state which has engendered the anxiety.

This is one of the 'chicken or egg?' discussions which keep
psychiatrists and lay people arguing happily amongst themselves, for anxiety is not always a primary condition. It can be a
symptom of many different psychiatric conditions: it is nearly
always found to a greater or lesser extent in people who are
depressed, and could almost be considered as part of the syndrome; and it is a prominent feature in the schizophrenic illnesses
– perhaps not surprisingly, as the varied and strange symptoms
which schizophrenic and schizotypal people experience are very
disturbing for them and would be enough to cause anxiety in the
most phlegmatic. When excessive anxiety exists by itself and
no other symptoms of psychiatric disease can be demonstrated,
it is described as an anxiety neurosis.

Various terms are used to describe anxiety. We all know when
someone is described as 'tense', and what we mean by the term;
we assume that they are as taut as a violin string, and as restless
as a tiger in a cage. People who are very tense are not only physically restless but their minds flit from subject to subject, just
as surely as a tiger paces around its cage, never still and never
settled. Tense people are also irritable – it would be unwise to go
into the tiger's cage and poke it with a stick; to prod the mind of
somebody whose anxieties are consuming all their thoughts
could be equally unwelcome, if less dangerous. Agitation is
produced in a very similar way to the other symptoms of tension,
but in agitation the physical restlessness is so extreme that its
emotional origins tend to be obscured.

In general medical practice the state known as 'free-floating
anxiety' is a constant source of problems and a trap for the

"I'M VERY WORRIED ABOUT TAKING
ANYTHING FOR MY ANXIETY"

unwary, whether doctors, relatives or friends, for that very reason – its source cannot be pinpointed. Someone suffering from free-floating anxiety has a chronic feeling of anxiousness and tension. The anxiety is ascribed to one cause after another and flits from one problem to another, like a butterfly moving from flower to flower. If one problem is solved the anxiety takes off and settles elsewhere. The apparent cause of the anxiety, the one offered to doctors and friends, may not be the true one, or even related to it. A young woman, insecure in her partner's love, may not express her anxiety by overtly worrying about whether he will be on time to meet her that evening, but instead may fret about her flatmate's lack of enthusiasm for the washing-up. Disaster can follow if people accept that any particular anxiety which a patient is at the time expressing is the underlying cause of all their troubles. A man, for instance, pursued by the bailiffs may claim that his worries are the result of his partner's misdeeds. Everyone rallies round, the partner is alienated, only for the true cause – his debts – then to emerge.

Indeed, Dr John Gray, in his book *Men are from Mars, Women are from Venus,* for a long time at the top of the bestseller lists, admonishes men for their habit of trying to pin down the cause of some anxiety or distress in a woman when in fact the spoken worry merely represents the most immediate problem from a pile of troubles which at the time have become overwhelming. Dr John Gray recommends that listening, however frustrating for the man who wants to be masterful and find a few solutions, is more efficient than for him to try to 'fix' some isolated and possibly unrepresentative burden. By listening, he will help the woman's worries come tumbling out, a process which may kick-start her own self-help mechanism. The trick which some men never acquire is to be able to look interested and concerned and yet provide nothing other than a listening ear; most women, on the other hand, are good listeners and will allow someone to unburden him- or herself, without looking for a quick solution.

Some years ago, a patient of mine, Alice, a lonely divorcee, was very concerned when she received a County Court summons to meet a sizeable builder's bill, which had been in dispute. A regular attender at the surgery – on this occasion with a persistent cough – and always with one worry or another, the immediate thought might have been that it was time for a few more Frisium, a potent anti-anxiety agent. But there was no doubt that the thought of being sued for £15,000, and possibly losing the court case, had seized her with fear, particularly as her bank were unhelpful, off-hand and critical.

Rather than handing out another prescription, it seemed that the time had now come to check Alice's financial situation to see how valid were her anxieties and how justified her bank's rudeness. Armed with a few simple questions, she then telephoned the manager. It transpired that her total assets were well over one hundred times greater than the disputed bill. My prescription on this occasion was for her to write a very sharp letter to the bank, saying that unless she received more co-operation in future she would find somebody else to look after her money.

Even as she left, all smiles, to have lunch with the bank manager, I knew that sooner or later another anxiety would take the place of the builder's bill, and another minor crisis cause a major upset, for Alice suffers from free-floating anxieties, and these will not rest until she has established a better-structured lifestyle.

Many people suffering from anxiety complain of physical symptoms which could be related to a serious disease, and so must be analysed. Heart and chest disease, cancer and sexually transmitted diseases are all common pegs on which anxieties may be hung. The doctor, confronted by a person who fears he or she has heart disease – and may well have symptoms to justify this – will be ever eager to settle his patient's worries. A series of tests will be arranged to exclude coronary heart disease, incipient cardiac failure, left-ventricular hypertrophy, dangerous arrhythmias of the heartbeat, and a host of other cardiac problems. Armed with a sheaf of normal results, the doctor may be rash enough to hope that he will have settled the anxiety and have an evergrateful patient. But not a bit of it. No sooner has the worry about the heart been settled than the free-floating anxiety will find another chapter in the medical textbook to account for the next batch of vague symptoms. This time it may be that dry cough: 'How do you know I haven't developed TB, doctor?'

We do not, of course, but we do know that repeated investigations will only make the situation worse, and the anxieties will float off to settle elsewhere. They do not necessarily have to settle on matters of health. They may be related to money, as in Alice's case, or family welfare, grandchildren's health or an aspect of the sufferer's own life. No sooner, for instance, has any anxiety about unpaid bills been settled, than the anxious housewife may start worrying that the house insurance is inadequate; once that is dealt with then she will be prostrated by concern that the children's school is educationally unsound and possibly a nest of paedophiles. The really anxious worrier will, if pushed, be driven desperate by anxieties over possible Chinese aggression, global warming, collision with a meteorite, or, of course, nuclear war.

Ironically, excessive worry – about health or anything else – can lead to physical illness. Many diseases are psychosomatic, or have a psychosomatic component. The obvious examples are those which may stem from an over-active autonomic nervous system, as may be found in tense, anxious, striving people. These include cardiovascular disease – strokes and heart attacks, hypertension, left-ventricular strain even in the absence of a high blood pressure – and, less demonstrably, Type II diabetes (the diabetes of later life). Some doctors believe that too early a benign enlargement of the prostate (enlargement of the prostate is part and parcel of ageing in the male) may also be related to a striving, ambitious temperament – others believe that the temperament and the enlarged prostate are both the results of high levels of testosterone.

More complex is the effect of excessive and persistent anxiety on the immune system. If the immune system is affected by personality, it could have some influence, albeit small, on the development of malignancies and resistance to infectious diseases. Dr Candace Pert, a neuroscientist, formerly of the Johns Hopkins University and now a research professor at Georgetown University, Washington, DC, explores the biochemistry of emotions in her book *Molecules of Emotion*. She demonstrates how the body, including the immune system, responds to emotion. Throughout the human body there are a multiplicity of receptors, which detect and receive various impulses, and trigger responses in the nervous system. Among other stimuli, receptors react to the presence and quantity of neurotransmitters – the chemicals which help transmit impulses from one nerve cell to another – the reaction of the receptors varying according to the mood and motivation of the person. The mood, in turn, varies according to the amount of neurotransmitter present. Serotonin, noradrenaline and dopamine, all of which act as neurotransmitters, are key players in the daily, and ever unfolding, drama of psychiatric health, and are constantly referred to in every discussion of modern mental health treatment.

Nature has given us a natural healing process, the immune system, which heals our burns, cuts and injuries; recognizes and repels disease-delivering organisms and works to eliminate cancerous cells. If people are oppressed by their worries and anxieties, if they are depressed and dejected, their immune systems may work less efficiently and their defences against disease become lowered.

Panic Disorders

Physical health problems apart, free-floating anxieties are one of the causes of panic attacks. The Greeks had no doubts about what caused panic attacks: Pan, the god of the forests, pastures, and fertility. Part-goat part-man and very lustful, he had the habit of lurking in remote spots in mountains and caves and was held responsible for the sudden inexplicable fear that can overcome the traveller alone in the wilderness. When a flock, again suddenly and inexplicably, stampeded, it was his doing; and he was blamed, too, for nightmares and any other feeling of terror that had no obvious cause. Hence the word 'panic'.

Panic attacks are brief episodes of intense anxiety, with all the symptoms of acute anxiety, but which last for only a short time, although the sufferer may feel washed out, knocked for six, for some time afterwards. Recurrent panic attacks can have very far-reaching effects on the patient's lifestyle, as on each occasion they may feel that they or one of their loved ones is doomed to die, or if not die be seriously ill.

It is interesting that panic attacks are of sudden onset and very often without any obvious precipitating cause. They are like clouds which suddenly appear in a clear, blue sky, totally unexpected. They can take the sufferers unawares and overcome them while they are in bed at night, or even when they are asleep, thereby waking them up. The patient is unaware of any particular dream or hypnagogic state – the very lifelike dreams which occur just before waking up or just after going to sleep – which could have induced it.

The Diagnostic and Statistical Manual of Mental Disorders IV has laid down that a panic attack cannot be diagnosed unless the patient has at least four of the common symptoms associated with an acute anxiety state – if the attack induces fewer than four symptoms, it is downgraded from a panic attack to a 'limited symptom attack'. Anxiety is defined as a 'diffuse, unpleasant uneasiness, apprehension or fearfulness stemming from antici- pated danger, the source of which is unidentifiable'. The physical symptoms include:

Changes in the skin: flushing, sometimes pallor, excessive sweating, etc.

Changes in the heart rate and rhythm: increased heart rate, sometimes irregularity

Changes in respiration: panting breaths which can lead to chest pain; tingling in the hands and feet and spasm in the muscles of the hands and feet

Changes in the gastrointestinal tract: nausea, even vomiting, intestinal hurry and urgency to defecate, sometimes incontinence – being 'caught short'

A genito-urinary response: the desire to pass water and sometimes incontinence

Feelings of faintness and dizziness: 'the vapours' of the nineteenth-century novelists

Weakness in the limbs: a sudden need to sit down, or seek physical support

Changes in the pupil: with anxiety or excitement, pupils dilate

Research has shown that although about 5 per cent of the population suffers from chronic anxiety states, including panic disorder, in which there are recurrent panic attacks, about one- third of all people will at some time have experienced a panic attack, and about 10 per cent will have experienced more than one, even though they are not chronic sufferers.

When anxiety state becomes manifest through panic attacks, it is often a result of a long-term stressful situation. This may be ongoing, such as the illness of a relative, or the grief associated with any other of the three 'D's – death, divorce or debt – or it might be a flashback to some past event. One of the characteristics of panic attacks is that their causes – when they can be identified –

are nearly always completely beyond the patient's control. For instance, the patient whose father's illness is found to be the root cause of their panic attacks is not, and never has been, in a position to influence their parent's condition and its treatment.

Panic disorder seems, like other forms of anxiety, to have a genetic basis. This may be seen from studies of twins, for instance, which show that panic disorder is five times more likely to appear in both twins if they are identical than if they are fraternal, and therefore genetically less close, even when their background and environment are identical.

The other background factors to panic disorder are also similar to those of other anxiety states. These include separation from, or the death of, a parent in early childhood – or even the loss of their love. This loss of love may be more perceived than real – as, for instance, after an acrimonious divorce of parents during the sufferer's childhood. Later the loss of the love of a partner or child, can induce anxiety disorders. Loss of self-esteem, another cause, is thought to stem from the acquisition of unrealistically high moral standards.

Sixty per cent of patients with panic disorder also suffer from severe depression. When depression is associated with a severe anxiety disorder, it may be more difficult to treat, and patients who suffer from both are more likely to be among the comparatively small minority of depressed patients who need continuous medication. Moreover, any underlying psychiatric problems tend to have a worse outcome than if the patient suffered only from depression, anxiety or panic disorders in isolation. Additionally, in someone who suffers from more than one of these sets of symptoms – anxiety, panic disorder and depression – the suicide risk is also increased.

Where drugs are involved, amphetamines, and amphetamine-type substances, including those like cocaine and Ecstasy, can induce recurrent panic attacks. These attacks may either be a feature of intoxication with the drug when the drug-taker is high, but more often they occur after the person has 'come down' and sobered up. Conversely, patients who suffer from panic disorders are up to five times more likely to take to illicit drugs or to consume excessive alcohol in the hope that the pharmacological effect of these substances will reduce the likelihood of an attack. Their optimism is misplaced. These drugs make the chance of having a panic attack more, not less, likely – and there is a well-known association between taking cocaine and sudden cardiac death, even in very young people.

Phobias

One of the better-known phobias is agoraphobia and it is frequently associated with panic attacks, although it can occur without any history of panic disorder. At least four of the symptoms of a panic attack are induced by a fear of being in a situation, physical or mental, from which there is no obvious and immediate escape – a fear that might be described as agoraphobia. Typical examples of agoraphobia are the fear of huge open spaces or the fear of crowds, whether the crowds are in an open space – for instance on a beach – or in a confined space: in a church at a wedding, perhaps. What these two situations have in common is that escape from either in the event of some little disaster might be difficult or embarrassing. The agoraphobic person thrust into public life will genuinely dread having to sit in the middle row in the front of the auditorium or, even worse, being exposed to general view as part of the platform party at a meeting. Equally, the singer in a choir may love the music but dread appearing on stage. On all these occasions the worry is, 'What will happen if I feel faint with all these people watching me?' At least one agoraphobic bride had two conversations running simultaneously as she took her vows at the altar in front of a packed church. One, whispered, was with her future husband, on what was going to happen if she fainted because there was 'no way out'; the other, out loud, was with the priest and congregation as she repeated her vows.

The agoraphobic patient will look for the end pew in a crowded church, or the last seat in the cinema row; they may be frightened of being too far from their car, or from their home, when they go out. Many are much happier if they have a companion or if they have a movable base – usually their car, which, if they can park close to their destination, means that they have a nearby home ground. They also reconnoitre possible escape routes – finding one not only provides some comfort, but having found a way out, they rarely have to use it: therapeutically, the important factor is knowing that they can escape if need be.

While some people with agoraphobia see their cars as a safe haven, others, on the other hand, find the enclosed conditions of a car both agoraphobic, with no way out, and claustrophobic, leading to a fear of enclosed spaces. Yet others have severe symptoms if they travel by air – aeroplanes are particularly frightening as there is obviously 'no way out', and it is not at all uncommon for a flight to induce a classic panic attack. The chest pain and palpitations often engender fears of heart attacks, and in my practice, which includes people who are constantly travelling, I regularly have patients who have been admitted to acute care wards all over the world. Interestingly, they have been overcome on a plane on some particular flight for reasons beyond their ken, although they fly routinely.

An unusual, but not uncommon, variety of agoraphobia is a fear of crossing bridges, known as 'gephyrophobia'. This fear isn't limited to crossing high bridges with a long drop on either side – although when the parapet is inadequate and the height precipitous the anxiety is, naturally, worse. I was at school with a very robust rugby-playing contemporary who was as brave as a lion on the games field and was blessed with a phlegmatic and detached temperament. He had, however, an Achilles' heel. Each day we had to cross a narrow bridge in order to ring the chapel bell and each day he was terrified. Even after a year of doing it, his five-yard walk left him sweating and palpitating.

There are countless other phobias. These fears usually start in childhood, but the phobic state may not be directly related to the childhood fear. They may be specific phobias, in which a person has symptoms of acute anxiety when confronted by a particular object or situation, such as blood, heights or, very commonly, insects and animals. Arachnophobia, a fear of spiders, is frequently encountered. Patients are usually fully aware that the phobia is absurd: what possible danger could a dying spider in the bath pose to anyone? Even so it is enough to induce a panic state in some people.

Another common phobia is a fear of birds, and especially their feathers. Margaret was a farmer's wife in those days when farms were not so specialized, and her role was to look after the chickens. Unfortunately she had a great fear of birds and feathers which was only matched by her determination to be a good farmer's wife. Twice every day she bravely went out to feed the hens and collect the eggs, but moving the broody hens was more than she could bear. Her real terror was exposed whenever a bird flew in through an open window. On these occasions, she would suffer palpitations, chest pain, breathlessness, sweating and weak limbs. She was especially unfortunate – most people who suffer from this kind of phobia can avoid close contact with birds. Margaret never took steps to overcome her phobia: she never became desensitized, or had treatment, but like the good Highlander she was, she merely put up with it – although there were beads of sweat on her upper lip.

Other people have a phobia about animals. An excessive and unreasonable fear of dogs is common. In our Norfolk practice we were joined by a new doctor, Dr Robinson, who had intended to stay for some months. Well-qualified, bright, athletic, even if somewhat arrogant, he seemed to be the ideal man for a long locum with the possibility of staying permanently. It soon became apparent that there was one terrible bar to his chosen career. He had a dog phobia. I was soon hearing stories from patients of how, for instance, a small dachshund had been spotted by the doctor before he left his car and how he had had to shout through the window to be escorted to the house. It was bad enough for him to have his rounds made miserable by a series of attacks of acute anxiety – even worse when he returned to the flat in our house. Our elderly and reasonably amiable spaniel wandered the premises and sometimes the luckless Dr Robinson would have to sit sweating and pale in his car for half an hour or so before one of my then young children came to rescue him. Within a month or two Dr Robinson had given up his plan to be a rural GP in England and had emigrated to Sydney.

Climatic phobias are mainly confined to a dread of thunderstorms and lightning. Otherwise brave and rational people are reduced to a shaking wreck, ears plugged, hiding beneath the stairs with the family dog, by some summer storm. More common is the fear of heights, which is similar to that of bridges. Unsurprisingly, it is made much worse if the sufferer has to look over the edge of a precipice or the parapet around a tall building: the sensation they feel is often described as vertigo. But it is not true vertigo, merely a sense of light-headedness and dizziness, probably induced by hyperventilation (rapid breathing, possibly made worse by the exertions of climbing). The symptoms of hyperventilation can be alleviated by breathing into a paper bag placed over the head so that carbon dioxide is breathed in again (plastic bags, of course, are lethal).

One disabling phobia which is too rarely discussed is social phobia – a fear of interacting with other people – into which shyness imperceptibly shades. Social phobias stem from the sufferers' fear that they might behave in a way which will lead to their humiliation or embarrassment – in essence that they are going to make a fool of themselves or even just blush excessively. They are terrified that they are being judged by those around them and that this judgement will find them wanting. Crossing the lounge of an hotel, mounting the platform at a public meeting, taking communion in church or meeting a group of strangers, all produce the unwelcome responses of extreme anxiety.

Social phobia will be intensified if the sufferer not only has to be present but is expected to talk once there. This would allow bystanders not only to judge his or her appearance but also their public speaking ability and conversational adeptness. Sitting in terrified silence, they fear their comments are considered foolish and irrelevant and that they will be forever damned as socially inept or boring.

Most patients with extreme social anxieties suffer from a generalized, social phobia which embraces occasions ranging from the Parent-Teacher Association meeting or dinner with the in-laws to a Buckingham Palace garden party. Not all social phobias are generalized – some may involve only one aspect of public life. The most common manifestations of social phobia are blushing, and a dislike of speaking, eating and drinking in public. Fear of eating in public is frequently concealed by those who have it, and represented as no more than a dislike of restaurants.

One well-known politician suffered from this fear of eating in public. When visiting a constituency, he would have drinks with his supporters before a meal, and then disappear to eat by himself under the pretext that he had a few bits of urgent business to complete, later joining the company for coffee. Surprisingly, this fear extended to his own dinner parties. He would greet his guests politely, hand them a pulverizing drink, and then explain that he had a few red boxes which had to be dealt with. He would be absent throughout dinner, leaving his wife in charge, and would reappear once the table had been cleared.

I studied him on many occasions and was initially unable to decide whether his refusal to eat in company was a very rational fear that some antipathetic photographer might take an unflattering picture of the coleslaw dripping down his chin, whether he really had had enough of the world and needed time by himself before he made a speech, or whether he, as I suspected, suffered from a variant of the common phobia of eating in public. Since his dislike of eating with strangers extended to small private parties it seemed clear that he had a social phobia – suffering it was a bearable price to pay for eminence and power.

The disadvantages of social phobia extend beyond eating in company or being the cynosure of all eyes at the altar rail. Sufferers may not only be limited in the holidays they take and in their interests, but they may have had to opt out of sixth-form college or university. Statistically, sufferers are more likely to lead solitary lives as they find it hard to make the close relationships which would have converted a date to a lasting alliance. Their suicide rate is six times the national average. Shyness, too, can be disabling but whether there are differences between extreme shyness and social phobias is a moot point.

Although only 3 per cent of people suffer permanently from social phobia, another 12 per cent have periodic symptoms. Those who suffer from social phobia should receive treatment from doctors, especially as there is a tendency for them otherwise to treat themselves by taking alcohol or soft drugs in order to give themselves the courage to face the feared situation.

As mentioned earlier, the basis of a social phobia is a fear of being humiliated or embarrassed in front of others, so that any sense of self-esteem is eroded. It is often found in those with low self-esteem and can therefore probably be dated to childhood and has similar causes to other sources of low self-esteem. The lower someone's self-esteem the easier it is for them to be humiliated, and the more likely they are therefore to be further humiliated in future – thereby compounding their sense of inadequacy and undermining their confidence.

However clearly defined phobias may be, their origins may be more complex than is at first assumed. It is easy to suppose that a fear, for instance, of cows, which is comparatively common in young children, never entirely disappeared and resurfaced as a phobia later when the sufferer was confronted by the very real problems of adult life. This may be too simplistic. Some psychologists maintain that a phobia is a manifestation of a general anxiety state and that the sufferer has subconsciously selected the object of fear as a suitable outlet for the expression of this anxiety. Just as general anxiety increases the impact of the phobias so, if these patients can plan their lives so as to avoid the phobia, their overall level of anxiety may then be reduced. A person who, for instance, is terrified of snakes will have no problems living in the West End of London.

The emergence of a phobia may happen by chance. It may be something, perhaps, which was causing some small anxiety when a greater worry first appeared. The developing person is unable to face the tensions and fears produced, for instance, by being part of a dysfunctional family, and subconsciously opts to find an outlet for his or her anxieties by pegging them to, say, spiders.

Delving into childhood experiences, remembering the time when Susie, the vicious terrier, bit you, and Grandmother demanded that you should be brave and ignore the blood pouring down a shin, may be a fascinating way to spend an afternoon but unfortunately the evidence is that psychoanalytical treatment doesn't help anxieties and phobias. Someone's family may have been totally dysfunctional, only one step away from the courts and charges of abuse, but there it is, all now twenty, thirty or more years ago. The concept of psychological treatment favoured by doctors concentrates on cognitive therapy, worrying less about the causes of the symptoms and more about boosting self-esteem so that they may be coped with. Cognitive therapy has had some success in the treatment of anxiety states. Other forms of psychotherapy have their advocates who assert that they are helpful in many cases.

Individual phobias in the past were dealt with by exposing the patient to the trouble, either by gradually increasing the stimulus, which is very time-consuming, or by a process called desensitization or 'flooding'. In flooding, the patient is subjected to the full horror of their fear so that in time they become accustomed to the worst it could do. Now the medical emphasis is on cognitive therapy, coupled with explaining the condition to the patient, persuading them to keep a diary of their fears and helping them to understand them.

Cognitive therapy can be combined with medication. For the sufferer from social phobias, for instance, the prescription of beta-blockers before a potentially pulverizing social event has become are a very popular treatment, especially as they reduce the palpitations, sweating and tremor. The patient thereby gains confidence that the outward and visible signs of their fear may not be noticed.

Other drugs used include various of the tranquillizer and anti-anxiety preparations. Benzodiazepines, such as Valium (diazepam) and Librium (chlordiazepoxide), have fallen into disrepute because of their alleged addictive qualities, although the occasional use of such benzodiazepine preparations as Frisium (clobazam) is justified. The non-benzodiazepine Buspar (buspirone) has become popular for the short-term management of anxiety disorders.

More recently, some of the antidepressants, in particular the ever-versatile 5HT-reuptake inhibitors (or SSRIs – selective serotonin reuptake inhibitors) have been shown to be of value: Prozac (fluoxetine) doesn't only help the anxious dog, as recent veterinary work and animal psychologists have shown, but also the human who is terrified of the poor quaking beast. Another antidepressant preparation, Manerix (moclobemide), an RIMA (reversible inhibitor of monoamine oxidase), is likely to prove effective in controlling many of the most distressing features of phobic conditions. Like all the MAOIs (monoamine oxidase inhibitors), it is not free of side-effects and care has to be taken to avoid a wide range of foods and many other drugs, with which it interacts. However, this disadvantage is much less pronounced than in older MAOI preparations – used in the treatment of phobias for many years – where the reaction to certain foods and drugs is potentially very dangerous to the patient. Recently, there have been very encouraging reports about the use of the 5HT-reuptake inhibitor Seroxat (paroxetine) in the treatment of social phobia: if only the Cabinet Minister had had one of these little white pills to swallow he might have been able to enjoy his chicken and chips with his party workers.

There is, therefore, hope for patients with phobias. And not just through medication – those with a fear of flying, for instance, can be cured by a course of desensitization treatment. This is so common that the therapy is conducted in classes, and, finally, at the last session, the class hire an aircraft and they all fly to France for a celebratory dinner.

Obsessive-Compulsive Disorder

Stories of people with obsessive-compulsive disorder, commonly known as OCD, frequently figure in the popular press. Obsessions are persistent, unwelcome thoughts, or impulses, which even the patient realizes are senseless but is nevertheless unable to ignore. The compulsions are repetitive rituals which have been adopted in an attempt to allay anxiety induced by the obsession. The person with OCD is torn between feelings of anxiety that if they don't perform the ritual which they realize is absurd, they will be confronted by some dreaded situation, and the desire to resist the compulsion because it seems so irrational. Until the compulsive ritual is started tension mounts alarmingly, but once it has been performed to the patient's satisfaction it provides some momentary relief from anxiety.

Many people with OCD have an obsessional anxiety about 'dirt' and 'germs' with which they feel others have contaminated the objects they have to touch, and they therefore adopt a complicated ritual in order to avoid this. One eleven-year-old boy was obsessed by the thought that his hands would pick up some dreaded germ during his everyday playground life, or off the door knobs at his school. He was also worried in case splashing from a puddle might transfer germs to his face, and was equally unhappy about walking around the bathroom after a bath, in case the floor was germ-laden. His bedtime ritual took a couple of hours. He undressed in the bathroom, had his bath and then had to walk on newly laid-down, unread, newspapers so that he could reach his bed without his feet touching the floor. Once in the bedroom he had a series of chairs arranged so that he could step from chair to chair, always suitably covered, until he reached the sanctity of his clean sheets. If at any time during his progress from the bath to the bed his hand touched something which might have been handled by others, or if he thought that his foot might have strayed over the edges of the clean papers, the whole routine, including the bath, had to be repeated.

It is not at all uncommon for OCD to become obvious in children of ten to fifteen, and some authorities suggest a third of all cases of OCD are first seen in this age group. In 75 per cent of all patients it is manifest by the age of thirty. C. S. Lewis, the well-known writer and university don, describes in his autobiography

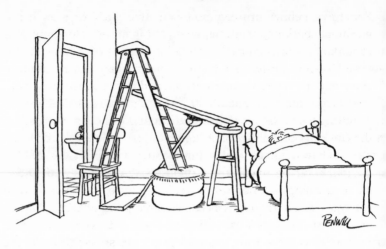

Surprised by Joy his own childhood ritual which, if not correctly performed, defeated sleep. A compulsion to have a bedroom meticulously organized, and laid-out in precisely the same way each night before sleep is possible is common.

Another patient, who held a commanding post in industry, always wanted the first appointment of the day at 8.30 in the morning. One day he wanted to see me urgently, but as the 8.30 appointment had already been booked, I suggested that he should come at 7.45. Although I had known him for twenty-five years, it was only then that he told me of his lifelong suffering from obsessive-compulsive disorder which, although it had complicated his daily timetable, had not prevented him from succeeding in the hard world of commerce and industry. Even to reach me, or his office, in time for 8.30, he always needed to start his cleansing ritual at 4.30 a.m. His ritual, planned to rid his body of the contamination from his bed, took three hours – 'You see why 7.45 would be a strain. I would have to get up at 3.45 to make it.'

These case histories illustrate how compulsive rituals interfere with people's ordinary daily life and in particular how they undermine a patient's efficiency by impeding their efforts.

Repetitive behaviours commonly involve such rites as hand-washing, checking, counting, repeating mantras or prayers. It is important to understand that minor degrees of ritualistic and obsessive-compulsive behaviour are common. Lesser compulsions may be seen in any group of children walking away from the playground. The small boy, for instance, who makes a ritual of hitting every second plank in the fence, or never stepping on the cracks, is probably doing no more than behaving as children have behaved for centuries, but if carried to extremes his behaviour could be an early sign of obsessive-compulsive disorder. Hand-washing is a normal hygienic measure, but, if carried to extremes, it too frequently becomes a symptom of OCD. Having one's clothes neatly arranged before going to bed is standard nursery teaching – being unable to settle unless everything in the bedroom has been precisely arranged, shoes all neatly in line and every object checked and touched, is unusual. Most people are anxious in case they have left a tap running or the oven turned on – to check once is a wise precaution, to have to check it time after time is abnormal.

Instances of obsessive-compulsive disorder are varied and distressing. Much of the data is anecdotal, and since the diagnosis is a matter of deciding the degree to which the person is obsessive, and most of those who have any hint of this condition are by nature anxious, some precision needs to be sought. This can be achieved by following the *DSM-IV* diagnostic criteria carefully. When this is done, many people who have been worried about their own minor obsessions, or those of their family, can rest assured, and those whose behaviour is causing serious inconvenience can seek help, whether from effective medication which is now more readily available or from psychotherapy.

The *DSM-IV* lays down the diagnostic criteria for obsessive-compulsive disorder. In full they are:

Either obsessions:
   recurrent and persistent thoughts, impulses or images that are
      experienced, at some time during the disturbance, as

intrusive and inappropriate and that cause marked anxiety
or distress;

the thoughts, impulses, or images are not simply excessive
worries about real-life problems;

the person attempts to ignore or suppress such thoughts,
impulses, or images, or to neutralize them with some other
thought or action;

the person recognizes that the obsessional thoughts, impulses,
or images are a product of his or her own mind (not imposed
from without, as in thought insertion);

Or compulsions:

repetitive behaviours (e.g. hand-washing, ordering, checking)
or mental acts (e.g. praying, counting, repeating words
silently) that the person feels driven to perform in response
to an obsession, or according to rules that must be applied
rigidly;

the behaviours or mental acts are aimed at preventing or
reducing distress or preventing some dreaded event or
situation: however, these behaviours or mental acts either are
not connected in a realistic way with what they are designed
to neutralize or prevent, or are clearly excessive.

In summary, those who can be said to suffer from OCD will,
at some point during the course of the disorder, recognize that the
obsessions or compulsions are excessive or unreasonable (this
does not apply to children): that the obsessions or compulsions
cause marked distress, are time-consuming (take more than one
hour a day), or significantly interfere with the person's normal
routine, occupational (or academic) functioning, or usual social
activities or relationships.

Treatment for obsessive-compulsive disorder has improved out
of all recognition with modern pharmacology. Anafranil (clomipramine) was the first drug to be used with success. It is primarily
an antidepressant but proved itself to be more efficient than

other tricyclic agents such as Tofranil (imipramine) and Tryptizol (amitriptyline). The introduction of the 5HT-reuptake inhibitors (SSRIs) proved a great step forward, and many of them have been shown to have anti-obsessive features. Faverin (fluvoxamine), Seroxat (paroxetine) and Prozac (fluoxetine) are three of the group which have been specifically licensed for this disorder. Cognitive behavioural therapy has also been widely used to treat obsessive-compulsive disorders and its usefulness has been confirmed by studies.

Post-Traumatic Stress Disorder

One of the bloodiest wars ever was the American Civil War. Few people realize that in a country which then had a comparatively small population, over 600,000 people were killed in the fighting. A combination of improved weaponry and inadequate medical facilities produced very many serious casualties who survived with their memories. The symptoms of post-traumatic stress disorder were described for the first time after the American Civil War but it was another 120 years, in the 1980s, before they were officially listed in *DSM-III* as a distinct diagnosis.

Post-traumatic stress disorder doesn't have to be related to war or even accidents or physical combat – a similar condition can be caused by sexual or physical abuse in vulnerable people. An interesting feature of post-traumatic stress disorder is why similar trauma results in such a variety of outcomes. The symptoms of post-traumatic disorder are now, thanks to the media, well known. Hyper-arousal is the situation in which patients are in an ever-ready state of alertness, subconsciously prepared for a re-enactment of the disaster. Someone, for instance, who has been involved in a bombing incident may show an excessive response to any loud noise, or a soldier back from combat may be irrationally upset by a car backfiring. The chronic anxiety not only produces these startle responses but many other signs of an anxiety state such as irritability, sleeplessness and unpredictable behavioural patterns. Flashbacks and recurrent nightmares are also common and may be triggered by such an everyday event as a clap of thunder; sometimes the patient may not even be aware of what precipitated it.

What causes post-traumatic stress varies from person to person. My father spent three years as a doctor in the trenches in the First World War. In his extreme old age I once asked him if he ever dreamed of the horrors of battle and of the carnage which it was his role to treat. He assured me he never dreamed of the war but he did have a recurrent nightmare when he was miserable or over-tired – his dreams took him back to the trauma of sitting exams at Cambridge.

Post-traumatic stress disorder can take many forms but nothing like so many as those attributed to it in popular myth. In some political circles it is now becoming accepted that the years of Conservative government started to come to an end as the result of the IRA Brighton bombing, and that thereafter Mrs Thatcher and her ministers individually and collectively displayed signs of post-traumatic stress disorder. Whether any of the people in the hotel at the time did experience these symptoms is not recorded, but what is certain is that any shortcomings in the then government's decisions and behaviour do not meet the criteria laid down in *DSM-IV*. As with governments, so with individuals, it is as well to know how psychiatrists, worldwide, define the condition and what they look for in a patient before it may be diagnosed. Mrs Thatcher may have had a depressed phase after she lost the leadership, but there was no evidece from her very robust response to the IRA bomb that she needed Faverin.

The diagnostic criteria for post-traumatic stress disorder are:

A   The person has been exposed to a traumatic event in which both of the following were present: the person experienced, witnessed, or was confronted with, an event or events that involved actual or threatened death, or serious injury, or a threat to the physical integrity of self or others; and the person's response involved intense fear, helplessness, or horror. In children, this may be expressed instead by disorganised or agitated behaviour.

B   The traumatic event is persistently re-experienced in one or more of the following ways:

recurrent and intrusive distressing recollections of the event, including images, thoughts, or perceptions. In young children, repetitive play may occur in which themes or aspects of the trauma are expressed.

recurrent distressing dreams of the event. In children, there may be frightening dreams without recognizable content.

acting or feeling as if the traumatic event were recurring (includes a sense of reliving the experience, illusions, hallucinations, and dissociative flashback episodes, including those that occur on awakening or when intoxicated). In young children, trauma-specific enactment may occur.

intense psychological distress at exposure to internal or external cues that symbolize or resemble an aspect of the traumatic event.

physiological reactivity on exposure to internal or external cues that symbolize or resemble an aspect of the traumatic event.

C   Persistent avoidance of stimuli associated with the trauma and numbing of general responsiveness (not present before the trauma), as indicated by three or more of the following:

efforts to avoid thoughts, feelings, or conversations associated with the trauma.

efforts to avoid activities, places, or people that arouse recollections of the trauma.

inability to recall an important aspect of the trauma.

markedly diminished interest or participation in significant activities.

feeling of detachment or estrangement from others.

restricted range of affect (e.g. unable to have loving feelings).

> sense of a foreshortened future (e.g. does not expect to have a career, marriage, children, or a normal life span).

D Persistent symptoms of increased arousal (not present before the trauma), as indicated by two or more of the following:
> difficulty falling or staying asleep
> irritability or outbursts of anger
> difficulty concentrating
> hypervigilance
> exaggerated startle response

E Duration of the disturbance (symptoms in Criteria B, C, and D) is more than one month.

F The disturbance causes clinically significant distress or impairment in social, occupational, or other important areas of functioning.

Hitherto treatment for post-traumatic stress disorder has been supportive psychotherapy coupled with systems designed to 'work through' the event which caused the trouble, so that they may reassess themselves and the incident. Cognitive therapy is useful in treating any ensuing complications of the condition.

Other patients may need a different approach. Experienced psychotherapists are becoming increasingly skilled at deciding who is likely to weather an emotionally traumatic event, and who is more likely to need long-term therapy. If the incident was a prolonged one, if the casualty list was heavy, or if someone close to the survivor, either physically or emotionally, was killed, the effect tends to be greater. If the person who has been in a life-threatening event has suffered from a similar situation previously, the outcome, perhaps surprisingly, is likely to be worse rather than better. It is another example of Lord Moran's theory of finite courage, mentioned earlier in this book. Many psychotherapists believe that a patient should be allowed to decide for themselves when and if they want psychotherapy, it shouldn't be foisted on them, and some will need no more than the support of common, decent neighbourliness. Martin Bell, the former war correspondent and now MP, in discussing post-traumatic stress disorder with Professor Anthony Clare on his radio programme, suggests that a frequently effective protection against the disorder is the presence and support of the Padre, who is familiar with the military scenario, the relevant action and the serviceman.

Recently greater emphasis has been given to medication: beta-blockers decrease anxiety, the tricyclic antidepressants improve sleep and also reduce the frequency of daytime flashbacks. MAOI antidepressants settle the patient generally, and, more recently, the 5HT-reuptake inhibitors have been used with success.

In general, many forms of anxiety may appear intractable, but can be helped in ways which could only be dreamed of forty years ago. Depersonalization is the comparatively common experience in which a person feels separated from their own body. Characteristically, it strikes out of the blue: someone is apparently happily walking down a street when suddenly they feel as if they are no longer inside their own body, it is as if they are watching themselves, and even as they watch, they are describing their own actions to themselves as if they were a commentator. Depersonalization is a symptom of many different conditions, whereas in depersonalization disorder it is not associated with anything else and occurs sufficiently often to cause distress. Psychotherapy is the standard treatment.

In my own practice, I have always found that patients with free-floating anxieties are the most difficult to help. The advent of the 5HT-reuptake inhibitors, or SSRIs, as mentioned above, has certainly transformed many people's lives, but those with free-floating anxieties frequently relapse under stress, and many are destined to become 'heartsink patients', despite cognitive or other psychotherapy and modern medication. In addition, many patients with anxiety disorders, of whatever type, find benefit from complementary medicine, with all its many disciplines.

3

Personality Disorders

Everyone has a distinct personality. The core of their personality is partly inherited and partly moulded by the events of early childhood and adolescence, and can be detected throughout the rest of their life. However, circumstances later in life, in adulthood, may well change the veneer presented to the world and may even – if the experiences have been sufficiently cataclysmic – alter a person's underlying temperament. There were few prisoners of war who didn't come back from the camps in the Far East feeling that they hadn't been fundamentally altered by their time in captivity. Likewise, educational, spiritual or physically challenging experiences may be transformative.

Some of the best-known people in the country, whose exploits fill our newspapers, whether the gossip columns, the parliamentary reports, the sports pages or the finance section, have personality disorders. Far more often, the life and times of the less talented with personality disorders don't hit the national headlines, but fill the pages of local papers in the reports of trials of petty offences.

People with a personality disorder have an abnormal temperament, often characterised by recurrent, maladaptive, inappropriate, even destructive behaviour. However, it shouldn't be thought that those with personality disorders are necessarily or even usually criminal; there are many forms of maladaptive behaviour which may be socially inconvenient and a nuisance but a trial only to the sufferer and their families. Those with a personality disorder who lack the audacity, charm and charisma of a Robert Maxwell may become no more than small-town, much-married fraudsters.

Scrooge wasn't the only man whose personality was changed to its roots by a hair-raising ordeal, although such transformations do belong more to the world of fiction than the real world. The police are always certain that the leopard never changes its spots and they take advantage of this characteristic to solve many crimes. However, a person's apparent character may alter almost beyond recognition. Oscar Wilde before he went to prison pursued his chosen lifestyle with panache, sophistication, urbanity and legendary humour. When he came out of prison, these finer aspects of his individuality had been blunted, his previous virtues had become a parody of themselves, and his proclivities coarse and gross. Those who had known him in his earlier days were shocked by the spectacle of a once fastidious man who had become gargantuan, with a subtlety replaced by crude explicitness. Prison still can have that effect.

Without emulating either St Paul or Oscar Wilde, and having a complete change of outlook, some degree of flexibility is a desirable feature in a well-orientated person. When someone's character is totally inflexible and does not fit in with the accepted standards of the culture in which they find themselves living, or when they are so inflexible that they cannot make even the minor, let alone the major, changes required by everyday living, it is considered an abnormal feature. Daily the newspapers carry stories of the rigid, inflexible parent who would rather be deprived of their child's love and company than accept that social mores have changed, and believes that throwing out the previously beloved daughter, with or without the white bundle, is better than condoning a different social code.

The degree to which such people's personal relationships, and their ability to fit into society, is disturbed by an abnormal personality will depend on its nature. Doctors have recently been encouraged to group these abnormalities into three clusters. Cluster A personality disorders are those which were previously only thought of as a cause of abnormally eccentric behaviour. Cluster B incorporates those who have an over-emotional and

83

dramatic personality, whose actions can seem abnormally selfish, manipulative and impulsive. Patients whose personality troubles are classified as belonging to cluster C have a character associated with neurotic disorders, described as the over-dependent, the avoidant, the co-dependent, the compulsive and the passive-aggressive. These traits will be explained later.

Each of the eleven personality disorders listed in the *Diagnostic and Statistical Manual of Mental Disorders* has been classified and can be slotted into one or another of these clusters. The designation of the cluster is included after the name of the personality disorder: Paranoid personality (A); Schizoid personality (A); Schizotypal personality (A); Histrionic personality (B); Narcissistic personality (B); Antisocial personality (B); Borderline personality (B); Avoidant personality (C); Dependent personality (C); Obsessive-compulsive personality (C); Passive-aggressive personality (C).

Paranoid Personality Disorders

The press was outraged when Mr Nicholas Soames, a minister in the Conservative government, described the late Princess of Wales as having a 'paranoid personality'. It is unlikely that Mr Soames had read the *DSM*, but few words are more misused in ordinary conversation than 'paranoid'. It does not mean angry, scared or irritated. Instead, it refers to a tendency to interpret the actions of other people or organizations as deliberately demeaning or threatening, and indeed the Princess did consider that the actions of the Palace officials, whom she called 'the enemy', fell into these categories.

The actress Nicola Pagett has openly admitted to paranoid delusions. She first became known to a wide public when she starred in *Upstairs, Downstairs*, and realized that for many years she had a manic-depressive nature, which eventually reached the stage where she needed urgent medical attention. Although Nicola Pagett's symptoms were not the result of an isolated paranoid personality disorder, but were the manifestation of more fundamental psychiatric problems, they do illustrate paranoia very clearly. They also demonstrate how destructive these traits may be to family, friends and workmates.

Nicola Pagett was convinced that her husband, Graham, was poisoning her and committing incest with their daughter. No amount of reasoned argument, even evidence, would convince her that nothing untoward was taking place. She also believed not only that the water in the water jug was poisoned, but that poison had been 'introduced' into the mains water supply and therefore the tap water was also contaminated.

The emotions felt by people when they are irritated by another person's seemingly unreasonable and destructive approach may well be those of anger, fear or exasperation but they are not necessarily paranoid – they may only be displaying a natural annoyance. Whether paranoid emotions are truly this or merely an understandable reaction, only those who know the full circumstances can judge. Not all those people who feel that society is targeting them are doing so because they are paranoid – many are making a sound judgement. In some the problem can be summed up by the well-known joke – 'Just because I'm paranoid doesn't mean people aren't out to get me'. People can be as cruel as hens in a chicken run and, as with hens in the chicken run, when one is slightly out of line and different, it will be savagely pecked.

There is nothing new in the term 'paranoia' being used to describe a wide variety of poorly defined symptoms of mental disease. The word 'paranoia' comes from the Greek for 'beyond reason'. In those classical times it was used to describe all forms of insanity, and only in the Victorian era was it given its current medical meaning.

Paranoid symptoms, like those of depression, can be a feature of nearly all psychiatric diseases. As well as of paranoid personality disorder, paranoia is a prominent feature of, for instance, paranoid schizophrenia; of paraphrenia, as the term would imply (where an elderly patient has a persistent paranoid delusion but the rest of their personality remains intact); of the more severe forms of depression; of sleep deprivation; of toxicity from many drugs; of senile dementias and of brain tumours. All these conditions have to be excluded before a diagnosis of paranoid personality disorder can be made.

Whereas many personality disorders are more common in women, men are more likely to suffer from a paranoid personality disorder. Paranoid personality disorders can be acute or chronic, they may even be shared. Shared paranoid disorder used to be known as 'folie à deux'; this is a strange condition in which two people who are closely linked emotionally share the same delusion – it is an uncanny experience having a conversation with them both at once. They can be so convincing about their delusion and so supportive of each other that the third party, often presumably the doctor, feels that the whole world is beginning to go mad – or, even more alarmingly, that he or she, the doctor, is.

As in all the personality disorders, the doctor has a checklist of signs and symptoms, and can tick them off rather as a Sunday paper reader might do the questionnaire at the back of the paper to find out if, for instance, he or she is happily married, upwardly mobile or a good lover. In the checklist for paranoid personality disorder four of seven characteristics must be present before the diagnosis can be made. Excluded from the definitions are those symptoms which would suggest an obvious diagnosis of schizophrenia or another diagnosable delusional disorder.

A patient with paranoid disorder:

Expects, without any true basis, to be exploited or harmed by others.

Questions, without any justification, the loyalty or trustworthiness of those people around them, including friends and family.

Reads hidden or threatening meanings into perfectly benign remarks or everyday actions.

Bears grudges and is very unforgiving of any insult or slight, however small.

Does not confide in others for fear that the information could be
  used against them.
Is easily offended, reacts with anger to the offence and counter-
  attacks.
Suspects, without justification, the faithfulness of spouse or
  sexual partner.

The paranoid personality is usually obvious by early adult life
and is more likely to be noticed by friends and family than it is
by doctors and psychiatrists. Doctors may be among the last to
hear of the paranoid fears of a patient, particularly if their worries are mild, because delusional anxieties often include fears
about their medical advisers, and expressing them is, rightly,
thought to alienate the doctor. Likewise, many lesser degrees of
paranoia remain unspoken because patients who suffer them
strive, unless they are grossly psychotic, to keep their beliefs to
themselves. They realize that these paranoid concerns are
unlikely to be well understood or received by those around
them. It is partly for this reason that paranoid people avoid
intimate relationships. However, they come out of the meta-
phorical closet when it is a matter of pursuing their interests in
litigation, and in battling to correct what they perceive as an
injustice.

The paranoid personality disorder may be difficult to treat not
because doctors haven't the correct medication in their medicine
cupboards, but because the paranoid personality expects that
others are out to silence them, if not to destroy them, and therefore regards the chemicals marketed by the pharmaceutical
company with the utmost suspicion. Patients with a paranoid
personality may become depressed, and conversely, those who
are depressed may become paranoid. Sometimes, therefore, when
antidepressants are prescribed – and are taken – they may have a
dramatic influence.

A quick personality appraisal of any large office organization,
or a rapid perusal of the chattier bits of a newspaper, will
immediately reveal candidates for inclusion in this category. If

they do come to the doctor's surgery, their complaints, criticisms and disruptive behaviour may make them very obvious in the queue, as any stress, which includes physical illness, tends to make paranoid patients worse, and they become even more quarrelsome and suspicious than usual. Textbooks advise doctors that they should expect to be neither trusted nor loved by patients with this temperament, and that the patients are likely to respond better to medical advice if the physician remains slightly aloof.

Even if paranoia is commonplace in all communities, sufferers rarely visit their doctor in order to seek help about their personality as they themselves can see little wrong with it. It is those around them who wonder why the sufferer is unable to keep friends or employment and if it can really be true that the world is so inhospitable. If the patient's friends and family are not aware of this personality disorder they may be misled into supposing that mutual colleagues or acquaintances are as untrustworthy and disloyal as has been suggested.

People with this disorder are sometimes tempted to ease the stresses they feel in their social life by drinking and illicit drug taking. It may not be pleasant to think that those around you are plotting against you but unfortunately having a perpetual hangover makes the situation worse. A hangover is one of the lesser causes of a minor paranoid state – as once the alcohol or drug has worn off the patient is left feeling more paranoid and edgy than before. Long-term drug abuse, in particular with cocaine, amphetamines, and similar drugs such as Ecstasy, is a frequent cause of paranoia.

Pinfold's troubles, so eloquently and minutely chronicled by Evelyn Waugh in *The Ordeal of Gilbert Pinfold*, bear lasting testimony to the ability of medication to induce paranoia. The description is reputed to have reflected Evelyn Waugh's own experience when he was overtreated with bromides. Although drug therapy, in the form of atypical neuroleptics, can revolutionize the lifestyle of someone who is suffering from a paranoid personality disorder, the chances of persuading such a person to swallow pills are small. Some doctors respond to the lack of co-operation by referring the patient for psychotherapy, but this can be a mistake – even Freud was very chary of treating these patients.

Psychotherapy is rarely successful in the treatment of paranoid personality disorder, as the psychotherapist may induce paranoid feelings unless he or she is very intuitive and adept at building a trusting relationship. Group therapy provides a fertile ground for paranoid fears. In their paper 'The Treatment of Personality Disorders', published in *Psychiatric Annals*, P. S. Freeman and J. G. Gunderson go so far as to say 'not a single report of successful treatment has ever been recorded'.

Schizoid Personality

While a person with a paranoid personality hears every derogatory whisper about them, and is cast into absolute gloom by the emotions these evoke, a person with a schizoid personality disorder is indifferent as to whether their actions are approved or disapproved by others. They are essentially loners, self-contained, doing a job as well as they can, minding their own business, and neither experiencing nor expressing emotion to any great depth. These are the characters who were portrayed in the Ealing films of the fifties and sixties, as admirably and aloofly running our embassies, commanding our armies or becoming withdrawn, but thoroughly decent, Oxford dons. Although it would seem that these fictional characters must have been born with a stiff upper lip, possibly accentuated by an unemotional education, psychiatrists tell us that in real life this distinctive personality, when carried to extremes, is only obvious in late adolescence or early adult life.

A diagnosis of schizoid personality is acceptable if a person has at least four of seven characteristics laid down in the *DSM*. Those with this condition were previously merely described as having an 'introverted' personality, but this is too imprecise as excessive introversion is found in many patients including those

"WELL, THAT'S TEN THOUSAND OF THE BLIGHTERS SLAUGHTERED
— ANYONE FOR A SPOT OF LUNCH?"

with schizophrenia. The *DSM*'s seven tell-tale characteristics of schizoid personalities are that they

Neither desire nor enjoy close relationships, and do not bond closely with other members of their family.

Choose solitary activity, whether at work, or in spare time.

Do not experience strong emotions such as anger or joy.

Are not particularly interested in having a sex life.

Are indifferent as to whether their actions meet with the approval or otherwise of others.

Either have no or only one close friend.

Are cold and aloof and do not return friendly gestures, such as a smile or a wave.

As in all personality disorders, the difference between an unusual character who slots adequately into a community, and one who can be said to have a personality disorder, is only a matter of degree. Another fictional character, Shaw's Professor Henry Higgins, the anti-hero of *Pygmalion*, has a classically schizoid personality: he chooses to live a solitary existence both at work and in his spare time; he doesn't display any strong emotions, anger or joy, and certainly isn't initially preoccupied with his sex life. He makes one close friend and doesn't give a damn what his mother, neighbours, colleagues or the world in general think about him, his activities or his dress sense. He would certainly never return a gesture, whether smile or wave, appropriately or with any warmth.

Patients with a schizoid personality will obviously have a very restricted social life, which is unlikely to bother them, but it may impair advancement in their chosen profession should it be one which requires conviviality.

Treatment is often not necessary but too few, when they require the support which could be offered by psychotherapy, accept it. Psychotherapists believe that if this help is accepted when offered, sufferers do benefit. Sufferers are often equally reluctant to take medication. The incidence of patients with a schizoid personality who lapse into frank schizophrenia is said by many authorities to be no greater than in the rest of the population. However, if their character does develop an obvious psychotic twist so that their sense of reality fades, and their thought processes become disturbed and deluded, they will respond to atypical neuroleptic drugs.

Schizotypal personality

The schizotypal personality is often, quite wrongly, confused with the schizoid. There are close family links between those with a schizotypal personality and schizophrenia, and an appreciable number of patients with this temperament do cross the borderline and later become diagnosable as schizophrenic. The condition is also dealt with in the chapter on schizophrenia.

People with schizotypal personalities may be found in every village, town and community: they are the interesting, unusual but frequently the 'bizarre' member of the community. They include the night-walking adolescent with shoulder-length hair who takes exercise hidden in the obscurity of darkness, clad in long black clothes. They are given to strange fanatical beliefs and are at the same time socially anxious. It is this social timidity which persuades them to wear clothes which extinguish their own persona and background, not always realizing that the very peculiarity of their clothes is as much a uniform as a dark city suit on a stockbroker would be in Threadneedle Street in the City of London.

The odd and eccentric schizotypal character isn't confined to youth. These people include in their number the traditionally eccentric aunt, the unconventional artist or art critic and the crazed professor who talks to himself even as he shuns other people. Their speech patterns may be unusual, but unlike those of a schizophrenic patient, are still perfectly coherent. Their speech is, however, rather vague and abstract. Their conversation has a tendency to digress so that sentences may be left incomplete. In their social relationships the schizotypal person may well be distant, and like the schizoid or schizophrenic patient, does not return gestures or facial expressions. A smile is not returned with a responding smile or a nod with a nod. Professor Calculus, of *Tintin* fame, is not alone; there are many like him in every community, not all of them with the excuse of deafness. The *DSM* lists nine characteristics and to achieve a diagnosis of schizotypal disorder one needs to score on at least five.

There may be ideas of reference (the condition in which the patient puts two and two together to make five). Many patients seem to refer to them when talking to me of 'coincidences', but they are coincidences which would seem to owe more to the imagination than to actuality.
Dislike of social occasions, which provoke excessive anxiety.
Odd beliefs and philosophies.
Unusual perceptual experiences, such as claiming to feel some

supernatural presence – the presence of the spirit of someone who has died, perhaps – but the sensation of a presence rather than sight or sound, they have not actually seen or heard them. (This must be seen in relation to the other symptoms – I have lived in a few haunted houses!)

Eccentric appearance and mannerisms, such as an unusual taste in clothes, often very anonymous, frequently black and extending to the ground.

A lack of close friends.

Using odd mannerisms to accompany their speech, which is vague and imprecise but grammatical and coherent.

Lack of empathy with other people, caused by lack of the appropriate gestures denoting friendship, the smiles, nods, waves, etc., which constitute social intercourse. Often they unwittingly display an aloof manner.

Some paranoid feelings.

Patients who have a schizotypal personality disorder may have short periods when they are frankly psychotic, with a breakdown of structured thought. People with this disorder are also more likely than others to have close relatives who are schizophrenic, and genetic studies confirm that the there is a relationship between this disorder and schizophrenia. From time to time neuroleptic drugs may be needed to treat schizotypal disorders, particularly in those patients who find it hard to maintain either satisfactory employment or to live a fulfilling life in the community.

Histrionic Personality Disorder

Histrionic personality disorder may be confused with another one of the personality disorders called borderline personality disorder. The two conditions have many features in common and may co-exist. More women than men have histrionic personality disorders and more women than men have symptoms which are shared with borderline personality disorder: in men it is the antisocial personality disorder which overlaps the borderline personality

It is said that women with a histrionic personality tend to be more sexually attractive and seductive than other women and pay undue regard to their appearance. This is only one of the many aspects of life in which they demand constant attention and, with it, approval and praise. They are centre-of-the-stage characters, who cannot bear it if the attention is off them and turned towards some other member of the group. They will immediately do something to bring the spotlight back on to themselves.

Not only are their emotions shallow, they are very obvious: just as still waters may run deep, so may storms in a shallow sea be particularly violent. Every minor emotion excites an intense reaction which is absurdly exaggerated. As in patients with antisocial personality disorders, they are impatient and demand immediate gratification of their desires. Shakespeare's vision of Cleopatra, many aspects of Marilyn Monroe's personality and those of a host of other film stars, illustrate the temperament. However, it is not necessary to go to Hollywood to find a person with a histrionic personality – they can be found in every group. Even a superficial analysis of the character of many public figures will reveal those who bask and shine in the spotlight but spit with anger or cry tears of rage and disappointment if ignored. Few, fortunately, are able to go as far as Cleopatra, who threatened to have a servant 'whipped in lingering pickle' if she was thwarted, however inadvertently.

People with a histrionic personality easily become bored and need constant excitement. Although casual friendships made by people with histrionic personalities tend to be superficial and easily abandoned, their long-term relationships are more variable. They make relationships with the opposite sex easily, but tire of their joint sexual repertoire equally easily. Even so, they become dependent on their partners and attempt to control them, thereby achieving both the reassurance of a regular partner and power – it seems that many do thus achieve a lasting partnership, provided that it is on their own terms. Others are more promiscuous and when sexually bored, look to indulge one romantic fantasy after another, always hoping that a prince or princess will come along. Possibly more often with women, but in either sex, the person with a histrionic personality may be sexually unresponsive once they have made a conquest.

Whilst women with this kind of personality attempt to dominate their partners, they may also be inordinately attracted by the dominant, successful, powerful man. Some will look for a glamorous and famous prince, who can satisfy their emotional dreams. Others search for the potent, commanding figure, perhaps someone like Aristotle Onassis, who fell for the allegedly histrionic Jackie Kennedy. These men, if not very appealing physically, are able to sort out all their women's problems (which have often stemmed from their impulsive behaviour and a lack of judgement) and help them to escape from the complexities of their life.

The health of people with a histrionic personality is frequently poor, and their physical symptoms, like their emotional feelings, tend to be exaggerated. As a result they are incapacitated by many day-to-day ailments which would be shrugged off by their more prosaic contemporaries. Women with the histrionic syndrome display 'la belle indifférence' more than other patients. 'La belle indifférence' is the phrase used to depict the manner of a patient who is obviously worried by a condition, recites to her doctor a long list of perceived symptoms, any one of which could be deadly, and then announces or implies that of course they are not worried – they know it's of no significance. These people are a particular trial to the medical profession, especially as after a doctor has been manipulated by the suppressed drama into carrying out some expensive investigation, they will say, 'Ah, doctor, I always knew there was nothing wrong.'

People with histrionic personality disorder are often very artistic and imaginative but, although intelligent, they rarely have a profound and sustained intellectual interest. Their forte is the quick, witty remark, again like Marilyn Monroe. Many could have been included in the category of people who used to be described as 'creative psychopaths', a term, needless to say, which is now considered politically incorrect and is no longer used.

Another parallel to a borderline personality is the tendency of histrionic personalities to occasional, periodic, transient, psychotic episodes, too short-lived to cause more than temporary concern. However, this is less a feature, if at all, of the histrionic personality. Although everybody will guess which of their friends and acquaintances have a histrionic personality, the *DSM* is strict about the terms of entry to the group; at least four of the criteria below must be met for a diagnosis to be made:

Constantly seeks approval, praise and reassurance.
Is inappropriately sexually seductive.
Is overly concerned with physical attractiveness.
Expresses emotion with inappropriate exaggeration.
Is only comfortable in situations where he or she is the centre of attention.
Displays rapidly shifting and shallow expressions of emotion.
Is self-centred, impatient and seeks immediate satisfaction.
Has a style of speech which is full of exaggeration and hyperbole, but is imprecise and lacks detail.

Narcissistic Personality Disorder

This is another example where there is an overlap of symptoms between the personality disorders. So many patients with a narcissistic personality also have a borderline personality disorder that many psychiatrists consider them one and the same condition. An antisocial personality disorder may also show symptoms of narcissism, with delusions of grandiosity. Narcissism is also found as a symptom in the histrionic and borderline personality disorders, and is not uncommon in patients who are depressed. The depressed state in these patients may be increased or triggered by the subconscious realization that they are not quite as splendid and all-powerful as they would like to believe. They may therefore have a subconscious fear that their position of power, whether real or imagined, is under threat, which produces persistent feelings of tension which may become manifest as depression. These symptoms start in adolescence or early adult life and persist. In order to diagnose a narcissistic personality a patient must show evidence of five out of nine symptoms listed in the *DSM*:

Reacts to criticism with feelings of rage, shame or humiliation. If sophisticated he or she may learn to hide these feelings.

Uses other people in an exploitative way to achieve his or her own ambition.

Has an excessive sense of self-importance, and so is described as displaying a pattern of grandiosity. Tends to exaggerate achievements and talents and expects others to accept unquestioningly this self-assessment.

Believes that any problems she or he may have are so rare, if not unique, that they can only be understood by other very special people.

Spends much of their time fantasizing about unlimited success, power, brilliance, beauty or ideal love.

Tends to feel that they are entitled to special favours and treatment. Not for them the last place in the queue, nor will they accept that the restaurant was fully booked.

Requires constant admiration and devotes considerable amount of time in making certain that he or she receives it.

Lacks empathy with other people and is incapable of understanding the problems they might have.

Narcissistic people are very envious.

Treatment of the narcissistic personality is difficult. Psychother-apy may help, but usually not group therapy. When narcissism is a feature of a depressed personality, treatment of the depression will sometimes achieve an improvement of the narcissistic state.

Antisocial Personality Disorder

'You're just a bloody psychopath!' is an epithet hurled at an opponent who has spilled someone's drink in a pub. After a spot of bother while driving, some fiercesome road-user may open your car door and shout in your face, 'What do you think you are, a psychopath?' Even the kind old lady, on hearing that a pensioner has been murdered for a few pounds will say, 'I am afraid he must have been a psychopath, doctor'.

The term 'psychopath' is an over-used insult and is now more likely to be heard shouted across a bar during a brawl than it is in a law court. This word, together with the allied 'sociopath', has been dropped from official medical terminology; the terms may be used by some lawyers, and are certainly current in the police force, but the official description of this personality disorder is 'antisocial personality disorder'. The press tend to employ the phrase 'personality disorder', without any further definition, as a euphemism for 'psychopath', thinking the two synonymous. The view that the term 'personality disorder' describes the same condition as 'psychopath' or 'sociopath' is gaining ground. It is frequently used in police court reports and is beloved by parents whose children have committed some frightful crime. I have had patients' relatives who have said to me, 'Eddie isn't a bad lad – he's got a personality disorder'.

These people, the Eddies of this world (they are usually male), although once described as psychopaths, are now said to suffer from an antisocial personality disorder. Their character and behaviour are such that unless they are very cunning, or very rich, they are almost inevitably going to clash with society and, in all probability, the forces of the law.

Doctors consider it unwise to make a formal diagnosis of antisocial personality disorder before a patient is eighteen, but everybody can remember contemporaries at school, who, long before this age, displayed very clear evidence of the symptoms which would later lead to a life of crime, and the diagnosis of this syndrome. Psychiatrists now accept that to make a definitive diagnosis of antisocial personality disorder in an eighteen-year-old, the patient must have displayed obvious antisocial behaviour before they were fifteen. This will include some of the standard signs of delinquency such as expulsion from school, theft, promiscuous sexual behaviour, aggressive behaviour (often including the use of a weapon), cruelty to animals, vandalism, early experimentation with drugs and excessive amounts of alcohol, and a general rebellion against authority whenever its rules prove inconvenient. Not unnaturally, the academic performance of these troubled young people often shows them to be under-achievers, not matching their apparent intelligence. It is not unusual to read the autobiography of some famous film star or entrepreneur and to wonder what would have been the pattern of their hell-raising life if they hadn't had a money-making ability to protect them from their own excesses.

Many doctors suggest that the condition can be detected long before the age of fifteen. Antisocial behaviour essentially starts as 'tricky' behaviour in childhood, develops into an aggressive bearing in adolescence and becomes typical of what is described as antisocial behaviour in adult life. Even as young children these people show evidence of emotional instability, lack of warmth, and no ability to forge loving relationships. They are often unresponsive, generally negative and refuse to fit in with whatever the family is trying to enjoy.

These children can stretch their parents' patience to its limits, an exercise which demonstrates clearly that many of the undesirable characteristics displayed by the child are inherited. A vicious circle is established; the difficult child, already a loner and antisocial, is increasingly rejected by his parents and thus becomes even more antisocial. The parents of antisocial children will of course themselves carry the same genes, and are therefore likely to be impulsive, potentially violent and to lack patience – they have in fact a personality which will exacerbate the situation. Antisocial behaviour is not spread evenly throughout society, but it can be detected at every level. It is also better hidden in the more affluent and socially powerful, but some or all of the same characteristics, both in behaviour and background, may be discerned.

People with antisocial personalities characteristically come from large, dysfunctional families, where love has been at a premium and there has been an excess of violence, whether verbal or physical, between the adults in the household. Various studies have shown that the parents of antisocial adolescents are not only neglectful but have no regular pattern of discipline, so that punishments are not only inconsistent but when they are administered tend to be unduly severe. It is not unusual to find that the parents of a child with antisocial tendencies are alcoholic; and that anger, poverty and broken marriages are prevalent. Thus role models tend to be faulty, with fathers who have been violent and with a criminal record. Not surprisingly, antisocial behaviour on the part of the mother is an even more likely way of inducing similar problems in the children.

Both home and school are likely to have been in deprived inner cities. At school many of these antisocial children tend not only to do badly and fail to reach their potential, but in quite a proportion their initial promise is probably less than that of other children. Sometimes they make up in charm what they lack in intellect.

As the adolescent becomes more aggressive, isolation from contemporaries increases. Some authorities divide those displaying antisocial behaviour into two groups: those who continue to be acceptable to their peers, even if they are opposed to society – described as 'socialized'; and those who become alienated from their contemporaries and act as privateers in a war against society – described as 'unsocialized'. If a child is antisocial in teenage life he or she has two chances in three of becoming an antisocial adult.

To be diagnosed as having an antisocial personal disorder, previously known as psychopathy, a person must be aged at least eighteen, have shown evidence of antisocial conduct before the age of fifteen, and display at least four of the following ten characteristics:

Inability to keep a regular job.
Failure to conform to normal social behaviour and the laws of
  the community.
Irritability and aggressiveness – hence repeated fights.
Failure to honour financial obligations.
Failure to plan ahead, and acting very impulsively.
Lack of regard for the truth.
Reckless disregard for safety – theirs and other people's.
Inability to act as a responsible parent.
Inability to sustain a monogamous relationship for more than
  a year.
Lack of a sense of remorse.

In adult life the person with an antisocial personality will have a
poor work record. There will be a history of aggressiveness,
which varies in expression and severity depending on the socio-
economic background of the sufferer: a rich tycoon will work out
his aggressive feelings by shouting at a waiter, and get away
with it, whereas an unemployed inner city labourer will become
involved in street fights, and may well be arrested. Financial failure, and in particular a failure to pay debts, is a common finding,
as is the ability to lie. As parent or partner, such people tend to be
neither responsible nor faithful, while they appear to have no
appreciation of danger and thus no regard for safety, whether
their own or anyone else's.

In general, antisocial personalities are indifferent to law and
order, whether laid down by the courts or dictated by custom, or
their own groups – and they feel no compunction in breaking
these laws in order to achieve their own ends. People with antisocial personalities act impulsively, usually to achieve immediate
gratification, and without regard for long-term consequences.
This does not mean to say that they cannot be manipulative. The
ability of prisoners to achieve parole by deceiving the authorities
into believing that they are filled with remorse and have become
good, godfearing citizens is proverbial. Outside prison, many
people with antisocial disorder will show great charm until they

are thwarted, having learnt that charm can help them achieve
their ends.

Treatment for antisocial disorder, and associated conditions
of earlier life, is disappointing. The high recidivist rate in patients with antisocial personality disorder is disturbing, but some
cases may respond to behaviour therapy, group therapy and antipsychotic drugs. There must be a genuine desire for change in
outlook, which is unlikely in a group of people who by definition
tend to be grandiose, inflexible and lacking in insight.

Work by the clinical psychologist Dr Robert Andrey has shown
that with careful selection a reasonable proportion, 25 per cent or
over, of prisoners who might be classified as having an antisocial
personality disorder will, following a harsh but fair prison
regime, together with group therapy, so modify their behaviour
that they do not re-offend. They may remain basically amoral,
unreliable and irresponsible, liars and cheats, but they have also
learnt that certain acts will land them back in jail, or make them
outcasts of society, and so avoid them.

'Psychopaths' are not confined to the brutal, recurrent
offenders whose exploits are recounted in the courts, nor to the
mean, remorseless petty crook, but are also found in the boardroom. Robert Maxwell, from a disturbed background, won
acclaim in the war for his bravery, but soon exploited the prestige
this gave him to chisel out a handsomely profitable living while
working for the British Government in Berlin. Thereafter he transferred his activities to London, where a combination of dishonesty, ruthlessness and, where necessary, charm, provided him
with a billionaire's lifestyle and all the women and other comforts
of life which money could buy. Like many people with an
antisocial personality disorder, he was also very paranoid and
spied on everyone, including his family. At the corner of his office
by his desk a cupboard contained a mass of bugging equipment
so that by moving a plug, or flicking a switch, he was able to listen
in to all the important rooms in the tower block from which he
directed his empire.

When we look at Cap'n Bob Maxwell's record and compare it

with the symptoms as listed in the *DSM*, we can see how his work record, his lawlessness, his indifference to the social norms, whether in the boardroom, the bedroom or on the benches of the House of Commons when he was an MP, revealed the flaws in his personality. The irritability and aggressiveness which landed him in a thousand conflicts are well recorded as are his repeated 'failures to honour financial obligations' or his inability 'to sustain a totally monogamous relationship for more than one year'. Needless to say, he also had a disregard for the truth and lacked any remorse. The courage he displayed during the war could equally well fit in with his personality, for, contrary to popular opinion, the psychopathic bully is not a coward, and may indeed be very brave. As mentioned above, one of the characteristics of the antisocial personality listed is 'a reckless disregard for his or her own or others' personal safety'. Anyone who has driven with someone who has an antisocial personality disorder doesn't have to go to the battlefield with Cap'n Bob, MC to find this out.

As in so many psychiatric conditions, the likelihood of developing an antisocial personality disorder has both a genetic and environmental component. In particular, it seems to be the father who may hand on the significant genes, whether to a son or to a daughter. The environmental factors probably account for the apparent predominance of the condition amongst people from a poorer socio-economic group as they are more likely to have been brought up in dysfunctional families and subjected to all the stresses and strains of inner-city life, as described earlier.

How to treat a disordered personality which is by its very nature impulsive and selfish, manipulative, lacks insight or such emotions as guilt or remorse – which constitute conscience – presents considerable problems. The patients themselves are unlikely to co-operate and in any case don't find their lifestyle entirely unsatisfactory. Dr Robert Andrey's work perhaps confirms that of Maxwell Jones in 1956, which suggested that peer pressure and a desire to live a more comfortable lifestyle could help. The police chief in the area where I was a police surgeon, however, never believed that the ageing psychopath had learned how to behave – merely that he had learned how to conceal his sins.

Borderline Personality

From Napoleon to Alexander the Great, the movers and shakers of this world have had unusual personalities. An analogy is that to succeed in life with an uncomplicated character is as difficult as pushing a knife though a cork, whereas a corkscrew, elegant and spiral, is designed to go through it with ease. The person with an absolutely straight personality may not achieve as much as those who have a twist to their character. However charming, kind and happy, without a twist they may lack the originality and charisma to accomplish great things. To expect the great to have flawless personalities might be to condemn them to mediocrity. Conversely, it is rare to find both fame and contentment.

Before her death, the Princess of Wales's personality was constantly discussed. After her death, many of those who had criticized her character and lifestyle then felt mean and filled with remorse lest they had not paid due regard to her achievements, and the compassion and kindliness which she so often displayed. One aspect of her life has been neglected. Despite any flaws in her character, and the scrapes they led her into, she has demonstrated, as no one else could have done, that a need to visit the psychiatrist's doesn't preclude a life which can have worldwide impact.

Cynics will claim that her good works were part of a well-orchestrated public relations campaign, but the truth remains that if she hadn't been able to empathize with people from every background – above all, the outcasts from society – the campaign would have been a failure.

Doctors who analysed her behaviour, even those who admired her accomplishments and generosity, settled on three possible diagnoses to explain her love of the limelight, her anorexia and bulimia, her suicide attempts, her seemingly motiveless rages, her bumpy friendships, and her difficulty in keeping staff; her, perhaps understandable, paranoia, even her love of excitement and danger. The possibility that the symptoms of her personality, as retailed to the press, could be fitted into the portmanteau labelled 'paranoid personality disorder' was discussed in the House of Commons amid uproar; there were regular hints that she displayed many of the features of a histrionic personality, but the emotionally detached psychiatrists who had the time to read the tabloids settled somewhat uneasily on the diagnosis of a borderline personality.

Certainly Diana's early background, as reported not only by the press but by members of her family and in her biography written, with her full co-operation, by Andrew Morton, is characteristic of people with a borderline personality. Her admitted feelings of boredom and emptiness, her impulsiveness, which she made sound quite fun, and the difficulties with interpersonal relationships were all there. The Princess of Wales recounts her problems in finding a worthwhile long-term goal within a rewarding career, a difficulty which gave her an ambivalent approach to public life so that one year she was renouncing it, only, within a few months, to achieve her greatest success, as an international figure in the landmines campaign. After this, there were rumours that she was again hoping, perhaps unrealistically, to disappear into anonymity. She also told of her great fear of abandonment and her dislike of loneliness – two very striking features, almost as diagnostic as the recurrent suicide attempts and threats, of the borderline personality.

There was always the danger that the Princess of Wales, like her uncle, might commit suicide, and this must have been a terrible fear for her family and friends. But although it may sound absurd, in the light of this risk, there doesn't seem to have been any evidence whatsoever that her personality disorders, if she did indeed have them, could have been confused with any of the major psychiatric diseases such as a major depressive state, or even schizophrenia.

The term 'borderline personality disorder' was first coined in 1938 by psychoanalysts and is the one which is now the accepted description. The definition of borderline personality disorder emerged from work in the 1960s and 70s and was defined in 1979. There have always been difficulties in diagnosing borderline personality disorders in some people, because of the overlap of its symptoms with those of other personality disorders, schizophrenia and manic depression. There is an obvious sharing of features with the schizotypal, histrionic, narcissistic and antisocial personality disorders, and with schizophrenia. The depressive episodes characteristic of a borderline personality could be confused with the black days of the depressive, or the wild spending might be seen as a symptom of hypomania. These impetuous, over-anxious, angry and impulsive patients, who have a suicide rate as high as that in the major psychoses, are mainly women.

When I was a young doctor there was a group of patients who were then known as psychoneurotics. These patients apparently had a neurotic personality but were subject to intermittent attacks of very brief psychotic episodes, in which a sense of reality breaks down, particularly when stressed. Other terms which have been applied are pseudo-neurotic, pseudo-psychopathic, latent schizophrenic, emotionally unstable personality disorder, borderline ambulatory schizophrenia, pre-schizophrenia, abortive schizophrenia. The multiplicity of names reflects the difficulty in defining the condition and there is still argument sixty years after its conception about whether the condition is distinctive enough to be classified separately. Even so, patients who are thought to have borderline personalities tend to keep their diagnosis over a period of time, but some have other personality disorders, such as histrionic or paranoid, added to it.

Skill and experience is needed to distinguish borderline personality disorder from all the other psychiatric conditions with which it can be confused. There are conflicting reports as to the number of cases of borderline personality disorder which are eventually reclassified. A study carried out in 1977 compared the effectiveness of diagnosis of schizophrenia with that of borderline personality disorder. The psychiatrists had few doubts about the patients they diagnosed as schizophrenic but there was considerable discussion about those designated as having borderline personality disorder. In fact, of the twenty-four test cases who were diagnosed as borderline, only one was reassigned to the schizophrenic group.

In another study, however, fifteen years after diagnosis, 24 per cent of those thought to have borderline personality disorder had clearly become schizophrenic. In the same trial 55 per cent of those who were originally described as schizotypal had developed obvious schizophrenia. In all the studies there is no one particular symptom of borderline personality which could be used as a marker for underlying schizophrenia. People with borderline personality fit into society more comfortably and have a better chance of a successful domestic life than do those with schizophrenia. They are also more likely to hold down a job, despite occasional short-term admissions to a psychiatric hospital.

Distinguishing borderline personality from the affective disorders, whether mania or, in particular, depression, is also tricky, but the failure rate in the diagnosis seems to be lower than with schizophrenia. 11 per cent of patients with a borderline personality later displayed symptoms of severe depression associated with an affective disorder. The converse is also true in another study, which found that a third of depressed patients showed signs of borderline personality disorder.

People with borderline personalities are essentially unstable in many aspects of their life. They have a constant restless feeling of boredom and a lack of purpose. Their interpersonal relationships tend to be fleeting, partly because these are characterized by over-adoration, too soon to be followed by unwarranted criticism and undervaluation. Yesterday's knight soon becomes today's blackguard. Unlike the schizotypal patient their inability to make a lasting relationship is particularly distressing as they have an abnormally great dread of being alone.

It is not only in their relationships that patients with borderline personality disorder are impulsive, but, as mentioned, their impulsiveness leads them into terrible problems, with reckless spending, promiscuity and excessive use of alcohol or drugs. They have a love of fast cars and find reckless driving stimulating. Their mood can vary very rapidly so that one moment they are irritable and anxious, depressed, almost suicidal, and the next they may be either quite normal or even over-elated. The mood swings are very much more rapid than in manic-depressive disease, more difficult to predict and do not usually respond to the same treatment.

Patients with borderline personalities often make suicidal gestures and threats, and may well commit suicide. Frequently, part of the suicidal gesture is self-mutilation: it is not uncommon to see someone with this condition with scratches and superficial cuts on the wrists, inflicted before they have taken an overdose. The anger is not always turned inwards against themselves; they can suffer from uncontrollable and intense rages. These can be triggered by an incident which would be shrugged off by the majority of people. Sometimes the rage may precipitate a suicidal gesture or attempt, but at other times it can lead to a fight or assault with potentially tragic consequences. In order to confirm diagnosis at least four of the following criteria as defined by the *DSM*, must be met. The person with borderline personality disorder:

Lives through a pattern of unstable and intense interpersonal relationships, alternating between extremes of idealization and devaluation.
Is impulsive in at least two of the following respects: spending; sex; substance abuse; shoplifting; reckless driving; bingeing.
Has wildly swinging moods, shifting from depression, irritability and anxiety to over-excitement. The depressive or other phases rarely last for more than a few days, often only a few hours.
Has inappropriate rages and lack of control.
Makes recurrent suicide threats or gestures or self-mutilation.
Has marked and persistent identity disturbance, manifested in difficulty in determining at least two of the following:

self-image; sexual orientation; long-term goals or career
choice; type of friends desired; preferred values (moral/
political, etc.).

Suffers chronic feelings of emptiness and boredom.

Has a frantic desire, and makes frantic efforts, to avoid real or
imagined abandonment.

Treatment for borderline personality disorder is similar to that of
the other personality disorders and there has been little success in
the use of the traditional antidepressants. The 5HT-reuptake
inhibitors have shown some success in reducing the severity of
the episodes of depression and the number of impulsive periods.
As in other forms of personality disorder, a combination of drugs,
psychotherapy and family therapy has been helpful.

The origins of borderline personality disorder are disputed
but most psychiatrists maintain that – despite the earlier names
for it such as 'ambulant schizophrenia', 'pseudo-neurotic schizophrenia' or 'latent schizophrenia' – there is no obvious genetic
association with schizophrenia. People who develop a borderline
personality claim that their childhood was unusually unhappy,
and these patients seem to have had a greater than usual likelihood of having been exposed to domestic violence and physical
and sexual abuse. Two large studies have both shown a higher
rate of childhood sexual abuse in those suffering from borderline
personality disorder than in other people. Not surprisingly the
parents of such people were more likely to have a history of mental disease, other personality disorders, alcoholism and to come
from a fragmented home; all of which could contribute to the
complaint often made by patients with borderline personality
disorder that they did not have the care which a child has the
right to expect.

There is one good piece of news to be garnered from the large
numbers of trials and surveys used to study the early life of
patients with borderline personality disorder. Although they
have all confirmed that the childhood of these patients was likely
to have been in a dysfunctional household, with aggression,

discord, marital separation of the parents, and with a greater likelihood than normal of physical and sexual abuse, simple separation was not a factor. Thirty years ago separation of a young child from its mother was thought to be enough to induce this syndrome. Now it is believed that other detrimental factors, including an adverse genetic background, are needed.

Avoidant Personality

Life is becoming more open and desperate shyness less common. In hospitals, offices and libraries twenty years ago it wasn't uncommon to have colleagues, usually women, who were terrified of being noticed, and yet harboured fantasies of being the life and soul of the party. What stopped these people from turning fantasy into reality was a fear of being adversely judged. They worried lest their clothes sense would be found wanting,

"I SUSPECT YOU HAVE AN AVOIDANT PERSONALITY"

their shoes unfashionable, their hair unbecoming, their figures unacceptable and their conversation trite. They were so tense that should they, in the course of their work, have to meet others, the encounter usually ended in failure. The awkward conversation was as short as possible, resulted in blushes and only served to confirm the person's view that they were as gauche as they feared. Modern life has reduced the number suffering from an avoidant personality disorder, and made the cases, such as there are, less severe, but they are still about and many of the criteria listed in the *DSM* can be identified.

The disorder, as it is defined in the *DSM*, revolves around a fear of being despised by society, a dislike of social events because of the unease and discomfort that they bring, and a timidity, whether expressed or not, in interpersonal relationships. Those with an avoidant personality are therefore anxious in social situations and avoid any change in their lifestyle which might increase social demands.

An avoidant personality may be found in conjunction with symptoms of depression, generalized anxiety disorder or various phobias. There is often a marked degree of suppressed anger and self-dislike at their inability to make relationships which they imagine might revolutionize their life. This personality disorder should not be confused with the withdrawn behaviour of people with schizoid personality – patients with an avoidant personality disorder would love to be the life and soul of the party, admired by all who meet them, with a mantelpiece covered in invitations, whereas those with a schizoid personality who also fight shy of close human contacts have no desire whatsoever for close friendships with confidants.

The *DSM* lists seven features of avoidant personality disorder. For a positive diagnosis the person in question should have at least four. He or she:

Is unusually easily hurt by any criticism or disapproval.
Has either no close friends or confidants, or only one, other
   than first-degree relatives.

Is unwilling to get involved with other people until he or she
can be certain of their approval.

Avoids social or occupational activities that involve significant
interpersonal contacts, seeks jobs where these are at a
minimum and refuses promotion if the social demands of the
job will be increased.

Is reticent in social situations, through fear of saying something
inappropriate, foolish or of being unable to answer a question.

Worries about showing signs of anxiety, embarrassment or
emotion, such as blushing or crying in front of other people.

Exaggerates the difficulties, even dangers, of doing something
outside the normal run of activities, and will, for instance,
cancel or refuse a dinner party for fear that it will leave them
exhausted, and be too much for them to handle.

Treatment is with psychotherapy, particularly the behavioural
approach, which encourages the patient to be more assertive and
to develop latent social skills. Cognitive therapy may also be
helpful, as it can correct faulty assumptions about self-worth
which sap the person's self-esteem. Some patients require tranquillizers for a time.

Dependent Personality Disorder

Depression is not the only psychiatric disorder which is revealed
by a person's posture and walk. Likewise, the voice can be a
valuable clue. One such clue is the childlike, high-pitched quality
of the voice frequently found in those with a dependent personality. People with this disorder are essentially submissive and lack
confidence.

Dependent personality disorder is found more often in women
than men. Women with the disorder display a spectrum of
symptoms, and have a pattern of behaviour, which would have
worried the suffragettes and would appal the modern feminist
movement. They are the archetypal 'little woman' who can be
guaranteed to have the master of the house's slippers warmed

and dinner in the oven. Men are not immune from this disorder: the diminutive hen-pecked man who figured in so many seaside postcards is a typical example of a male dependent personality. The type still exists.

A person with a dependent personality allows others to make all the important decisions in their life, is not prepared to disagree openly, even if they do mentally, with those around them and is ready, even pleased, to undertake the unpleasant or dreary tasks of life, if it will win them favour. They are the doormats of life. Like those with a narcissistic temperament, these people resent criticism, and like those with a borderline personality, they have a great fear of being abandoned, whether through the end of a close relationship, or death. The *DSM* suggests that five of nine characteristics must be present before the diagnosis can be made: the dependent personality:

Is unable to make everyday decisions without an excessive amount of reassurance.

Allows others to make important decisions for them.

Does not stand up for their own beliefs, even when they know that they are right, in case their determination produces rejection.

Does not start to do things of their own volition, but would rather wait so as to be able to fit in with, and please, others.

Is a willing volunteer for a menial task, if it will increase feelings of gratitude.

Hates to be alone.

Becomes very upset if a close friendship ends.

Will go to great lengths to avoid being abandoned or left.

Is easily hurt by criticism.

In general these people lack self-confidence, long to be part of a close relationship and are prepared to sacrifice their independence in order to achieve this. Similar symptoms can be found in patients who have a histrionic, schizotypal, narcissistic or avoidant personality disorder; many with dependent personality disorder also develop signs of general anxiety disorder and a depressive syndrome.

Group behavioural and cognitive therapies are all helpful. Group therapy is particularly favoured, as the discussion it engenders encourages the patient to put forward their own point of view forward, and not to be subservient to others. Treatment with drugs only provides short-term help and the ultimate aim must be to encourage the person to be happy without being a dogsbody.

Obsessive-Compulsive Personality Disorder

Captain Mainwaring of *Dad's Army* could be said to have had an obsessive-compulsive personality disorder without having obsessive-compulsive disorder, OCD. This so often figures in stories in the press of people of all ages, frequently children, whose lives are devastated by pointless rituals, and is described in chapter 2, 'Anxiety Disorders and Phobias'.

Captain Mainwaring suffered, like so many people, from an inflexible and perfectionist nature. Although he tried hard and had a willing team, his very perfectionism sometimes prevented the Walmington-on-Sea Home Guard Company being quite the efficient military force he intended. However, he loved his lists and rules, his schedules and his hierarchy, and what did it matter if the principal object of his Company, to defend Walmington from the Germans, was undermined by the time he spent on these activities? The important thing was that Sergeant Wilson did just as he was told and displayed as much devotion to duty as he did. Captain Mainwaring, like others with an obsessive nature, had a financially mean streak, and he worried terribly if Jonesy didn't pay the sixpence owed. Not that he necessarily wanted the money, but its absence would have spoilt the completeness of an account book.

In pre-Thatcherite days, having an inflexible and perfectionist nature was even considered advantageous in, for example, accountants or those, like Captain Mainwaring, who were bank managers. If occasionally decisions were delayed because too many lists were drawn up and too many possibilities considered, this was dismissed as unimportant when compared to the advantages of having an over-conscientious but scrupulously honest character. The obsessive-compulsive personality disorder describes this kind of nit-picking personality. Those with it have frequently been ridiculed from an early age, for it is often recognizable in children.

People with this condition are more likely to be male than female, and tend to be pessimistic and to lack confidence, but at the same time they are ambitious, competitive and have therefore a traditional Type A personality, which is characterized by a striving, competitive nature. Many also suffer from hypochondriasis, may be generally unhappy, and may even develop a major depressive illness. Although lampooned in comedies, their rigid personality and their love of detailed, accurate work makes them excellent engineers and company secretaries, as well as bank managers and accountants. Tragically, their obsessive nature and their Type A personalities gives them a higher than average chance of having to swap their desk for a bed in intensive care for treatment of a coronary thrombosis, or an early stroke.

People with obsessive-compulsive personality disorder are so inflexible that they may become depressed if they are prevented from carrying out their daily routines or if the rest of the world doesn't live up to their high standards and fit into the slots which have been allocated to them. In early life the obsessive-compulsive person may well have been brought up with a strict, rigid family discipline and in a household where any display of emotion was considered weak and undesirable.

For the diagnosis of personality disorder, the *DSM* lays down nine points, of which five must be positive:

Perfectionism that interferes with task completion.
Preoccupation with details, rules, lists, orders, schedules, organization, at the expense of the achievement of the major objective, 'cannot see the wood for the trees'.

An insistence that others should do something in exactly the same way as he (as it is more often 'he') has ordained.

Excessive devotion to work, to the exclusion of spare-time activities and interests, even if there is no economic necessity for this.

Indecisiveness and procrastination.

Over-conscientiousness, scrupulousness and inflexibility on matters of morality, ethics and social values.

Difficulty in expressing affection.

Meanness and a lack of generosity in giving money, or time, when there is unlikely to be any personal gain.

The hoarding of worthless and worn-out objects, even though they have neither sentimental nor practical value.

In these lesser manifestations of the obsessive-compulsive disorders, treatment is unlikely to be necessary. It is hard to visualize Captain Mainwaring sitting around in group therapy. However, if he had become depressed by his temperament, his treatment, as with other disorders, would have been recently revolutionized by the introduction of the 5HT-reuptake inhibitors.

Passive-Aggressive Personality Disorder

'Dumb insolence' was the popular name for a display of passive-aggressive behaviour in the army. During the Second World War persistent dumb insolence was more formally described by military psychiatrists as passive-aggressive personality disorder. Although the resistance to unwelcome authority shown by those with this disorder is always passive, the army psychiatrists recognized that the underlying emotion was one of aggression.

Passive-aggressive people subtly resist pressure to work harder, or to conform to the demands of what is expected of them. They will run an errand but take an unconscionably long time doing it. They will acquiesce in a request to wear a certain type of clothing but it will be subtly inappropriate. In all their defiance they are usually too manipulative and cunning to refuse outright to co-operate but, rather, achieve their own ends, and bolster their own self-esteem, by being devious.

This syndrome can occur in either sex and may show itself early in the behaviour of the bolshy, rebellious child or adolescent. People with the disorder often lack self-confidence and may fear that they will perform badly. Their behaviour may therefore be an example of what George Bernard Shaw once referred to as an 'unconscious acceptance of incompetence'. In order to make the diagnosis as laid down in the *DSM*, five of the following features should be apparent. The passive-aggressive person:

Procrastinates, so that deadlines are not met.

Becomes sulky, irritable or argumentative, just like an adolescent when asked to do something he or she does not want to do.

When dragooned by someone else or by circumstances into doing something they do not want to do, they seem to do it deliberately slowly or badly.

Protests without justification about 'unreasonable demands'.

Blames a poor memory and avoids obligations by claiming to have forgotten.

Resents any suggestions as to how his or her productivity can be improved.

Does not do his or her fair share of the work, thereby obstructing others in their tasks.

Is unreasonably critical of people in positions of authority and scorns those whose role it is to command.

Treatment is aimed to help the patient understand their hidden feelings of hostility to authority and why these might have arisen. In the past, dumb insolence rarely resulted in a soldier having a severe punishment but it did prevent promotion. Likewise, showing civilians the consequences of their difficult behaviour and then providing support as they try to change has been known to be helpful. Drug therapy is rarely indicated but may be useful in the few cases when the sufferer's troubles land them in difficulties severe enough to cause clinical depression.

Other Personality Disorders including Premenstrual Syndrome, Sadistic Personality Disorder and Self-Defeating Personality Disorder

The *DSM* does not cover all the peculiarities of personality which can cause social and professional difficulties for the sufferer, and for those who come in contact with them. The symptoms which are displayed are often sadly similar and could broadly be described as syndromes even though they have not yet been described as such. They may not be easily defined, but they are equally trying.

There are exceptions which are already sometimes classified as personality disorders. The first of these is premenstrual tension. This is such an important condition that the only excuse for giving it so little prominence is that it is usually treated by gynae-cologists, although classified by psychiatrists. Premenstrual tension is a term which was replaced in the best Harley Street circles by the description 'premenstrual syndrome'. The super-scientific doctor is even more precise and now sometimes refers to what the rest of the world calls premenstrual tension or premenstrual syndrome – or simply PMS – as the 'late luteal phase dysphoric disorder'! This is a phrase which connects the disruption of mood and psychological equilibrium associated with the hormones produced by the ovary during the late, 'luteal', phase of the cycle after the ovum has been discharged on its journey to meet a quest-ing sperm. The syndrome has a hormonal basis and is almost certainly connected to the normal physiological changes which follow the varying levels of ovarian hormones which are experi-enced during the cycle. The amount of progesterone increases during this phase. Progesterone may be a hormone which admir-ably prepares the inside of the womb for a fertilized ovum but it does little for the serenity of the woman.

Several generations of doctors taught, and were taught, that

PMS was essentially a middle-class complaint and predominantly affected women in their later thirties until the menopause. Closer examination of the statistics shows that this is not so, a class bias is unrelated to any difference in mood, working-class husbands are just as likely to have household items hurled at them as their better-off neighbours. The apparent difference is that middle-class families complain to their doctors about their symptoms whereas their more phlegmatic fellow citizens just accept it as an fact of life.

The textbook *Gynaecology* edited by Shaw, Soutter and Stanton (Churchill Livingstone) suggests that only 5 per cent of women are completely free of symptoms, even though many women are unaware of the subtle changes which accompany the latter part of the cycle, while the body is preparing itself for a pregnancy. PMS mimics many of its features, ranging from a protuberant abdomen and relaxed joints to some emotional turbulence. Fingers and toes, hands and feet are not the only parts of the anatomy to become puffy, the brain too swells but the skull doesn't expand to accommodate it. The poor pinched brain is as sensitive in the premenstrual woman as is the swollen brain of the hard-drinking younger man with a hangover. Most people expect the drinker with the hangover to have an oedematous brain and to be like a bear with a sore head – they are not always as sympathetic to the suffering premenstrual woman. In these women, changes in serotonin levels have also been recorded, hence the suggestion that 5HT-reuptake inhibitors, such as Prozac or Seroxat, could be of value in treatment.

Gynaecology quotes 'aggression, anxiety, crying, clumsiness, depression, irritability, loss of concentration and tension' as being the most common symptoms. In milder cases the woman frequently complains of being 'always on edge before a period'. In extreme cases PMS can lead to heavy drinking, assault, child abuse, problems at work, car crashes, criminal behaviour and suicide. It is even quoted by lawyers as a defence for murder charges. PMS should only be diagnosed when at least one symptom disrupts the normal pattern of life, whether professional, domestic or social. Technically the term shouldn't be used to describe a patient's symptoms if there is evidence of other psychological malaise at other times or throughout her cycle. This may, to some extent, be rather a quibble as psychiatric problems are liable to become very much worse, and more disabling, in the premenstrual phase.

Treatment is disappointing. If the PMS is secondary to some definable gynaecological disease, the upset of the menstrual period would of course be less if the problem is corrected. If the patient suffers from other psychological disorders her PMS will benefit if these are treated. Treatment for those with primary PMS who have no obvious gynaecological problems, or no clearly underlying psychological trouble, has been disappointing, despite an enormously varied range of therapeutic regimes which have been tried. Vitamin B6 has been widely recommended and has its advocates, as do oil of evening primrose, and diuretics. Oil of primrose is successful in some cases but the results of trials have been disappointing; likewise, B6 is worth a try, and helps more often than can be accounted for by coincidence. Research has failed to show any advantage to taking diuretics unless there is clearly demonstrable tissue swelling, in which case, patients may benefit from the diuretic Spironolactone. The role of progesterone in PMS is much disputed. Despite the suspicion among some doctors that excess progesterone might actually be a cause of PMS, other doctors have continued to prescribe it without any good scientific evidence that it is very effective. Removal or destruction of the ovaries is effective but drastic, and would only be considered as a last resort in severe, disabling cases.

Flashman of *Tom Brown's Schooldays*, and, very much later, the anti-hero of a host of other books, was the archetypal bully. Bullying, however, is often much more subtle and the essential ingredient of the person who is a bully is that they derive satisfaction from being cruel and being able to belittle other people. Bullies may well be aggressive but their behaviour is frequently far more sophisticated than the bruising actions of the football hooligan.

People who derive aberrant pleasure from being bullies may be described as having a sadistic personality disorder. It is often exhibited in their relationships with family members or with junior colleagues at work. Interestingly, those people who rely upon mental bullying but are themselves not physically violent may very often be intrigued by violence in others, and may be, for instance, collectors of weapons, instruments of torture or pictures of brutal episodes. In general the bully displays an indifference to others' feelings and indeed the bully may take pleasure, or may be amused, by seeing their humiliation.

The difference between the sadistic personality disorder and the sadistic paraphiliac is that the latter obtains sexual satisfaction from the suffering of his victims. Many people who are cruel to animals are also violent, or pathologically unkind, to children or other dependants. Doctors, and other health professionals, make a point of having a pretty good look at the whole household if someone within it is obviously brutal to animals in their care. Bullies with a sadistic personality disorder frequently have features of antisocial or narcissistic personality disorders, and like those who suffer from these disorders may well have been bullied themselves and abused physically or psychologically.

Just as not all sadists derive sexual pleasure from sadism, not all masochism has a sexual bias. Emotional masochists are described as suffering from a self-defeating personality disorder. Those with self-defeating personalities are very much more likely to be women than men, whereas, perhaps as could be expected, sadistic personality disorder is much more common in men.

These self-defeating people reject help even as they are attracted to situations which will inevitably make them suffer, and likewise they avoid relationships where they may actually derive pleasure and be cared for. They become involved in partnerships where it is inevitable the end will be painful, they reject promotion even though they may have worked for it, they will sabotage their own record and reputation by some self-defeating device, and they discount all encouragement and praise. The very rejection of others' advances induces rejection themselves and increases the likelihood of suffering from depression and excessive feelings of guilt.

People with personality disorders are another group of heartsink patients in the surgery queue and the despair of the criminal courts. Treatment of all personality disorders is difficult and some would say almost impossible, as in most instances the person shows little desire to change. They are perfectly happy with their behaviour and it causes them little anxiety unless the people they offend become so aggrieved that the provoked reaction starts to destroy their own lives. Sometimes patients, as they grow older, seek a more rewarding lifestyle than the one to which their personality has condemned them. These patients therefore are usually only driven to seek help if their behaviour is such that it induces anxiety, and then they usually need the prompting of others, whether close members of the family or an employer. In those personality disorders in which antisocial behaviour may lead to criminality, sufferers may be forced by the courts to seek help. The courts are amazingly over-optimistic about the chances of success.

People with a personality disorder have an abnormal temperament which is characterized by recurrent maladaptive, inappropriate and often destructive behaviour. The behaviour may be self-defeating or antisocial, sometimes both. There is much discussion as to whether people with, for instance, an antisocial personality disorder, are 'mad', and the responsibility of psychiatrists, or 'bad' and the preserve of the police and the prison service. In the not too distant past, psychiatrists accepted more responsibility for those with personality disorders but their patients have tended to prove resistant to treatment and all doctors like their patients to get better. At the same time, the psychiatrist's ability to treat recognized psychiatric disease has improved, but as it has done so, treating patients has become more time-consuming. The improvement in treatment has coincided with a shortage of in-patient accommodation; as a result, psychiatrists are loath to see their few beds filled with people with personality disorders, sometimes gravely antisocial, who have little chance of improving.

In some cases, modern medication, in particular the 5HT-reuptake inhibitors and atypical antipsychotics may help. Others will perhaps benefit from cognitive therapy, but intense psychotherapy is often less effective. In general, psychotherapy should be directed towards encouraging the patient to understand the difficulties their behaviour causes them, and therefore the ways in which it can be modified, rather than an analysis of either their deepest thoughts or the causes of them, which may only increase feelings of resentment without providing a means of eradicating them.

Many with obvious but not gross symptoms of personality disorders may stand out from their contemporaries. The Princess of Wales and Florence Nightingale were exceptional examples of people with personality disorders who nevertheless revolutionized attitudes. The empire builders and conquerors may well have had the withdrawn, cold, detached, unemotional schizoid personalities which made them great commanders, but even Robert Louis Stevenson despite his devotion to Fanny Osbourne, the great love of his life, had some remarkable schizoid features and dined happily, but formally, as the locals rioted around his house. Many well-known artists – Salvador Dalí and Paul Gauguin, for instance – may have had schizotypal (and, in Dalí's case, narcissistic, even histrionic) tendencies. And the life histories of some of the Old Masters give clues to personalities which were not run-of-the-mill and could well have filled several pages of psychiatric notes.

In a lesser way, hundreds of thousands of idiosyncratic, non-conformist and sometimes wayward, people are benefiting society, even if the characteristics which make them distinctive might not always be totally desirable. Conversely, others whose personality characteristics are, by definition, extreme, enduring, inflexible and maladaptive, inevitably cause distress to others and interfere with the person's ability to cope with life.

Many people can have one or two characteristics of a personality disorder without in any way being classified as being abnormal. Having the agreed quota of symptoms laid down in the *DSM* is essential for the overall diagnosis. It is also important to realize that the severity of the symptoms matters – they should be marked enough to be obvious to family and friends and severe enough to make interpersonal relationships strained.

Disorders of Impulse Control

A shopaholic, an arsonist who burns down his neighbour's barns and straw ricks, a gambler who has lost all his money before he returns home on payday, a kleptomaniac who can't resist stealing the silver snuff boxes at a party or an unhappy young person who twists and pulls at their hair until they have bald patches, all these people may be suffering from one or other of the same group of psychiatric troubles – disorders of impulse control. Some doctors even include an obsessional traveller, a person who is only happy for a short while after returning home and then soon starts to plan the next trip.

In impulse control disorders a sufferer is unable to resist the temptation to do something which may well be harmful to themselves or to others, even though they are aware of the unfortunate results which will follow. The normal pattern of behaviour is that the patient suffers from increasing tension and excitement before they perform whatever act is their particular penchant. They carry it out, experience pleasure and gratification, followed by an immediate relaxation. If the act was antisocial it may be followed by self-reproach and remorse, whereupon the whole cycle tends to repeat itself. Some psychologists feel that the objective is to relieve the pain of the tension rather than to experience pleasure.

In the past paraphilia, alcoholism, drug addiction and even eating disorders have been included among impulse control disorders but they are now classified separately. Psychotherapy designed to give patients insight into their condition is often helpful. Other associated conditions may make the situation worse and these should be treated.

4

Schizophrenia

Schizophrenia, and its treatment or the lack of it, has become one of the great social issues of today. The shadow of schizophrenia extends far beyond the households of people with the disease. The general public, alerted by sensational stories, are aware of the horrors which can be associated with schizophrenia, but less aware both of the extent of the problem and also of the numbers of people with the disease who are coping admirably and bravely.

More hospital beds are devoted to the treatment of schizophrenia than to any other medical condition. There are more patients in hospital with this disease than there are suffering from cancer or heart disease. This is particularly remarkable as most people with schizophrenia are treated outside hospital, and many of these are living near-normal lives. One way of appreciating the numbers suffering from schizophrenia is to realize that if the 80,000-strong crowd filling Wembley Stadium is representative of the population in general, 800 of that crowd will be in need of treatment for schizophrenia.

Although treatment has improved out of all recognition over the last forty years, it is still not ideal and there is the perennial problem of persuading patients with schizophrenia to continue to take their medication. Treatment failure, for whatever reason, is the basis of a hundred and one shock-horror newspaper reports. It has been the impetus behind the founding of SANE, a charity which advises people tormented and distressed by unresolved, and often untreated, psychiatric problems, and the Zito Trust which investigates violent acts committed by psychiatrically disturbed people in the community.

The problem is that if members of the medical profession miss the diagnosis of schizophrenia and underrate a patient's grasp of reality, or their tendency to violence, they risk being pilloried. Conversely, doctors fear that if they overstate the case, they will stigmatize a person, often only of student age, and will have blighted their future – perhaps indefinitely. Furthermore, the realization that the shortage of funds and hospital beds has made adequate care of patients with schizophrenia no longer possible has driven many talented psychiatrists to abandon their careers as a result of the constant anxiety these cases engender in the community.

Daniel had both physical and mental illness, he suffered from schizophrenia and from cerebral palsy, which confined him to a wheelchair. He suffered from delusions, and furthermore he thought that his ideas and views were controlled by an outside source and that others knew what he was thinking about. Worry about his schizophrenic symptoms destroyed whatever peace of mind his family might have had, but when he went into a residential home the staff there seemed to have neither the patience nor the facilities to deal with his troubles. Daniel became extremely depressed and his family found it hard to talk to somebody who seemed to be 'in charge'. Daniel finally attempted suicide but even this didn't bring to him the help which he needed. His problems remained unsolved, his condition a disaster waiting to happen.

Schizophrenia is one of the most dreaded diagnoses which a doctor can deliver. It is frequently wrapped up in euphemisms: 'a bit depressed', 'rather over-sensitive', 'not very well socially orientated' – all of which are true but all of which avoid using the term 'schizophrenia'. A leading article in the medical journal *The Practitioner*, although written twenty-five years ago, sums up the view of schizophrenia that is still widespread today: 'So dreadful is its outlook, that some psychiatrists never diagnose it and employ the word only in a descriptive sense.' The description 'schizophrenia' is more than a label – it is a diagnosis on which the correct treatment, and even a patient's health or life, may depend.

The stigma of schizophrenia hampers both correct diagnosis and treatment. The diagnosis is only comparatively rarely straightforward; one problem is that it is mainly a disease of young people, whose behaviour may be antisocial or bizarre, in the view of their elders, even without any psychiatric disturbance. The more celebrated the family, the more reluctant doctors are to make the diagnosis, but the genes which transmit a susceptibility to schizophrenia ignore Debrett's list of the titled and famous, and are blind to social distinctions.

Both Sally Roberts's parents were famous artists and household names. Sally had always been the odd one out in the family. However, she did well at school, where she was a perfectionist, and, as was expected of her, went on to university where she soon established a reputation as a student writer and actor. She also took a prominent part in left-wing student politics and was particularly concerned about the starving millions in Africa. In her third year she started to become unnecessarily and excessively worried about her work; at the same time her relationship with her boyfriend broke up and her equilibrium was destroyed. She became acutely depressed and, although an insomniac, spent most of her time in bed.

Sally developed a great fear of people. Initially she only acknowledged feeling alienated from her family and friends but later admitted that she thought that they were constantly talking about her and criticizing her every move – they were planning, in her opinion, to interrupt her studies and send her to her grandmother in Wales. In consequence, she interpreted all sorts of perfectly standard happenings in everyday life as part of a great plot to banish her. As in so many cases in which a patient is clearly suffering from delusions, there was a grain of truth in her fears: her family had indeed hoped that she would go for a period of recuperation to her grandmother, but they were not conspirators, sending messages to each other in mysterious ways, as she imagined.

Sally became increasingly withdrawn and, when she spoke, her face was contorted by strange grimaces; her clothes, previously

Schizophrenia
amusingly eccentric, became distinctly odd, she refused to get up, and lost all her enthusiasm for her studies. Instead she became preoccupied with environmental causes. She began to hear voices, not frequently but regularly – they admonished her for a multitude of mistakes and shortcomings. As would be expected, she avoided all social contact, and became incapable of making decisions.

Later, she described her daily mood: 'It's only in bed that I don't think. I can't stand not being able to talk to people, I have nothing to say to them, I have only thoughts about myself. I am on a different wavelength from the rest of the world and alienated from all the people I once knew. I just can't make up my mind, even the simplest decision will take all morning to solve, and then I have second thoughts. I know I am a failure, but I don't need to hear this from a voice.'

Sally remained ill for months. She went home, and then to her grandmother, but was able to return to her university the following year and obtained her degree. Still determined to correct the environmental ills of the world, she worked in developing countries, but was usually moved on as her perfectionism and lack of rapport with others caused strife. Finally she was invalided home with 'a nervous breakdown'.

To her parents' extreme reluctance, and with her own lack of co-operation as she had little insight into her condition, Sally was referred to two psychiatrists. Possibly overawed by these eminent people, who both immediately emphasized the importance of the symptoms of depression, Sally hid her other more psychotic symptoms, which were left unaddressed and untreated. They finally surfaced when she confided in her GP, who immediately prescribed antipsychotic medication, which dramatically improved her state of mind.

Sally was then referred to a third psychiatrist who specialized in psychotic disorders. This move was greeted by her parents with anger as well as horror – at a pinch they would accept that a Roberts could be depressed, but not that one could be schizophrenic. By this time Sally had been unfit for work for two years but the continuing deterioration of her state of mind, and the implications of this to her future, seemed of little consequence to her parents when compared to the trauma of a diagnosis of schizophrenia. However, the psychiatrist agreed with the GP's diagnosis, changed the antipsychotic for another, more modern one, and since then Sally – so long as she takes the treatment, and doesn't undertake too stressful an occupation – remains well.

The general public's views about schizophrenia haven't kept pace with improvements in treatment, and fears and preconceived ideas remain, intermittently fuelled by frightening accounts of atrocities committed by schizophrenic people, which give a distorted account of the disease. Only recently, parents have said to me that they had hoped that their son's or daughter's mental symptoms might have been the result of a brain tumour, despite the probability of malignancy. They were in fact saying that they would prefer that their child died rather than suffer the symptoms and stigma of schizophrenia.

Listen to any serious radio programme, and time and time again a person who has two conflicting sides to their personality like Jekyll and Hyde – kindly, gentle, churchgoing at one moment, rough, brutal and selfish at other times – is described as schizophrenic. Likewise, a politician who holds two totally different points of view, a fascist in relation to foreign affairs but a liberal on social problems, is described as having schizophrenic opinions. Whatever their problems, they are not schizophrenic. Nor do they even have a schizotypal personality disorder. In fact the description 'schizophrenic' is a total misnomer.

The definitions of lesser conditions similar to schizophrenia are a semantic minefield. Doctors talk of schizophreniform disorders and schizotypal personality disorders, but there is general agreement that in those families in which there is obvious frank schizophrenia there are other members who suffer from varying degrees of the same symptoms – such as odd thought patterns, peculiar behaviour, magical thinking, depression – and yet are not at the time psychotic. Some of these people could be said to have schizotypal personality disorders.

Schizophrenia is an illness of the mind, a chronic mental disorder, in which in its acute stages there is a loss of contact with reality; it is therefore in medical terms one of the psychoses but not, despite modern lay language, the only psychosis. For instance, patients with manic-depressive illness may also themselves sometimes suffer from a psychosis which can cause them to lose touch with reality; and there are also the organic psychoses which range from fever and subsequent delirium, exposure to toxic chemicals, including an excessive amount of alcohol taken over a long time, and the dementias of old age – such diseases as Alzheimer's and Lewy body dementia.

The essential features of schizophrenia are described in the *Diagnostic and Statistical Manual of Mental Disorders*, or *DSM*. Schizophrenia is the presence of characteristic psychotic symptoms during the active phase of the illness resulting in the person functioning below the highest level previously achieved; and in children or adolescents, failure to achieve the expected level of social development and academic achievement. To be defined as schizophrenic, the illness must have a duration of at least six months that may include characteristic prodromal – i.e., early warning – symptoms or residual symptoms. At some phase of the illness schizophrenia always involves delusions, hallucinations, or certain characteristic disturbances in affect (mood) and the form of thought. The diagnosis is made only when it cannot be established that an organic, physical factor initiated and maintained the disturbance. The diagnosis is not made if the symptoms are due to a mood disorder or schizoaffective disorder, e.g. if they are clinically depressed or manic (over-elated) or if they suffer from a schizoaffective disorder (described later).

Schizophrenia affects every aspect of a sufferer's life. The more dramatic symptoms have obvious impact. It is difficult for a computer programmer, for instance, to remain fully functioning and competent if their attention is not entirely on their modules and modems but is distracted by inner voices reinforcing paranoid fears of espionage and murder, plotting associates or families. After a sleepless night riven by anxieties, it is not surprising that an already unusual taste in clothes is compounded by untidiness and grubbiness.

Schizophrenia also alters the emotions and mood: at least 70 per cent of all schizophrenic patients are clinically depressed; many at other times are either hypomanic or manic (extravagantly elated and overexcited); and some from time to time are too inert and emotionally blunted to have a well-defined mood. Schizophrenia, by interrupting normal thought processes, produces delusions and hallucinations, and even changes the way a person walks, gestures and stands. As would be expected, the relationships people with schizophrenia have with the rest of their family, friends, and even casual acquaintances, are altered and sometimes damaged irreparably. Schizophrenia doesn't only leave a patient feeling depressed, but in a hundred and one subtle ways their relationships are sabotaged by their personalities and they are left feeling isolated and excluded from the mainstream of social life.

Who does schizophrenia affect, and what chance does the reader, or his or her children, have of developing it? Would a different lifestyle have kept it at bay?

The overall chance of the average man or woman developing schizophrenia is accepted as being one in a hundred, but this statistic needs amplification as the incidence varies so much from group to group and family to family within a country. Men tend to suffer their first diagnosed attack of schizophrenia three to five years earlier than women: the peak time for initial diagnosis in men is between the ages of fifteen and twenty-five whereas for women it is between twenty-five and thirty-five. Women also sometimes suffer from schizophrenic breakdown at the time of the menopause. It is thought that the female hormones, oestrogens, may have a protective role.

An argument, sometimes unnecessarily fierce, has revolved around the incidence of schizophrenia and its relative concentration in specific groups of people. It is found that the number of cases is greater than would be expected, for instance, in inner cities. No one disputes this. More politically contentious is the apparently disproportionate number of cases of schizophrenia found in certain communities of second-generation immigrants, particularly African-Caribbean.

One view is that a seemingly excessive number of cases of schizophrenia in an immigrant population will be the result of differences in cultural behaviour which are neither comprehended nor accepted by the host nation and would not necessarily be considered indicative of schizophrenic disease in their home countries. This view is not universally accepted, and is the subject of vehement disagreement. The protagonists of this opinion hold that the apparent evidence of high numbers of cases of schizophrenia in second-generation immigrants is not so much the result of the genetic susceptibility of some races which could predispose them to schizophrenia, but owes more to the result of the conflict between their own cultural habits and the set behavioural patterns of the host nation.

Theories abound about the possible causes of any disparity between the incidence of schizophrenia between an immigrant community and the host nation – should, indeed, any such discrepancies exist. Hard evidence, however, is in short supply, and many authorities will even deny that inner-city life predisposes to schizophrenia. It has, however, been suggested that those who have a wanderlust, and may find it hard to settle, may also show other signs of a schizotypal personality disorder or of schizophrenia. Some of those who are compelled to travel by circumstances may be vulnerable because of their temperament; others may be subjected to stress because this enforced journeying would tax anyone's resistance. Additionally, it would be surprising if a vulnerable personality did not respond unpredictably to the hostility which is often exhibited by a host nation.

Most authorities assert that more cases of schizophrenia are found in deprived inner-city areas than in the lush, green countryside. Various explanations are offered as to why there is such a concentration of schizophrenics in depressed inner cities. There is the suggestion that these depressed surroundings tend to uncover schizophrenia in people who are genetically predisposed to the disease, but who would possibly otherwise have been very talented. Those living in areas of social deprivation have to compete with all the attendant problems of urban decline which may be too great a burden for a finely balanced mind.

Other psychiatrists have observed that schizophrenic patients drift towards the inner cities because they are unable to compete in more affluent surroundings. A third theory is that those with a schizophrenic tendency enjoy the anonymity and the escape from family and community pressures which inner-city surroundings, albeit sometimes bleak, afford: there are no Joneses to keep up with, no parents to live up to and few standards to be upheld.

Financial and domestic insufficiency may therefore uncover any vulnerability to the disease while, in other cases, the 'social drift' hypothesis may explain why the socially insecure and embattled drift to the inner cities.

Sally Roberts's case history was discussed earlier in the chapter. She was, as we have seen, eventually diagnosed as having schizophrenia. Although this label hadn't been applied to any other members of her family, the family's abundance of talent was matched by more than a fair share of eccentricity, as so often happens. Just as schizophrenia is found in greater numbers of people in some communities than others, so is it found more often than would be expected in some families. To this extent schizophrenia is a familial disease – that is to say, some families have more cases than would occur by chance – rather than a disease in which the strict rules of inheritance can, as yet, be charted.

Families with schizophrenia do not behave like Mendel's sweetpeas, which obeyed simple and clearly defined laws of inheritance. For example, none of the hypotheses of genetic inheritance which explain how Huntington's chorea, a form of movement disorder associated with dementia, is passed down through the generations can be applied to schizophrenia. It is

herefore assumed that in certain families there is a genetic predisposition to schizophrenia, a vulnerability to the disease which
may or may not be uncovered by a wide variety of adverse circumstances.

It is unlikely that any single gene transmits a tendency to
schizophrenia; it is probably a multi-genetic characteristic.
Although Huntington's chorea has many different signs and
symptoms, these are easily recognizable, very distinct and follow
obvious physical changes. Conversely, human personality which
is so altered by schizophrenia is bewilderingly complex, and it is
not always easy to relate the physical and biochemical changes,
which can now be demonstrated, to specific changes in personal-
ty. It seems that there are probably several different genes
involved in the formation of the person's personality and temperament, and that the seed and soil concept holds. That is to say,
if the seed – the inherited liability to the disease – is raised in a
perfect environment, all may be well; but if the soil is unsuitable,
the propensity to the disease may be triggered.

Statistics which are as dry as dust to the rest of the population
are of fundamental importance to people in whom there is a fam-
ly history of schizophrenia. Doctors are regularly asked about
the likelihood of a patient developing it themselves, or, especially
if they were to marry someone from a family with similar
problems, the chances of their children being affected. All too
frequently Cupid fires an arrow at two people with similar psychiatric tendencies. The earlier schizophrenia appears in a person,
the more likely it is for their relatives to show signs or symptoms
of it or similar psychiatric problems. Overall, if one parent has
schizophrenia, a child has a 12.3 per cent chance of developing
the disease. If both parents have schizophrenia, a child's chance
of developing it increases to 37 per cent (some authorities have
suggested the figure might be as high as 46 per cent). There are
differences of opinion concerning the risk to a person if their
brother or sister and one parent have schizophrenia. Varying
estimates suggest that the risk may be as low as 14 per cent for the
sibling, while other researchers favour a much higher figure.

Given that the diagnosis of schizophrenia is often difficult, this disparity is not surprising.

The variations in figures collected by different authorities may result from different interpretations of the strict criteria necessary for the diagnosis of schizophrenia. As has been mentioned, in those families in which there is frank schizophrenia, similar, but lesser, disturbances in personality are commonly found. Certain features of the genetic patterns of the inheritance of schizophrenia are, however, obvious, even if the exact figures vary. The figures given in the table below are not written in stone but represent a summary derived from different sources. Nonetheless, we are all vulnerable: someone with no schizophrenic relations still has an approximately 1 per cent chance of developing the disease.

Risk of Developing Schizophrenia

Relationship to schizophrenic patient	% risk
Parent	4.4
Sibling	8.5
Sibling with one parent affected	14.0
Child with one parent affected	12.3
Child with two parents affected	37.0
Uncle/aunt/nephew	2.0
Identical twins	40 to 50
Non-identical twins	8.5

The days are long gone when it was fashionable to blame a patient's schizophrenia on their family upbringing. Nevertheless, studies of identical twins raised separately show that environment, as well as genetic inheritance, has a strong influence on the development of schizophrenia. It seems that people inherit a tendency to schizophrenia which may make them vulnerable to other factors, possibly environmental, including abnormalities of pregnancy and complications of delivery. The physical environment, such as chemicals in the atmosphere, or the emotional milieu are also significant factors. As mentioned, it is unlikely that any one gene is responsible for the increased susceptibility which renders a patient prone to schizophrenia; instead it is thought that there is a multiplicity of genes which may contribute to any liability. In time these genes will be uncovered.

There are many unanswered questions about the familial and genetic background of schizophrenic patients. One of the factors which has intrigued doctors for many years is that in Britain a larger number of schizophrenic people are born during the late winter and spring than would be expected, and that the rate is lower at other times of the year. The suggestion is that during the winter months, and in particular in December and January, many pregnant women catch the prevailing winter viruses, and, in the later stages of pregnancy, it is one or more of these viruses which predispose a child to show signs of schizophrenia when older. Although this has become an established theory in Britain, and in general seems to apply to the northern hemisphere, and certainly also in Australia, the results have not been confirmed by all studies in other countries with similar climates.

Is Tancred, the timid, sensitive child of the highly strung artistic couple who live near the surgery, merely like his mother, or is he showing the first signs that – like his grandmother – he is going to develop schizophrenia? The doctor doesn't know the answer, any more than do the child's parents. They will just have to watch and wait.

Many authorities think that there are early signs and symptoms that herald future trouble. A prospective study published in *The Lancet* in 1994 showed that there were differences in speech, social integration and muscular co-ordination at a very early age in those who were later found to have developed schizophrenia. As time passed these pre-schizophrenic children showed increasing disabilities, until it was possible to say that their unusual behaviour, the harbinger of calamity, could be described as the first stage of the disease.

Loss of ability at school, coupled with increasingly eccentric behaviour and a failure to live up to earlier promise, gave way to abnormal moods as the child climbed the academic ladder. The children may have become wildly and irrationally elated or depressed, and began to show unusual patterns of speech and adopted bizarre ideas and interests. Their eccentricity was often manifested in an enthusiasm for cults, esoteric religious groups and strange philosophical beliefs. They may not have all thought they were abducted by aliens, but their enthusiasms were not the typical ones of the average fifteen- or sixteen-year-old.

As discussed, not least of the problems in diagnosis is that many of the initial symptoms in young people are deceptively similar to those exhibited by normal but slightly rebellious adolescents. Doctors have to make very exacting decisions based on probability after all the patient's symptoms have been assessed in relation to their cultural background. Labelling illness is always complex and fraught with problems. The diagnosis may require hours of interview time, which is not always available. Relatives frequently feel that due regard is not given to their own observations and accounts of a patient's behaviour. Valuable diagnostic information is also rejected on the grounds that it may only be hearsay evidence – and therefore dismissed as being no more than anecdotal testimony, even gossip.

Some patients are enormously relieved to have a label applied once a diagnosis is made. It makes them realize that they are not alone in their troubles, and they feel that once the nature of the disease is recognized, help will soon be at hand. Other patients are appalled and angry. They share the widespread view that to have schizophrenia is to be stigmatized. Some have said that to them it seems as if they have been given a life sentence. Many even resent the idea that they are ill – schizophrenic patients are notorious for their lack of insight. Even more patients don't like to be categorized, and consider that even if the doctor is right, to be labelled 'schizophrenic' is denigrating and depersonalizing.

Peter Wilson's early years illustrate the difficulties of diagnosis. As in many cases, a retrospective study shows that Peter Wilson's schizophrenic disease could have been traced back to childhood. When he was a small boy he was never the scruffy over-excited child rampaging around the playground; he was always clean and immaculately dressed in grey flannel trousers and a smart red-and-black blazer, his spectacles were invariably well polished and he was always very upset if he dirtied his clothes and knees. Neither popular nor unpopular, Peter remained on the edge of the crowd during the rough-and-tumble of the mid-morning break. He was a wary watcher rather than a player and didn't display the wild and irrational behaviour exhibited by some young children who later develop schizo-phrenia. However, Peter at this age did have unusual patterns of speech and an obsessive interest in religion, and these, with his other characteristics, are seen as warning signs in some cases of incipient schizophrenia.

Adults liked Peter: he was quaint, unusually grown-up, smiled rather distantly and was always polite to other parents and the teachers. He knew all the answers at the Sunday school; at school and at home, as he was obsessional – everything had to be just right, including the degree of his parents' approval. As Peter grew older his obsessionalism and religiosity increased. He became a lawyer, a respected man in his local community, and although his metaphysical reasoning sometimes perplexed his partners, he was good-hearted and any minor eccentricities were tolerated. After a while, however, Peter's religiosity became such that he relinquished all hope that fellow men could provide the answers to life, and he determined that only God would resolve his perplexities. With God firmly on side, Peter now felt that it would be possible to plot a way through the complexities of life, and that contemplation, reading and prayer would reveal the secrets of this world and the next.

Peter became more and more lost in meditation, and as he did so found one 'truth' after another and became increasingly excited by his discoveries. He neglected his clients and his family, he talked only of his 'research', and finally decided it was easier to talk only to God – shouting, laughing and gesticulating as he did so. He neither ate nor slept. Eventually he had treatment and made an excellent, but slow, recovery. A new partnership was found which did not carry the same level of responsibility, and he settled down into a quieter, happier, and less introspective world.

Schizophrenia can start suddenly, perhaps precipitated by some unexpected stress – childbirth, severe illness, surgery, examinations, a change of job, house or lover – or it can creep on gradually as it did with Peter. Most cases are diagnosed in adolescence or young adult life but in others it is not obvious until the patient is a pensioner. The best service family and friends can do is to take note of the changes in personality and to accept that the increasingly lonely life the sufferer is leading could be abnormal, as could their confused thoughts and beliefs, excessive mood swings and insomnia. If the person shows obvious signs of delusions, hallucinations or marked depression, the diagnosis becomes even more likely. Medical help should be sought as early as possible, for the sooner the patient is treated, the better the long-term outlook.

Susan, a hairstylist in Pimlico, had been brought up by her widowed mother. She had been subject since adolescence to attacks of depression and on one occasion had made a suicide attempt and had been admitted to hospital. There had been no previous record of her displaying any psychotic symptoms but she now went to see her doctor as she was hearing voices. The voices had taken control of her thoughts and independence of action. They were telling her that she was evil and that she had better kill not only herself but also other people, including her GP. Her doctor arranged for Susan to be admitted to a psychiatric hospital, a course of action with which Susan was totally in accord, as she was frightened that she might be unable to resist the commands. She made a good recovery after taking atypical antipsychotics.

There was a time when schizophrenia was entirely 'blamed' on the parents and how they brought up the child, as well as on the behaviour of other members of the family and on the child's early educational influences, rather than on the inheritance of a genetic susceptibility. Fortunately it is now accepted that this extreme scapegoating of parental behaviour is unjustified and counter-productive. Nobody can be blamed for the nature of their own genetic make-up. Even so, the way the family deals with the distressing and inconvenient signs and symptoms of schizophrenia is of extreme importance.

Many parents will have sympathy with the father of one eighteen-year-old boy who had an acute psychotic breakdown while at school. His doctors thought that the stress created by a series of examinations might well cause a relapse, and it was decided he should not go to university. Searching for another career, his father suggested that as his son's only skill other than those of academia was sailing, he should gain experience by signing on as a crewhand on an ocean-going yacht. No job could have suited a highly sensitive, schizotypal academic less – crowded conditions and no physical privacy. Any lack of good social skills, essential for a harmonious relationships in a tightknit team, could easily have led to rejection and could then well have precipitated another breakdown before the yacht was beyond the Scillies. Fortunately the boy's family doctor suggested a safer alternative: 'How about an expensive sailing school with some good lodgings near by?'

A key phrase when dealing with the inter-relationship between a person with schizophrenia, or any of its allied conditions, and his or her close family is the term 'expressed emotion'. The term seems to be a misnomer, as the emotions it refers to are not spoken demands but the undercurrents generated by fervent feelings which run through all families. These feelings are usually unexpressed but are greater in those that are dysfunctional and may be brought out by the discordant note often struck by someone with schizophrenia. Even so, the term 'expressed emotion' is now so widely used by doctors, healthworkers and their patients that it is customarily known as 'EE'.

A troubled, tense atmosphere – expressed emotion – is more common in the households of schizophrenic patients because some of their relatives, having the same genetic background, may have similar but less marked personality changes. They may also have a greater dislike of being judged than do the rest of the population and may resent the flashes of intuition so often displayed by many people with schizophrenia, an ability which, ironically, they may share. The patient with schizophrenia or one of its allied conditions is not only very sensitive to outright criticism which, however well meant, may never be forgiven, but is adept at detecting covert hostility, or censure. Conversely, overprotection, particularly if prompted by feelings of parental guilt, can increase the patient's sense of inadequacy: 'Not only am I hopeless, and leading a useless life, but I am making my parents' life miserable, too.' Children are all too well aware that they carry many of their parents' ambitions on their shoulders, and for some children this burden may be so heavy that they crumple.

Expressed emotion is a measure of the disappointments, tensions and emotional undercurrents which run through any family. It is composed of unspoken but implied criticism, adverse comments, uncalled-for advice, hostility and jealousy, which although found in every household is present to a much greater degree in a family where the normal dynamics are disturbed if one or more of its members are suffering psychologically. The greater the expressed emotion in a family, the more likely there is to be someone suffering from schizophrenia in it, and the less well any schizophrenic patient will fare living at home. High EE has little influence on the first attack, but is a very important cause of relapse. If symptoms of the disease are already present, they are likely to become worse; if the symptoms have been lost, they are likely to return. The atmosphere of the household – and, in particular, any impossibly high parental expectations – is thus of vital importance in determining whether a susceptibility will become an actuality.

Schizophrenia appears to be more common in the poorer socioeconomic classes and in those people who have had a difficult early home life. It is, however, probable that class bias is overestimated and that these apparent differences may be partly explained by the capacity of money – and a secure background, whether institutional or domestic – to lessen the effect of the symptoms, or even possibly actually to diminish them. In many of the schizophrenic-type illnesses, given the right circumstances, the sufferers are merely seen as eccentric or bizarre and can continue to live an exceptionally successful life. My Oxford tutor, discussing with me the psyche of some of the best-known dons of the time, suggested that if these idiosyncratic people had been less clever, and had not had such a privileged early background and good education, rather than being admired as intellectual giants and considered amusingly eccentric, they would in all probability have been part of a drifting population in some downtrodden urban area.

The distinction between schizotypal personality disorder and schizophrenia can be very fine. In general terms, the patient with a schizotypal personality disorder has many of the milder characteristics of the psychotic patient with schizophrenia. Some people with schizotypal personalities are highly imaginative, creative, brilliant – even if eccentric. They have great powers of perception, and their tendency to paranoia may even enhance

"WHAT MAKES YOU THINK OTHERS ARE OUT TO GET YOU?"

their ability in commerce, industry and the arts. If these attributes are over-accentuated, however, a paranoid idea can become a psychotic delusion, and slightly bizarre social aloofness may spill over into unacceptably inappropriate behaviour. The impoverished speech in schizophrenic patients may be mirrored in those with a schizotypal personality disorder by a vagueness of expression and sometimes by the rather endearing habit of never ending sentences, so that they trail away into nothing. As John Dryden so neatly expressed it in the seventeenth century, 'Great wits are sure to madness near allied, And thin partitions do their bounds divide.'

However, in general, schizotypal people are very much less likely to be the eccentric Oxford don, and are more likely to be the odd suspicious person furtively walking down the street or sitting alone in a pub. Their thoughts tend to dwell on the magical, and they have wary, eccentric habits. They are solitary and lack close friends.

The signs and symptoms of schizophrenia may be all too obvious. In one Norfolk marshland family I looked after, four out of the seven by then middle-aged children of one family were schizophrenic. No one could doubt that Jim Rook, one of the sons, had inherited the family troubles. He was paranoid, and, as such, thought that the world was full of his enemies plotting to do him down and ravish his wife. He came to the surgery one night to report that his wife was bleeding heavily – would I go and see her. As we went in through the cottage door, he took the twelve-bore off the hall wall, sat me down opposite his wife and levelled the gun at my chest: 'Now, doctor, I want to know what's wrong with my wife.' This posed a problem: if I was to examine her, would I be shot as a rapist? If I didn't give an answer, having failed to examine her, would I be shot for incompetence? I decided to examine Mrs Rook, came to the conclusion that her heavy bleeding was the result of fibroids, and gave the watchful pair my verdict. Mr Rook went to the door and hung the gun in the hall. He came back in again: 'Thank you, doctor, I am glad I didn't have to use the gun. Won't you have a glass of whisky?'

The episode of Jim demonstrates both paranoia and inappropriate reaction. Having threatened his doctor with a gun for half an hour, he thought that a smile and a glass of whisky was recompense enough. It was a help. On another occasion I visited his brother, Roger. Just as I reached the gate there were wild shouts from a gesticulating Roger. Remembering Jim, I stopped, and Roger came round from the back of the house and led me in through the kitchen. He told me that he was concerned because he had set a booby trap with another shotgun from the family armoury attached to black cotton stretched over the garden path leading to the front door. If I had stumbled on the cotton the shot might have taken my legs off below the knees. He was certain that people were creeping up his path at night and peering through his windows, and he was going to get them.

The third brother was milder. He quietened his moods and dissipated his anger by taking exercise. He walked around the country lanes with a heavy sack of stones over his back, varying the load according to his degree of tension. As I came back from night calls to ill patients I would pass this strange hunched figure, bent double under his therapeutic burden, and exchange a jolly wave.

The Rooks's troubles might all be described as positive, florid symptoms of schizophrenia, which in their case were based on persecutory, paranoid beliefs. Schizophrenia has very many different symptoms, so many and so varied that the general belief now is that they are unlikely to be the result of one particular disease entity but rather are a syndrome – a collection of symptoms. Only in very few cases, even in the early stages, does a patient show the complete range of symptoms described in the textbook. In most patients, the type of schizophrenia from which they are suffering tends to be classified according to the most prominent of the symptoms.

Symptoms are likely to be modified by the character of the sufferer, and those around him or her, as well as their cultural background and environment. Schizophrenia is not like mumps. In mumps, the swelling in the parotid gland in front of the ear looks and feels much the same whether the patient is rich or poor, educated or untutored, comes from Iceland, New York or central Africa. In schizophrenia, on the other hand, these different circumstances will all affect the way in which the disease manifests itself. This can make the diagnosis difficult and sometimes lead to inadequate or inappropriate treatment.

Traditionally there are five subtypes of schizophrenia; their definition, however, is now becoming increasingly blurred as the complexities of the disease and the varied nature of the symptoms have become accepted. Categorizing the symptoms into patterns of disease can be useful when deciding on treatment. However, too ardent a search for defining symptoms may confuse the diagnosis, because most of the symptoms appear in more than one of the subtypes. The important difference is between the positive symptoms and the negative symptoms.

An earlier division of subtypes of schizophrenia with their typical symptoms has now been superseded, but the terms may still be found in older accounts of the disease, and are often used in ordinary conversation:

Simple: insidious loss of drive, interest, ambition and initiative; associated blunting of affect

Hebephrenic: marked disorganization of thinking; primitive, disorganized and regressive behaviour

Catatonic: marked abnormality of motor behaviour, mannerisms, stereotypes, posturings, stupor, excitement, speech disorder

Paranoid: delusions of persecution or grandeur – frequently associated with hallucinations; tense, suspicious, often hostile and aggressive

Paraphrenia of the elderly: well systemized delusions remaining unchanged for many years; no associated disintegration of personality

More recently, a user-friendly, more readily understood division of schizophrenia into five subtypes has been introduced into the latest edition of the *DSM*:

DSM-IV Division of Schizophrenia into Five Subtypes

Disorganized: disinhibited; poor organization, personal
appearance and grooming; inappropriate emotional responses;
age of onset usually before twenty-five
Catatonic: adopting bizarre postures, extreme excitability
Paranoid: delusions of persecution, older age of onset and better
functioning than in other subtypes
Undifferentiated: characteristics of more than one subtype; this is
the most common way for schizophrenia to manifest
Residual: has had a schizophrenic episode and thereafter shows
residual symptoms without any evidence of continuing
psychosis

Before discussing the individual symptoms of the various subtypes the division between positive and negative symptoms has
to be clarified. This difference has considerable clinical importance, as it may determine treatment. Fortunately, the new
atypical antipsychotic drugs are to a varying degree able to ease
both positive and negative symptoms in a majority of patients,
but any additional treatment directed at a particular manifestation of schizophrenia may well be selected as a result of the
assessment of the symptoms displayed by the patient.

Positive Symptoms:
Delusions: strange beliefs, often paranoid, quite foreign to the
person's background, which cannot be shaken by logic or
reason, e.g. secret agents are watching and preparing to
attack, or aliens from outer space are invading earth. Or the
sufferer may suffer from grandiose delusions and believe he
is a popular celebrity, a member of the Royal Family, or a
second Virgin Mary or Jesus Christ.
Paranoid beliefs: including the delusion that the patient's
family have become enemies plotting to murder or otherwise
harm the individual. They may think that innocuous
coincidences are evidence of conspiracy or evil intent.

Hallucinations: the sufferer hears, sees or smells things which are not there. The most common hallucination is hearing voices, which may, for instance, give orders to commit suicide or leave home to escape persecution.

Thought reading: people with schizophrenia often believe their thoughts can be read by others, or that thoughts are put into their mind to control them – these symptoms are described as part of abnormal passivity.

Negative Symptoms:

Symptoms of emotional numbness, apathy and social withdrawal.

Difficulty in communicating with friends or others.

Lack of motivation.

Inability to care about or cope with everyday tasks such as getting out of bed, washing and dressing.

The following symptoms are commonly found in schizophrenic patients but are not among those which are useful to the classification of positive or negative because they occur in both:

Direct eye contact avoided; ill at ease with people.

Thought confusion; muddled incomprehensible speech.

Positive symptoms are those which are commonly portrayed when, for instance, a schizophrenic patient is described in a book or a film. These positive, florid symptoms are, it is said, characterized by excesses. They include delusions (and therefore paranoid beliefs), hallucinations and bizarre behaviour. Although patients with positive symptoms often suffer from hyperexcitability and even manic behaviour, they may also show signs of depression: 75 per cent of all patients with schizophrenia suffer from a manifestation of depression at some time or another.

It was, for instance, Jim Rook and his family, with their dangerous paranoid beliefs, who sprang to mind as an example of schizophrenia, because of their positive symptoms, when thinking of schizophrenia in Norfolk, and not their near neighbour,

Mrs Haversham. Her schizophrenia was characterized by negative symptoms. She was a kindly, although paranoid and deluded, person who lived a reclusive life, but was so lacking in motivation and felt so depressed that she rarely got out of bed before lunch and had usually retired upstairs before dinner. But she didn't sleep and her nocturnal wanderings irritated her much older husband. He looked after himself, Mrs Haversham having long since ceased to worry about the cooking, let alone the washing up.

Negative symptoms reduce the patient's intellectual and emotional reserves. Many become emotionally blunted and intellectually slowed. Often they are depressed and lethargic to the point of being inert. A common everyday manifestation of this lethargy and inertia is that, like Mrs Haversham, they suffer from difficulty in getting up. Parents who have an adolescent son or daughter with schizophrenia may be enraged to find them still in bed at teatime, but sometimes what they condemn as idleness is a symptom of the disease. Young people wouldn't be blamed for their spots if they had measles, nor should they be castigated if a lack of enthusiasm for living, and a fear of confronting the world, keeps them in their bedroom.

Most patients with schizophrenia suffer from anhedonia, the smart term for an inability to experience pleasure, a lesser form of depression. They may also suffer severe degrees of depression, too, as part of the negative symptoms associated with the disease. It is thought that these changes in mood may in part be determined by the misery they suffer as the result of their delusions, paranoia and hallucinations, and the terrors these induce.

It has been noted that if schizophrenia worsens, the depression, rather than keeping pace with it, may sometimes even slightly improve. This, it is suggested, is because the patient's degree of insight is becoming progressively less so that he or she may be becoming blunted to the problems the disease is producing. More often, however, patients are all too well aware of their problems, even if they don't have insight into what is creating them. Not unnaturally, they feel pretty miserable about their plight.

Depression may well be an integral part of the actual disease process, irrespective of whether the patient has insight. The post-schizophrenic depressive state is also sometimes reactionary – the patient recovers from their psychotic interlude only to discover that the world has moved on, they have been left behind and in being left behind have they have also lost their standing in society. The emotion which precipitates the depressive state has been compared to that of prisoners when they are released. Although back in the community, they find that they have been stigmatized by their disease, and are without their status, job and the respect of their peers. Finally, some of the depressed state of the schizophrenic patient stems from their need to take medication. Invaluable as these are, they don't make life a bundle of fun. It is hoped that the new atypical antipsychotic drugs will have fewer side-effects and, as they are also much more useful against the negative symptoms, will tend to jolly people up.

The general mood of patients with schizophrenia, even when they are not depressed, is frequently blunted, so that they do not scale the heights of emotion, nor experience the pleasures, enjoyed by other people. In other cases, social response may be inappropriate, so that a little chuckle greets news which would be more appropriately received with a solemn face, or someone else's disaster may provoke laughter.

One particular patient with schizophrenia, Harry, the brother of my friend Alan Edwards, clearly illustrates both blunting and incongruity of response to emotionally charged events, and also social withdrawal. Not surprisingly, Harry lived alone. Their aged father lived with Alan, a North Country tycoon. Sadly, their father died suddenly and Alan felt that he should drive down to break the news to his schizophrenic brother, who lived in Brighton. He stopped in London in order to talk to me about the best way to tell his brother. After much discussion we agreed upon a choice of words, how the scene should be set and the measures which should be taken if the brother was either inconsolable or became difficult and aggressive.

When Alan reached Brighton he found his brother in the

larder. Harry was reluctant to come down from the steps, where he was rearranging hundreds of tins of baked beans. Undaunted, Alan gave him the details of their father's death while his brother carried on sorting the tins. Harry paused for a moment and then said, without any flicker of emotion, or display of sadness or regret: 'Well, I'm rather busy at the moment. Perhaps we could talk about it later, when I have finished cleaning out the larder.' Alan was surprised at his brother's complete lack of feeling, but bore no grudge about the 600-mile return journey he had undertaken. His reward, he felt, was that his brother's life had been so little upset.

The families of schizophrenic patients often do not understand negative symptoms and just interpret their relative's apathy and social withdrawal as laziness. The mental health charity SANE, which has done so much to explain psychiatric illnesses to the general public, says that in its experience negative symptoms irritate and distress families more than positive ones. Relatives would rather live with someone who is obviously bizarre but active, rather than depressed, lacklustre, inert and unemployed. Patients with negative symptoms feel that they are not understood and that it is a struggle to communicate with their family. These negative symptoms include feelings of guilt, shame, inadequacy, a disturbing flattening of emotion, a shrinking of the vocabulary when speaking, and sometimes a lack of relevance and meaning to the words when they do speak.

So all-pervasive, too, is apathy in patients with negative symptoms that they lose interest in their own appearance and domestic surroundings and in keeping a job. They take little exercise and show no desire to mix with the rest of the community. Dancing, for example, with its ritualized sociability, represents hell for people with schizophrenia or a schizotypal personality.

Not surprisingly, schizophrenic patients with a surfeit of negative symptoms lose any sense of pleasurable anticipation and they find themselves unable to experience the normal pleasures and delights of a domestic life. Emotional numbness extends to their libido, which withers, for, unlike those patients with mainly positive symptoms, they have no appetite for sexual activities. Hitherto, it has been more difficult to treat negative symptoms than positive ones, but with the atypical antipsychotics the situation may change.

Patients suffering from a predominance of negative symptoms – with increasing withdrawal from society and apathy, loss of interest, emotional blunting and academic under-achievement – frequently display symptoms in their teens, and these may at first excite little comment. Initially, the behaviour of people with schizophrenia may be characterized by little more than odd mannerisms and actions; sometimes these are disturbing to their families, and at other times treasured by them. Friends and strangers often find idiosyncratic behaviour slightly amusing and – if it doesn't go too far and become embarrassing – the approach is often summed up by the rhetorical question, 'Isn't he (or she) a character?' Only if the disease grows worse does the true import of these small oddities of behaviour become apparent.

Jim, despite his strange manner, was a successful lawyer. He was known in his office as being mildly eccentric, and as such people accepted his behaviour even if he was sometimes so aloof and distant that he not only didn't reply to questions but appeared not to have seen the questioner. At home, life wasn't so easy. There, Jim's 'eccentricity' was closer to paranoia, and he was convinced that his wife was having an affair, or in fact affairs, and found confirmation for this in the flimsiest of evidence, or even mere suspicion. In time, his anxieties over her imagined amorous misbehaviour were compounded by his belief that she was also stealing from him. The more she protested her innocence, the more abusive and violent he became. Fortunately, the violence was confined to smashing up the house rather than his wife.

Jim's doctor had been aware for some little time that all was not well and he arranged for Jim to see a psychiatrist, who treated him with antipsychotic medication. After a period of in-patient treatment Jim returned to his wife and was able to resume his job. His wife reported that although he couldn't yet be described as normal, he was no longer violent or accusatory.

This type of schizophrenia, however, when the symptoms are pronounced, does account for the large number of schizophrenic people who live rough or who have drifted into prison, having committed some petty crime. Living rough is never an easy choice for someone with schizophrenia, but many fear contact with other people, and control by authority, to a greater extent than they dread deprivation and the indignity of life in a doorway.

Even though a schizophrenic patient may not show extreme paranoia or grandiosity, or exhibit the grotesque symptoms of a severely deranged mind, their illness is such that their thoughts are so disorganized that they no longer fit into standard society. Their life has in fact been reduced to an uncomfortable and lonely chaos. Frequently, the absence of extreme symptoms may have delayed diagnosis, but the patient's own lack of insight or of faith in medicine may have also contributed to their condition and kept them away from the doctor's surgery, and possible help.

Many patients with schizophrenia show inappropriate social behaviour. 'Inappropriate social behaviour' is a portmanteau description for a wide variety of small quirks of behaviour which can ruin a patient's integration into society. Someone, for instance, who disregards the normal but unspoken rules of society and stares too long and hard at a drunken man in the bar may find himself being hit for, as it seems to him, no very good reason. The person behaving inappropriately – in this case staring – does not understand normal cultural concepts of space.

Harold, for example, had been educated very expensively by his elderly parents but – regrettably, in his parents' view – he was not academic and went to earn his living in the Middle East, where he suffered a psychotic breakdown and was bundled home. Each day, for a time, he used to come and see me, but even by sitting in the waiting room his behaviour inevitably seemed to engender a complaint. My receptionist couldn't understand why the dark-suited bankers were alienated by this strangely dressed but perfectly clean and well-spoken young man.

As soon as I had watched him through the waiting room doors, the reason was obvious. The other patients, when they came in, picked *The Times* or *Telegraph* off the table and hid behind it, seemingly oblivious of everything going on around them. They politely pretended that the other patients were not in the room. Harold, on the other hand, came into the room, stared at each one, minutely and in turn, and as he assessed them they shifted uneasily in their chairs. Even after he had finally sat down, he jerkily leaped to his feet from time to time and paced to the window. If he did pick up a paper, he always put it down as soon as someone else came in so that they, too, could be subjected to his quizzical gaze. He ignored their polite nods, or glared, but when they glared, he smiled. Even if his choice in clothes, and barber, had been more traditional, his lack of understanding of appropriate social response would have made him an unwelcome member of any surgery queue. His behaviour caused a general unease which the other patients found hard to define, even though this didn't stop them from mentioning Harold's presence in terms of anxious disapproval and complaint.

Although what is considered inappropriate behaviour varies from one group to another, in general nobody likes to have someone they are talking to come as close during a conversation as many schizophrenic patients do, who lack an understanding of personal space. Patients with schizophrenia are also notorious for their disorganized and inappropriate conversation, as they do not always comprehend the limits of what is allowed or not allowed, and when it is allowed, in conversation. Nor do they know which questions are too personal to be asked by a stranger or, if they are to be asked, the type of facial expression which has to be adopted to soften their impact. Not only is their conversation inappropriate, but very often so are the gestures which accompany it. A statement which should be met with a solemn face and a weighty comment is greeted with smiles, or possibly ignored completely. When condolences would be in order the patient may respond with jocularity.

Although schizophrenic patients have feelings as fragile as the finest glass, they themselves, because of their lack of social finesse, are frequently too blunt, being both over-sensitive and over-defensive, when expressing an opinion. They can become insultingly personal while arguing and can be embarrassingly insensitive to other people's feelings. Telling white lies may be baffling and alien to their character, for they retain the unrealistic innocence of childhood speech. While straight talk may be acceptable from the toddler in the nursery – 'Grandpa, you have old arms, old hands, and an old face' – it is seldom welcomed in the office, or the saloon bar of the George and Dragon.

It is not only speech which can be inappropriate – clothing, too, can strike a discordant note. It may be a disregard for convention, no more odd and worrying than an eccentric physician I knew who used to wear carpet slippers with a morning coat and striped trousers, but some clothing can give rise to real disquiet. Too often this unease seems to be caused by a black overcoat, stretching to the floor, together with a dark shirt and long lank hair trailing over the eyes and collar. Many schizophrenics' posture is characteristically self-effacing, their neck permanently bent forwards, so that eye contact may be reduced to a bare minimum. Failure to make eye contact is a marked feature of all schizophrenic patients, a feature which is very noticeable, whether they are suffering from positive or negative symptoms.

Schizophrenia disrupts a sufferer's thoughts and renders them, and their conversation, illogical and tangential. Patients who have this severely disturbed thought pattern can be very irritating to talk to. Their conversation does not go from A to B to C to D and constructively onwards until a conclusion is reached, but round and round in circles. Questions which require a definite answer are replied to with a riddle – like Ophelia's replies in *Hamlet* – presumably meaningful to the patient but meaningless to everyone else.

On other occasions the schizophrenic patient will reply to the question with a fleeting, indecipherable smile, or they may just ignore the question and continue as if it had never been asked. They are very often impatient, and so wrapped in their own thoughts when talking in a group that they do not wait for a pause in the conversation but cut across it. Conversely, on other occasions, the natural timidity of those with schizophrenia prevents them from inserting their contribution into the conversation at the correct time. Their words of wisdom, or otherwise, may then be out of phase with the run of the conversation and create an embarrassed silence when eventually murmured. If the rest of the party is polite and socially adept, however, a hasty restructuring and backtracking can spare everybody's feelings. If those who are chattering away are inconsiderate or insensitive, the shy person may be subjected to a glance of surprise or scorn, and the ignored patient's fragile self-esteem takes another battering.

Conversation is conventionally a two-way process, in which good manners dictate 'who bats when and for how long'. However, many schizophrenic patients tend to be insensitive to these niceties; some don't say enough, others, all too often, may inflict their thoughts and views on whoever happens to be within earshot. Frequently when the condition worsens, the sufferer becomes increasingly withdrawn and uncommunicative, and negative symptoms may start to become predominant.

Catatonic schizophrenia, which is now very rare, usually starts later – in the teens or early twenties. Essentially it involves disturbances of motor activity, that is to say, of physical activity. The patient may be immobile, withdrawn, silent and of course unresponsive, or may be agitated, excited and restless. There are marked mood changes, with rapid and unaccountable swings from the over-elation of hypomania to discordant depression and deep gloom. There are many positive symptoms in catatonic schizophrenia, when the patient may suffer from hallucinations and delusions.

In the past, catatonic schizophrenic patients would, far more often than today, have periods when their thought processes and physical movements were so inhibited that they stayed for long periods as still as a statue. Not only might they adopt these statuesque positions themselves but at other times they could be put into a posture by someone else and maintain that posture for some time. As this has some similarity to wax modelling, it is known as 'waxy flexibility'.

For many years, in a London club, a particular member would adopt a certain pose – for instance, with one arm outstretched or held aloft – after breakfast and would sometimes remain in that same pose for four or five hours. New members may have been astonished, but the older members and the staff were entirely tolerant. Long before the club member showed any signs of her psychiatric problems, the die to determine her future had perhaps been cast in her mother's womb and in her own early life, for her grandmother and four of her grandmother's six siblings had either died in a mental hospital or committed suicide.

The club member's mother was able to cope with life provided that her children went to a boarding school at a very early age and her husband kept an eye on the workings of the household. The mother didn't waste her days and although thought eccentric, she was in fact ahead of her time, and had embraced the green movement in the 1930s, devoting her life thereafter to the demanding task of preserving hedgerows and footpaths.

Abnormal thoughts are a characteristic of all schizophrenia. What is considered abnormal in a person will very much depend on the social norm in the community in which that person is living. Mystical beliefs and the belief in one's own mystical powers, which might be well accepted in West Africa or the West Indies, might be considered distinctly bizarre in Paddington or Preston. Schizophrenic patients have many unusual patterns of behaviour, small rites, without which they feel lost. This may be part of an obsessive nature some display. Sometimes, for instance, the patient feels compelled to walk in a certain way, performing pre-ordained steps, just as determinedly as if they were carrying out the complex movements of a Scottish reel.

Schizophrenic patients have to endure many disruptions to an ordered thought process. Some of the stranger ones are grouped together under the term 'passivity phenomena' and include thought-broadcasting – the feeling that one's thoughts are not one's own and can be heard, and are thus available to everybody.

Non-schizophrenic people dismiss too readily the amount of worry and unhappiness that this fear can cause.

Patients can feel that their minds have been opened up for general scrutiny. How many people would really like their thoughts, hopes and feelings accessible to all those around them? 'What a silly ass that man is, as ignorant as he is ugly' is a thought better kept to oneself. It may be acceptable that God, to whom all hearts are open, and all desires known, and from whom no secrets are hid, is privy to our minds but it is an alarming thought that the rest of the railway carriage might share His skill.

Other patients sometimes think that their thoughts have been 'sucked' from them, in which case the term used is not 'thought-broadcasting' but 'thought withdrawal'. Yet others think, not that their own thoughts are being withdrawn or broadcast but that other people's thoughts are being inserted into their minds and that their powers of reason are no longer under their own control. Thought-insertion is so classic a schizophrenic symptom that when a patient suffers from it the diagnosis is usually obvious.

Ben had worked in a chemist's shop before he decided to join the police. Initially his thoughts were all of law and order and the value of the work that he was hoping to do. He had come from a sheltered background and was rather shocked by the conversation and language, and even behaviour, of some of his fellow recruits, who didn't seem to have his dedicated approach to life. He was left even more appalled by his confrontation with the murkier aspects of humanity. He started to turn down invitations to go to the pub or to parties. Ben spent more and more time by himself despite the friendly concern of some of his colleagues. He wanted to control his thoughts but, bit by bit, thoughts as actual words started to come into his head, and they were very embarrassing, all too often sexual. Whatever he was doing, these words and phrases came back, so that sustained thought became impossible and everything became jumbled in his mind, and became mixed up with worries about disgrace and damnation. His work suffered, his manner became bizarre, and he was finally found wandering in the woods convinced that he was a satyr.

Schizophrenic patients' troubles don't end with feelings that their thoughts are being broadcast, withdrawn or that others are being inserted into their minds. They may also worry that the same thing can happen to their feelings and their responses to them. They believe that the emotions they experience are then not the genuine ones that they should be experiencing, but ones 'grafted' onto their psyche by some outside force. Likewise, they fear their responses can be 'controlled' by an alien agency.

When a doctor says that patients have 'poverty of speech' it not only means that they may be abstracted and uncommunicative, but that even if the patient is chattering away, the person they are talking to may unfortunately be little wiser at the end of it. Some schizophrenic patients' vagueness in expression is coupled with a habit of endless repetitions, a combination of qualities which can make conversation very hard to follow.

Similarly, not all the physical gestures of schizophrenic patients are understood, although when a good rapport is established with patients they may explain them. I have seen several patients who shake their heads like a two-year-old child. It is not quite certain why babies shake their heads, other than to find a method of communication with adults, but more than one patient has told me that in their case it was to shake the cobwebs from their mind and to sort out their thoughts. Others, like children, indulge in head banging, usually only symbolically, they may suggest, because they are disturbed by what is going on within their heads. However, at other times, like a child, they may bang their heads with considerable force.

Schizophrenic patients often have a love of heavy metal music, jangling and discordant to most people. Some sufferers have said that they play this at such a volume so as to drown the voices in their heads, just as the head bangers and shakers intend to beat the offending part and dislodge the fiends. It may also be as a protest at their own cluttered and deranged thoughts, which are causing them such bewilderment.

Barely a week goes past without a paper carrying the story of some disastrous misdiagnosis of schizophrenia which has resulted in mayhem. Many of these catastrophes stem from paranoid delusions. Paranoid schizophrenic patients are convinced that they are being 'got at', if not by the whole world, by an individual or an organization which is plotting against them and is preoccupied with achieving their downfall. The persecutory thoughts are frequently reinforced by auditory hallucinations – not only are the Russians or Chinese plotting to seize or destroy their victim, but the patient can hear warnings of the plotters' evil intent. The voice can sound absolutely normal, just as real as if someone was talking across the dinner table.

Voices may be friendly or hostile, congratulatory or condemnatory, co-operative or destructive. Voices can sometimes goad the patients into acts of violence, at other times alarm them into defensive aggression – many patients with paranoid schizophrenia commit their apparently hostile acts because they adhere to the old military principal of the advantages of the first strike. Sometimes the voice is recognized – it is frequently that of a loved one – at other times it is unknown, unrecognized and the patient may not even remember if it was male or female. Comparatively often, a patient who suffers from paranoid schizophrenia, apart from their fixed delusions, may be quite rational about other aspects of their life. Paranoid schizophrenic patients often develop the first signs of their condition later than do those suffering from other types of the disease.

Freda was a strange, retiring woman. She found making friends with her neighbours difficult, and, as they said in the neighbourhood, she kept herself to herself. David looked after her wonderfully, he usually tolerated her unpredictable moods with a smile and only occasionally allowed himself the luxury of a mild grumble. Only when her husband died did the village realize how much she had depended on his ability to anticipate the family's needs. Without him she became increasingly disturbed and she became convinced that she was the queen. This would have been a difficult role for her to fulfil had it not been that the ticks of the sitting-room clock gave her the necessary orders to perform her duties. Like all queens, she had enemies, but fortunately she had learned how to recognize them: her enemies carried large red bags.

That orders stemmed from the clock were not her only delusion, she also heard other voices when she went shopping. The voices stopped her thinking about what she had gone out to buy and she wandered disconsolately around the market stalls. It was bad enough that the voices upset her, but she also worried about their effect on the village children who hung around the streets. She found that the way to deal with the voices was to laugh so loudly that the noise of her laughter drowned the voices' obscenities and left the children uncorrupted. Not unnaturally, the sight of Freda stalking the market and the sound of her raucous unamused laughter attracted the attention of the authorities. Now, after treatment, she is back home again, quiet, distant but apparently able to manage by herself.

Not all the delusions that paranoid schizophrenic patients suffer from are persecutory – like Freda's, they may be grandiose. At its most absurd the patient thinks that they are the Prime Minister, or the hitherto undiscovered son of a member of the Royal Family, but in its lesser forms it may be no more than an unrealistic self-analysis of their own abilities. This lack of ability to judge their own ability doesn't only apply to the would-be writer whose writing is without merit, and often pseudo-philosophical nonsense; or the artist whose picture is incomprehensible – it also applies to the clerk who thinks that he or she should be managing director, or the district councillor who yearns for Downing Street. In perhaps the most interesting cases of all, these may lead to grandiose delusions – grandiosity. There is no medical student who doesn't remember the case of the little old woman who was convinced that she was Princess Margaret.

In milder forms, grandiosity excites both sadness and embarrassment. Bill Eastbrook was the son of a brilliant mathematician who had an eccentric but successful lifestyle. Bill himself was clever but not so clever that his eccentricity and disorganized behaviour could be incorporated into an effective university career. He took refuge by becoming more and more solitary, retiring

"COULD YOU BE HENRY THE EIGHTH
WITHOUT THE EATING HABITS?"

to his rooms to write his masterpiece, a long novel. He carried his manuscript everywhere but no one was allowed to see it. Finally, it was unveiled at the end of one term, and two or three of his closest friends shared a bottle of wine as they were introduced to his book. The book lacked any distinction, it had no clearly defined plot, in fact suffered from a surfeit of plots. Its language was convoluted, the terminology obscure; in short it was without merit and was more than a little bizarre.

Like many people with a personality which would now be described as schizotypal, Bill was convinced that he was genuinely a latter-day Dickens, if not Tolstoy. He only wrote once again, a short story, very much more telling than his magnum opus, but having been once rejected by the literary world, he was convinced that no one was interested in his book, and he never even tried to have it published. A lack of self-critical ability extends across the creative arts. Sufferers, for instance, competent to play hymns on the church organ or perhaps the guitar in a pub are certain that they are Bach or John Williams. The mortification which so often follows rejection can trigger a relapse.

Bertrand had been hearing voices for so many years that he had become used to them. After a time it wasn't only the voices: there were the inner convictions and the certainty that he was an important military man who was under the direct command of the Prince of Wales, whose voice gave him orders. Even this might have been socially bearable had not Bertrand believed that as he had worked for the Prince for so long, the Prince now knew things about him that he would rather no one knew. Furthermore, he knew things about the Prince which no one should know and as a result he thought there was a grave danger that he might be obliterated by *Them*. Not only did the Prince of Wales talk to him, but Jesus, too, had a word from time to time. Jesus suggested that he should join a militant anarchist group, but luckily Bertrand, who had been seeking treatment unavailingly, rejected Jesus' advice and instead decided to set fire to some local scrubland so that he would be admitted to hospital. The device worked and now so long as he continues to take medication he remains well and the voices are bearable.

Paranoid delusions and grandiosity are considered to derive from the same disordered reason. In terms of outcome after treatment, it may even be more encouraging to the patient to have symptoms of paranoia. Delusions are divided up into delusions of reference, delusions of control, paranoid delusions and grandiose delusions. In delusions of reference, there is a belief that events which most people would consider pure chance – the coincidences of life – are in fact planned with special reference to the patient, usually to inconvenience or damage them. There are also frequently messages from on high, which are portents from the supernatural, warning of the plots which are being hatched against the patient. The patient looks at perfectly normal events and, as the expression has it, adds two and two together to make five. The patient may, for instance, be certain that a TV presenter,

163

or a preacher in the pulpit, is referring to them, and has a special message for them.

One variant in the usual pattern of delusions of reference is commonly heard in a doctor's surgery. Many patients suffer from delusions which may not only be about the supposed intrusive, bad, or even threatening, behaviour of other people, but may inspire fears about their health and misconceptions that their body is diseased. They may be convinced that their illness is more serious than others suppose, and they can then easily find other hypochondriacal symptoms to support their own initial faulty diagnosis. The everyday trivial aches and pains, which most people suffer intermittently, they interpret in a way which confirms their own deluded beliefs.

Often the delusion starts because the doctor may have said previously that the patient had, for instance, a minor abnormality of the kidney. The patient may have accepted this happily enough at the time, even believed the doctor's reassurance that the abnormality was of no clinical significance – but then all their fears will have come flooding back when they experienced some slight pain on passing water. A more phlegmatic character would have attributed the discomfort to over-indulgence in rhubarb or strawberries, or perhaps the use of highly scented soap, but not a deluded hypochondriac. The situation suddenly becomes clear. It is a cancer of the bladder and the truth is being hidden while they are being secretly treated. There can be no doubt about it – why else did the patient's wife want a new bathroom on the ground floor and a change in the holiday plans, why else did the family diet suddenly contain so many more carrots and tomatoes? It all now suddenly makes sense. The ubiquitous, all-powerful *They* all know about the cancer, but are not letting on. *They* have been watching him to see how he was doing, *They* had to find ways of giving him drugs without his knowing. At first he thought it was no more than the lacing of his food with drugs, but later he knew that he was being given radiation treatment through the walls of the house next door. This is of course why the local electricians called. All that talk about rewiring hadn't fooled him.

In delusions of control, schizophrenic patients have a belief that their thoughts, emotions or physical movements are controlled by an external power. Disorders of the thought process in a schizophrenic patient bring about a loosening of associations. Ideas therefore are not expressed succinctly and the connections between them may seem totally incomprehensible or bizarre to those not experienced in following a particular person's distorted logic. This type of thinking, in which the patients no longer go from A to B to C and so on, but jump about so that the connections between each of the thoughts is abstruse, is called 'knight's move thinking' after the crabwise advance of the knight on the chessboard.

There are two other conditions affecting the patient's thoughts, and therefore their conversation: thought block and neologism. These speech abnormalities are very striking when they are encountered. In thought block there is a sudden interruption, without obvious cause, in the direction in which the patient's thoughts are flowing. Neologism is the inclusion in a patient's conversation of words made up by the patient, which sound real enough, often rather impressive and learned, but which have no real meaning and cannot be found in the dictionary. Although they are not true words, they can resemble them and sometimes, from a distance, sound as if they fit into the general conversation.

Peter Borrow's case illustrates both thought disorder and paranoia in schizophrenia. A colleague from the House of Commons asked me to have a chat with Peter, one of his constituents, who was making threats against the Member's wife. Unfortunately the constituent's doctor did not take these threats very seriously, and considered that the patient was suffering from a personality disorder, was 'bad' rather than 'mad' and that the best treatment for him was to go into the local prison.

Although, when I met Peter, he displayed many of the patterns of behaviour characteristic of schizophrenia, I was struck above all by his choice of words. They sounded most impressive, for his conversation was studded with technical terms I had never heard before. I stood on his doorstep and if it hadn't been for the rest of his demeanour I would have been overwhelmed by his erudition. He was a very keen, if not a very knowledgeable, student of English and did not take offence when I asked him for the precise meaning of some of the words. But his evasive replies made it immediately obvious that they were neologisms. However, his strange vocabulary didn't disguise the genuine anxiety he was experiencing as a result of his delusion that the Fascists were now in league with the local Communists and together they were going to encourage the Russians to land at the local airbase. So great was his fear that his country was in danger, that he felt honour-bound to do something about it and the best he could do, in his opinion, was to galvanize his MP into action, and the surest way of doing that would be to threaten the MP's wife. He had every intention of carrying out his threats.

People with schizophrenic and schizophrenic-type conditions with thought disorders can even be irritating when they give a decipherable answer. This may not be a definite 'yes' or 'no', but is couched in vague, noncommittal terms: 'could be', 'I may', 'per-haps', 'possibly'; or they may procrastinate, frequently offering the reply, 'later'. The problems caused by this vagueness, possibly partly adopted so as to avoid the criticism that a definite opinion might bring, are compounded by the habit which nervous schizophrenic patients sometimes have of speaking not only dis-jointedly, but in a mumbling, low, small voice.

The general view is that a hallmark of the schizophrenic patient is the hearing of voices. This phenomenon has been the crucial clue in numerous films, books and plays, and in real life it has caused alarm in tens of thousands of households. The voices come in four types. There is the second-person voice, when the voice talks to the patient, just as if they were across the dining room table – Banquo's ghost without a ghost. Conversation and the stream of orders are direct and the voice may or may not be recognized.

In third-person voices, the patient is aware of someone

discussing him or her, in general as if he or she were not there. The effect is similar to the way in which a doctor may discuss a patient lying in bed as if they were not there, or the style of conversation when two mothers might talk about a child playing around their feet.

In the running-commentary voice the voices keep up a commentary on the patient's actions. The patient is referred to in the third person: 'Steven shouldn't have done that, he just won't get away with it.' Some years ago, a prominent and very good London surgeon was apt to worry his patients by commenting on his own actions and techniques, sometimes critically, as if they were not there. The patients liked to think that he was thinking out loud but those with medical knowledge were always worried and feared that some inner voice was at work and he was recounting this voice's comments.

In a thought echo, the fourth type of voice, patients have a sensation that the inner voice has the ability to echo their own thoughts, which it repeats.

Although auditory hallucinations are the most common form of hallucination in schizophrenia, they are not the only ones. Patients may very occasionally have olfactory hallucinations – strange smells: and in these cases it is very important to exclude a physical cause, such as a tumour. Visual hallucinations may be the result of such conditions as Lewy body dementia, a variant of Alzheimer's disease, or the hypnagogic hallucinations of narcolepsy, experienced when patients are in the twilight zone between wakefulness and sleep, but they can also be a symptom of schizophrenia.

Mrs Deacon, a patient of mine when I was in general practice in Norfolk, was suffering from schizophrenia and had regular visual hallucinations. Her symptoms also included depression. We tried to maintain her dose of psychotrophic drugs on an even keel, but it needed regular modification. Every now and again an increase in the dose of antipsychotic drugs would be needed to take away the vision of the Virgin Mary, who used to visit Mrs Deacon regularly. At other times a return to antidepressant therapy was required, for without antidepressants she was apt to feel suicidal.

When crisis struck the Deacon family, her husband, who looked after her excellently, used by day to rattle at my door, or by night throw pebbles at my bedroom window: 'Doctor, doctor, it's the visions again. She needs the Stelazine.' After a few doses, the Virgin Mary would disappear from sight. At other times, there would be a call for a visit as Mrs Deacon was threatening to take her own life – then chat, reassurance, regular visits and a reissue of the antidepressants, and within two or three weeks she would be back at her cleaning job and the Deacon household could expect a few months, or even a year or two, of calm.

In paraphrenia, an elderly patient may have one well-entrenched paranoid delusion while the rest of their psyche remains reasonably whole, so that their personality is sufficiently intact for them to continue to lead a normal life in the community. Paraphrenia is not a diagnosis made in younger patients.

There are a variety of symptoms which are experienced by patients with schizophrenia which are not exclusively confined to schizophrenic people but which, when exaggerated, certainly point to it. They vary from a strange condition known as 'echopraxia' to a heightened sensory awareness, including acuteness of smell, sight, hearing and cutaneous sensitivity. Echopraxia is a strange phenomenon. In a milder form, it is often seen when two very close friends or lovers are together. On these occasions one person's movements tend to echo those of the other. Echopraxia carries this to pathological limits, when there is obvious, immediate imitation of the other person – one pulls at their ear, the other pulls at theirs. This condition is different from stereotyping, when a patient simply repeats the same purposeless movement, over and over again.

Patients with schizophrenia also complain of changes in their libido and sexual response. Many schizophrenic patients with negative symptoms are too withdrawn, even without their medication, to establish emotional relationships with those they feel drawn to sexually. Many of the earlier antipsychotic drugs blunted sexual feelings; others, among both the older and the newer drugs, may not reduce libido, but may cause impotence in men or lack of lubrication in women. However, those with schizophrenia who have a multiplicity of positive symptoms, but are not withdrawn, may have very strong sexual urges without have the social competence to establish a normal, loving relationship. Intimacy – which most people consider the foundation of a good sexual relationship – is not their strong suit. Schizophrenic patients therefore find themselves making use of the services of prostitutes to a greater extent than most members of the population, and when they do make advances to other people, these are often clumsy and socially inappropriate. In some cases the ineptness of their actions creates actual fear. When a relationship is established, the actual sex tends to be very physical, with an over-emphasis on the need to obtain sexual gratification.

As physical sex, even if it is only masturbation, is important to many schizophrenic patients, any drug which takes away their ability to enjoy sex may be rejected. It is surprising how few doctors ask about this, but it is not surprising that patients will not volunteer this information without being prompted. The doctor then may be left wondering just why this pleasant and otherwise co-operative young man hoards or destroys, but doesn't swallow, his tablets.

Many of the minor symptoms of schizophrenia, minor even though they can make the patient's everyday life difficult, are shared – but to a lesser degree – by people with a schizotypal personality disorder. This can be manifested by a sometimes tedious worry about the pronunciation of words, grammar and in particular punctuation. In people who have this trait, this punctilious interest in words is part of the obsessive aspect of their nature.

Such a man was William Tucker, a pre-war academic, who had, through no fault of his own, a difficult life as the war had cut short his academic life. Eventually, in his early fifties, after years of mundane jobs, and social and financial ignominy, he achieved his just deserts – someone recognized his intellect and abilities and he was appointed to an important job in industry. All went well for several years, until one day William told the chairman that his punctuation in the Annual Report was incorrect. William proceeded to put the commas where they should be. The chairman was not at all pleased to receive an impromptu and public lesson in grammar and insisted that his message to the shareholders should go out as he had written it. William said that no letter with which he had had anything to do could be sent out if the grammar was not correct and he would rather resign than allow this to happen. Despite his years in the economic wilderness, and his battle to re-establish himself, he stuck to his principles and resigned.

Prognosis and Treatment

Schizophrenic patients who are paranoid and suffer from delusions and hallucinations are not only more likely to commit suicide, but are also more likely than others suffering from schizophrenia to commit acts of violence against other people. Most schizophrenic patients are anxious, timid, frightened people, who would like to remain obscure and unnoticed, but there is no doubt that a schizophrenic patient is more likely to commit or attempt to commit homicide than the rest of the population. Although only one per cent, or thereabouts, of the population have a formal diagnosis of schizophrenia, 8 per cent of people who have committed or attempted to commit murder are schizophrenic. A schizophrenic patient is four times more likely to be involved in non-fatal violent acts than an otherwise similar member of the general public.

Another outcome is suicide. About 15 per cent of people with schizophrenia commit suicide. Many commit suicide early in the disease, before either they or their families have become accustomed to the diagnosis, its symptoms and the change in lifestyle that it may entail. Schizophrenic patients may, like many other psychiatric patients, commit suicide when they start to get better. When very ill they may be too unaware and inert to realize their problems, or may be too indecisive to damage themselves. Other schizophrenic patients commit suicide on a sudden impulse. Mood swings from elation to deep depression occur much more quickly in those with schizophrenia than in other forms of depression and there may be no precipitating cause that would be obvious to a rational person.

In some cases suicide, like other forms of violent behaviour, may be the result of delusions, which create unhappiness, or, less commonly, the commands of hallucinatory voices. It has been recorded that patients with hallucinations and persistent delusions are more likely to commit suicide than those suffering from schizophrenia in which other symptoms predominate. Schizophrenic patients are a hundred times more likely to commit suicide than to murder. This, however, will be of little consolation to the victim's family.

In general, the life expectancy of a schizophrenic patient is about ten years shorter than the standard for the rest of the population. Not all the deaths are from suicide. Smoking, for instance, takes its toll. The majority of schizophrenic people smoke heavily, as each cigarette tends to give about twenty minutes' relief of tension – but it also means an increased incidence of heart disease. Another possible factor may be cardio-vascular complications caused by some of the older psychotrophic drugs; recently there has been a similar problem with Serdolect (sertindole), one of the new atypical antipsychotics, which has since been withdrawn.

Schizophrenia is not necessarily a progressive disease. The course of the disease is very variable. Some authorities say that one-third of patients recover completely, others that two-thirds recover to the point that they can continue in society. It used to be said that a quarter recover to the extent that they are able to go back to their old job, a quarter return to work but in a less stressful role, a quarter are capable of looking after themselves in society but have problems with earning an adequate income, and the remaining quarter suffer from a chronic illness and need constant support.

The Concise Oxford Textbook of Psychiatry divides the outcome of schizophrenia into five. One fifth develop an acute illness but make a complete recovery, and another fifth have recurrent acute episodes and recover between each of these episodes. The other three-fifths have chronic disease, divided between those illnesses which have an acute origin and those which started insidiously. Eugen Bleuler (1857–1939), a pioneer in the treatment and understanding of schizophrenia, followed his patients for many years. He determined that 20 per cent made a full recovery with no recurrence, 35 per cent recovered in between repeated episodes, 35 per cent suffered a chronic mild psychosis but had severe exacerbations, and 10 per cent deteriorated to the point where they needed continuous care. Other doctors have a slightly less cheerful approach, believing that one-quarter will become chronically psychotic, one-quarter will make a good enough recovery never to require re-admission to hospital, and that half have some obvious disability, but that the severity of the symptoms wax and wane. The same accepted prognosis says that 70 per cent have, whatever the outcome, depressive symptoms of some type or another, and 15 per cent will continue to suffer delusions or hallucinations. In schizophrenia the outcome is not only very variable but it is usually impossible to predict with certainty which patient will follow which course, although there can be clues to their future.

Although it is true that, in general, schizophrenic patients do less well than those who have an affective disorder, whether depression or mania, the pattern of the disease is, thankfully, as with other psychiatric disorders, increasingly being modified by the introduction of new drugs. Family and patients nearly always ask the doctor for a prognosis, but wise doctors refuse to give one. The doctors' tutors in their medical youth will have told them to be 'guarded', a wonderful medical term for humming and hawing, for it is impossible to be certain of anything when dealing with patients who have schizophrenia. However, it is right and proper that the doctor should explain that many make an almost complete recovery and are able to go back to their jobs, provided that these do not cause unreasonable strain.

Schizophrenic disorders do not always run a smooth pattern; in some cases the symptoms come and go. But when discussing prognosis, there are some signs which point to a good outcome. A sudden onset of symptoms is considered a favourable sign, particularly if the trouble can be laid at the door of some external event; if this is so, the breakdown may, to some extent, be considered a reactive condition. A reactive breakdown is particularly likely to have a good prognosis if the patient has a well-ordered home background, so that their domestic and even sometimes professional life continues. One consequence of good professional and domestic support is demonstrated by the frequency with which married schizophrenic patients do better after their first attack than do those who are divorced, single or widowed. The presence of the positive symptoms of schizophrenia when first diagnosed, and the absence of too many negative symptoms, which, all too often, slowly and insidiously increase in their severity, is a good prognostic sign.

The signs which tempt a doctor to be even more cautious than usual about prognosis are of a slowly progressive illness. The negative symptoms which are discouraging include loss of eye contact, marked withdrawal, paucity of speech and thought, emotional blunting and intellectual regression. As if to underline the hazards of the insidious onset of the disease, those patients who had early symptoms and warning signs of possible trouble ahead in childhood tend to have a worse prognosis.

Those who have had previous attacks also tend to do less well, as the more attacks there have been, the worse the outlook. As an extension of this, those who have previously had a schizotypal personality, and in fact may have appeared no more than slightly bizarre to the rest of the world before they had a schizophrenic breakdown, also fare less well in the long term.

As far as treatment is concerned, the outlook for the disease has never been better. The atypical antipsychotics, introduced in the last five years, promise a revolution in the treatment of schizo-phrenia and of allied conditions. Whereas there was opposition to the older neuroleptic drugs used to control schizophrenia, the new forms of treatment have received a degree of unity in their acceptance from the medical profession and psychotherapy never previously witnessed. Soon, it is hoped, the impaired functioning of the brain of patients with the disease may be corrected, and the symptoms, which are now so devastating, kept at bay.

Quite apart from any treatment with drugs, the ways in which patients' relatives and colleagues relate to sufferers is crucial to the development of the illness. People with a schizotypal person-ality disorder, even if they are not schizophrenic, not only find integrating with their families difficult, but also all activities which involve interpersonal relationships. In each and every one of them they fear being judged. Every social occasion, every meet-ing with strangers, even the daily confrontations in the office, shop or factory, can be as demanding to them as an appearance in the magistrate's court, or a cross-examination at a university oral examination, would be to others. They sense they are being appraised and, as many are depressed and paranoid, they assume (perhaps correctly, as their social manner may be inappropriate) that their performance will be found wanting by those who don't know them.

Family reaction to a schizophrenic person's behaviour is par-ticularly important. Any comment which can be misunderstood or considered unnecessary, particularly if made by a member of the family, is particularly wounding. The patients long to have family life like other people's, they want to be able to enjoy holi-days, celebrate Christmas, birthdays and weddings in an atmos-phere not riven by expressed emotion. They wish to have the warm and close emotional relationships with other members of their family, which they can see other families enjoying, but they are constantly thwarted by an inability to respond appropriately to joking banter or loving gestures. They are left mourning their lack of emotional rapport with those to whom they should be closest, and regretting the family rows this induces.

Ideally, schizophrenic patients should live near their families and have ready access to them. If they have to live with their families, everyone must remember that the patient's inability to reciprocate the standard expressions of love and acceptance from which others derive such comfort intensifies their feelings of inadequacy and thereby increase their isolation.

The definition of schizophrenia is all-important when following the pattern within a family group. The very strict definition of schizophrenia has resulted in its under-diagnosis, but it has been found that people with similar conditions, but without the essential diagnostic features demanded by traditional psychiatrists, are much more common in those families in which there is schizophrenia and a similar family pattern can be shown in these instances. These conditions include schizoaffective disorders, other disorders with schizophrenic features, psychiatric conditions which resemble schizotypal personality disorders and other psychotic troubles, in particular extreme depression, mania and the manic-depressive psychoses. All are found more often in some families, and particularly in those in which other members have an agreed diagnosis of schizophrenia.

My psychiatric mentor once said to me, when looking at the relatives who had come to visit one of our patients, 'It's a toss-up which of the family should be in the bed, and which should be encouraged to go home. It is probably chance, but it could certainly depend as much on their social and financial background as on the integrity of their thought processes.'

An illustration of the importance of the physical environment and the influence of interpersonal relationships acting on genetic susceptibility, was expressed by another of my teachers. He taught that choosing the right environment and human companionship was much more important when treating patients with the schizophrenic-type diseases than it was when dealing with people suffering from disorders of mood, like clinical depression. His generalizations about the relative importance of environment and its influence on inherited susceptibility when considering schizophrenia and its allied conditions – as opposed to the influence of environment on genetically linked affective disorders, such as depression – are often true even if they cannot be justified in all cases. My teacher's theory was that it was easier to wrap mildly schizophrenic patients, or those with a schizotypal personality disorder, in an environmental cotton wool, and thereby protect them from the world's harshness, than it is to help depressed patients whose depression may not lift, however comfortable their surroundings. Likewise, shielding a depressed patient from the slings and arrows of society may not always influence the likelihood of a recurrence, whereas choosing the correct regime for a patient who has suffered from one of the schizophrenic-type diseases may be crucial in preventing a relapse. People with schizophrenia, or schizophrenic tendencies, need shielding from the harshness of society – too many of their refuges once provided by the state have been closed.

A patient with mild symptoms of schizophrenia who is rich may make a charmingly eccentric duke, but if he was a railwayman his behaviour would lose him his job, and he would probably end up on the streets, where all his symptoms would be exacerbated. The cotton-woolling against woeful circumstances, which is sometimes so effective, can also be very expensive. As Virginia Woolf said about the protective qualities of a comfortable, secure and accepting environment, 'Those comfortable padded lunatic asylums which are known euphemistically as the stately homes of England.'

Before discussing the new atypical antipsychotics, which represent a major advance in the treatment of schizophrenia, the older antipsychotics must be considered. They are still being prescribed, and still have their uses, which are likely to become more limited as time goes on.

The use of the older antipsychotic drugs relieves the symptoms produced by delusions, hallucinations and disordered thought, so that even if the patient is still experiencing these symptoms, the unhappiness, confusion and unbearable tensions they produce are alleviated. The antipsychotic drugs also have some effect on the negative symptoms which tend to make the patient apathetic, withdrawn and depressed. The more acute the symptoms, the greater the improvement which is noticed after treatment.

The disadvantages of all antipsychotic drugs is that long-term use is essential in order to prevent relapse, but the side-effects of the older antipsychotics can be severe. The patients will often refuse to take these older drugs because they feel that they over-sedate them, leaving them, and their life, lacklustre. They may also cause various physical changes. They affect periods in women and potency in men. Women may develop a discharge from the nipples, galactorrhoea; men may develop breasts and complain of impotency. Both sexes put on a large amount of weight. In patients who show reluctant compliance, antipsychotic depot injections may be used.

The more distressing and disabling adverse effects of the older drugs involve the central nervous system. These include Parkinson's-type symptoms and akathisia – which is usually euphemistically referred to as restlessness but the restlessness can be so intense that the patient is greatly disturbed by it. Unfortunately the symptoms of akathisia can be similar to those of the disease and, as a result, the doctor may be tempted to put up the dose and make the situation worse rather than try another drug. Another neurological side-effect which is better recognized is tardive dyskinesia, in which the patient suffers involuntary movements, particularly of the facial and neck muscles, so that they may spontaneously grimace. These neurological symptoms are not always related to the dose or to the length of time the patient has been taking the treatment. It seems that there may be a susceptibility to some drugs in some people. Jaundice may also be an occasional side-effect of the older antipsychotics, or affect the blood count; very occasionally they can give rise to trouble with eyesight. Treating the tremor and other symptoms of Parkinson-ism induced by the treatment with anti-Parkinson drugs is not recommended as it may precipitate tardive dyskinesia, which may not always disappear once the drugs have been withdrawn.

Little wonder that the introduction of the atypical neuroleptics, which offered relative but not complete freedom from the neurological adverse effects of the older antipsychotics, was welcomed. The first of these was clozapine (Clozaril), but this is only prescribed in hospital practice to patients who are unresponsive to other antipsychotic drugs. Its great disadvantage is that it may cause potentially dangerous changes to the blood count. There are now at least four other atypical antipsychotics with a safer side-effect profile: amisulpride (Solian), olanzapine (Zyprexa), quetiapine (Seroquel) and risperidone (Risperdal). As experience of their use grows, minor variations in their action and side-effects will probably determine which drug is prescribed for which patient.

The atypical antipsychotics are so much more free of side-effects than the older, conventional antipsychotics that there is much greater compliance from the patients, who are otherwise notoriously reluctant to continue with their treatment once they start to feel better, and the worst of their terrors and anxieties are alleviated. The atypical antipsychotics are also better at treating the negative symptoms as well as the positive ones and may be effective in cases which have failed to respond to earlier treatment. They very often bring about a marked improvement in cognitive function, so that patients are able to think more logically, and therefore improve their ability to communicate. Likewise, compared to other treatments the patients are more cheerful and less agitated and anxious, and so there is very often a reduction in aggression, whether verbal or physical.

It is found that when patients are prescribed these new drugs, they need far fewer admissions to hospital, and so any additional expense may be more than compensated for by lack of in-patient costs. Patients' failure to comply with treatment when having community care also bears its own price, not only in terms of money but also in human misery. To improve the medication for schizophrenia is an essential step in furthering any schemes for greater use of community, as opposed to hospital-based, psychiatry. Up to 60 per cent of patients who were previously deemed untreatable using conventional drug therapies have shown

ignificant clinical improvement with carefully selected atypical
ntipsychotics; in particular there is a reduction in hostile
ehaviour with clozapine.

There is enthusiasm over current research at the Institute of
'sychiatry. This research may herald a whole new understanding
f how the brain's function and structure is disturbed in schizo-
hrenia. It may not only provide the explanation of how and why
typical antipsychotics work, but also be a valuable diagnostic
ool which will demonstrate the cause of a patient's troubles and
ive warning that they could have difficulties in the future. There
s evidence that the sooner schizophrenic or schizophrenic-type
ymptoms are treated, the less likely the person is to suffer
lisability.

The team at the Institute of Psychiatry have been studying the
ctivity of the human brain in the living patient and, for the first
ime, the dynamic effects of medication on the brain in schizo-
hrenia. It is hoped this technique, functional magnetic resonance
maging, or fMRI, will provide images of brain activity based on
hanges in blood flow in the brain. There is evidence that the
typical antipsychotics reduce the degree of abnormality of blood
low observed in the brains of patients with schizophrenia; this
as raised the hope that they may therefore be not only treating
he symptoms of the disease but removing its cause by providing
ome return to normality.

5

Alzheimer's Disease

Even while President Reagan was still presiding at the White House, his choice of words and the slowness with which he replied to questions revealed early symptoms of Alzheimer's disease.

During Reagan's second term, a British television programme was devoted to a discussion on the frailties of the health of world leaders. In it, a clinical psychologist who had minutely analysed President Reagan's speech and behaviour explained why it was possible to deduce from the President's public appearances that his cognitive faculties were waning. The psychologist was even alive to the President's habit of brushing aside any inability – as, for instance, when failing to remember the names and positions of foreign politicians, or when displaying uncertainty about the name of the town he was in. This could perhaps happen to any inveterate traveller, but to a trained and knowledgeable observer the pattern of President Reagan's conversation betrayed the true state of his intellect years before Reagan, very bravely and public-spiritedly, told the world that he had Alzheimer's disease.

At about the same time, an old friend of mine – a British politician and former Minister – and his wife came to see me. The politician was as charming as ever; in conversation which dealt mainly with the past when we had both been in the House of Commons, he was witty, erudite, urbane and interesting, but he had little to say about the current political situation. He told me how his memory for recent events had slipped and recounted how, the week before, he had set off on a short journey to see a friend and had amazed himself by arriving at the Redbridge roundabout on the other side of London, many miles away and far off course. We all hoped that this was an example of benign memory loss, for the memory of nearly all older people declines – as long as the rest of their personality remains intact, they are merely showing a sign of ageing as common as greying hair. However, it wasn't many months before the true diagnosis was obvious: the former Minister's general condition began to deteriorate and his personality to disintegrate. He died several years later in a nursing home, by then quite unable to recognize his family or even to recall his own identity.

Dementia the hallmark of Alzheimer's, is a dread word, but it means no more than a deterioration of intellectual ability in a person who is fully conscious. It needs to be distinguished from other problems which can mimic it, whether psychological ones such as depression; physical ones that cause the loss of ability to speak or to remember; or delirium and mental retardation from some specific cause. An increasing general awareness of Alzheimer's has had the advantage of bringing dementia to the public's notice. It is now acceptable to say that an elderly relative has Alzheimer's, whereas before it sounded dismissive and

" WE PUT THAT UP IN CASE WE GET ALZHEIMERS"

insensitive to suggest that Great Uncle Tom had senile dementia. But there are disadvantages: so acceptable has the term 'Alzheimer's' become that doctors as well as laymen are apt to describe all forms of dementia as Alzheimer's. As a result, some patients are not treated who could be, and other patients are given the wrong treatment. The terms used need to be clarified: dementia is an all-embracing term for mental deterioration resulting from physical changes in the brain. Alzheimer's disease is only one of the problems which can induce these changes.

In the general population, Alzheimer's causes 55.6 per cent of cases of dementia, but in the over sixty-fives 75 per cent of dementia cases are the result of this disease – which means it is overwhelmingly the most common cause of dementia. Of other dementias, about 20 per cent are the result of Lewy body dementia, which has features of both Alzheimer's and the dementia which may be associated with Parkinson's disease. Also common is vascular dementia, a condition which used to be known as multi-infarct dementia, in which parts of the brain are deprived of oxygen because of haemorrhage or clots of one sort or another – little strokes. Parkinson's disease causes about 7.7 per cent of cases of dementia and another 10 per cent or so may be the result of brain injury or of other diseases, including malignancies.

In order to diagnose dementia, doctors need to satisfy themselves that the patient is showing at least three out of five common diagnostic features: loss of memory, a shrinking language, loss of topographical sense – i.e. a loss of sense of direction and an inability to know where they are – changes in emotional outlook on life, and an increasing inability to think ahead and to plan without being overwhelmed.

Some forgetfulness is almost always associated with ageing: older people notice that it takes longer to find the right word and that names tend to evade them. If it is no worse than this, they should take heart as it may fairly be described as benign memory loss. In Alzheimer's disease, however, memory loss may become particularly obvious, so that those suffering from it display an all too evident shrinking vocabulary and, with it, a diminishing skill

in the use of language. It was these characteristics which were clear in Reagan's later interviews.

In early Alzheimer's disease patients often start to lose their sense of direction and forget the geography of their own district. By the later stages of Alzheimer's, the patient may be regularly led home by the police, having been found wandering in the streets. Finally, the person may be unable to make their way around the inside of the house. Recently, a guest with Alzheimer's was at a dinner party; he left the dining room to go to the kitchen, a journey he must have made a thousand times before. He reappeared five or ten minutes later: 'Could someone tell me where the kitchen is?' He had forgotten the geography of the house he had been visiting for forty years.

Agitation when carrying out trivial tasks is another early sign, a state of mind partly caused by lack of confidence, which also accounts for the uncertain temper which some older people develop as their cognitive functions decline. At the same time, changes in a person's emotional outlook on life result in a deterioration in the quality of their relationship with their family, friends and associates. One of the inevitable behavioural changes of people with Alzheimer's is their response to those around them. In many cases, the patient's spontaneous rapport with other people is dulled; but, conversely, in other instances, the patient with Alzheimer's disease may initially show some lack of inhibition, which can result in an over-enthusiastic reaction to everyday social stimuli. Thus the hostess who greets her guests with a polite European kiss may to her surprise be rewarded with an enthusiastic hug; or the little joke expected to prompt a smile suddenly becomes a cause of rumbustious mirth.

George Robinson was a retired army officer who carried his profession's traditional reserve to extremes. When Alice, his previously equally quiet wife, first developed Alzheimer's disease, the first indication to George that something was wrong was when at parties her voice and laugh could be heard above the general chatter. Later, her behaviour became increasingly uninhibited and inappropriate – not quite unacceptable, but to a shy man distinctly embarrassing. At about this stage in her deterioration he began to notice that her memory was failing. Handbags, spectacles, pens and travel tickets were mislaid; then George began to notice that Alice could no longer be relied upon to complete a simple journey without getting lost.

The changes in Alice's character were quite different from those that, in addition to a failing memory, can occur in all elderly people. The personality traits which have always distinguished them from their contemporaries, and added piquancy to their characters, become exaggerated so that the older person is all too often a caricature of what they were like when they were younger. An easygoing youngster may become an absurdly jocular and irresponsible older person. A careful, meticulous financier may become stingy and pedantic, with so little intellectual flexibility that he is dogmatic and entrenched in his views.

There are few people who have not had personal experience of, or at least witnessed, the misery Alzheimer's and the other dementias usually cause to relatives, though some of the dementias, particularly in their early stages, are equally if not more distressing to the patients. It is harrowing for family and friends to watch a once intelligent, charming and socially adept person progressing from being merely forgetful to suffering severe short-term memory loss, until finally their intellect disintegrates entirely and they become disorientated, deluded, agitated and restless.

Although there is no single specific cause for Alzheimer's disease, in many cases there seems to be a family history. Alzheimer's is three to four times more common in patients who have had older relatives with the disease. It is also much more common in women than men, and – although to some extent this disparity can be accounted for by the greater longevity of women – in the minority of people who develop Alzheimer's in their early fifties or younger, there is a real preponderance of women. When there is evidence of Alzheimer's disease in someone under sixty-five, it is described as 'pre-senile' Alzheimer's. About 4 per cent of the population are affected by Alzheimer's by the age of retirement at sixty-five; this increases to over 20 per cent in those over eighty.

Alzheimer's is an insidious disease. Although characteristically its first symptom is loss of memory, this may have widespread ramifications and affect other aspects of the patients' lives. Even before it is obvious to them or to those around them, it can, as mentioned earlier, induce a general lack of confidence which permeates all other aspects of the patients' behaviour and contributes to their agitation.

The memory loss is initially of the short-term variety, of recent events, whereas for a time the patient may still have a reasonable memory for happenings long since past. It is, however, perhaps worth noting that although the patient may be quite certain that his or her memory for distant events is undimmed, careful research shows that it is not as good as he or she would believe – a phenomenon immortalized by Maurice Chevalier in his frequently quoted song from *Gigi*, 'I Remember it Well'. As time

185

progresses, the memory loss worsens and patients' general personality and intellect begin to degenerate, so that they become less flexible in their lifestyle, their interests become narrow and they are unable to understand new concepts or to adopt new skills.

Not only memory suffers but other evidence of damage to the higher centres of the brain becomes obvious and the whole personality disintegrates; at a later stage of the disease these defects become more and more prominent. With the increasing cognitive loss, there may be specific neurological symptoms, so that speech, which to begin with slows down, later becomes halting and may be garbled.

Changes in personality and cerebral function are reflected in changes in the anatomical structure of the brain. When examined, the brain of an Alzheimer's patient is seen to be atrophied. Its folds have become shrunken and the crevices (the sulci) between them widened, while the ventricles – the hollow spaces within the brain – have expanded as the surrounding nerve cells have died. Looked at under a microscope the brain structure is no longer so neatly arranged and has become disorganised.

There are also microscopic changes within the nerve cells which show the formation of characteristic neurofibrillary tangles of nervous tissue and of plaques composed of beta-amyloid, an abnormal protein. These changes are scattered throughout the cerebral tissue. A recent article in the *British Medical Journal* suggested that the role of amyloid in Alzheimer's disease is not that of a mere bit part but rather that of one of the lead players. It seems that beta-amyloid does not just happen to be present in the brain of patients with Alzheimer's disease but may actually be responsible for the death of the neurones, or nerve cells, and is thus the cause of the ultimate destruction of the patient's mind.

The neurofibrillary tangles form inside the nerve cells which are responsible for sending out impulses from the brain and which therefore control all aspects of our intellect, as well as our physical functions. In time these tangles kill the cells and that part of the brain dies for ever. The beta-amyloid protein plaques collect between the cells of the brain, and interrupt the action of the neurotransmitters which allow the messages to go through. Both tangles and plaques are found in many different parts of the brain, especially the cerebral cortex and the hippocampus. Plaques are, in particular, found in those parts of the brain which are responsible for sophisticated behaviour: our personality, use of language and forward planning. They are also found in the parietal lobe, which is involved in movement, and in the temporal lobe, which includes the hippocampus, and is an important seat of memory.

The appearance of plaques and tangles is an inevitable accompaniment of dementia but suprisingly the degree of dementia is not always proportional to their extent. Some people, for instance, may show massive microscopic changes but only moderate intellectual loss; in others there may be little change but a considerable loss of function. What is certain is that in any individual case, the patient's deteriorating condition is mirrored by an increase in the number of tangles and plaques. Whereas neurofibrillary tangles are diagnostic of Alzheimer's and similar dementias, it is common to find amyloid plaques in other conditions – for instance, such plaques are found in Parkinson's disease, concentrated in a different part of the brain. This disease is a disorder of movement with tremor, muscle rigidity, disturbances to gait, and loss of facial expression. Only some patients with Parkinson's disease develop dementia. Amyloid plaques may even be found in people not suffering from dementia without much apparent effect.

For these, and other, reasons, Alzheimer's should never be accepted as the cause of a dementia until other possibilities have been excluded. In particular, pseudo-dementia, a manifestation of depression in the elderly which can mimic Alzheimer's, must first be eliminated.

The Ernest Saunders case will be long remembered in the City of London for the intricacies of Guinness's financial dealings. In medical circles, the case will go down in history as the most public instance of the ease with which the differences between early Alzheimer's and depression in the elderly may be confused.

Ernest Saunders's doctors had pleaded that his dementia was incurable and the result of Alzheimer's, and that he was therefore to ill to serve the sentence for financial malpractices for which he had been convicted. Unfortunately some of the psychiatrists giving evidence to the court came to the wrong conclusion, and their misdiagnosis was as public as their confusion. Once Mr Saunders was released into more congenial surroundings, he cheered up, his symptoms cleared and he was able to resume a career in the City.

Although many thought the outcome of the Saunders case was only an example of what could be achieved by hiring a clever barrister, it was in fact an instance of a failure in medical diagnosis, later readily admitted, rather than an example of skilful advocacy. Unfortunately, such a misdiagnosis is by no means rare, and as treatment for Alzheimer's has only recently become available, many elderly people suffering from depression are thought to have dementia and therefore be beyond medication, and so are neglected – untreated, they become crippled with the type of depression which used to be known as senile melancholia.

Difficult as it is to tell early Alzheimer's from depression in the elderly, there are differences which are apparent to doctors used to dealing with psychiatric patients. In general, it is said that patients who are depressed tend also to show some other classic signs of depressive disorder: they have diurnal variation of mood (more cheerful later rather than earlier in the day), loss of appetite, have early-morning waking; while, although they suffer from loss of memory, they are usually able to recall the major events of their domestic life and their own personal background. They may not be chatty, and may talk slowly, but the depressed patient, when coaxed into giving an answer, usually makes good sense and has normal elocution.

Depression becomes increasingly common in older age groups and may be characterized by irritability as well as anxiety and, all too often, some paranoia. The paranoia can be intensified by diminishing sight and hearing, which increase the patient's sense of vulnerability. Older patients especially become less fastidious about their appearance and their toilet. Any individual's particular deficit will be related to the areas of the brain which have been most affected by the degenerative changes in the nerve cells. Very often the alterations in their intellect are so slowly progressive that they may be indiscernible even to those closest to the patient, until they are so severe that some disaster occurs. In other instances an unrelated occurrence, major surgery or an accident, for instance, may destroy the older person's deteriorating grip on reality.

Delirium, too, must always be distinguished from dementia, whatever the cause of the dementia may be. Delirium is the confused state which follows usually transitory damage to the brain, whether by toxins, such as are associated with many illnesses, or by brain injuries. It is therefore found in those who have had accidents; have suffered some forms of stroke; have taken drugs, whether prescribed or otherwise; have an inflammatory disorder and a high temperature, or have even overindulged in alcohol.

Parkinson's disease, although it is often thought of as an entirely physical problem by the lay public, can also have a mental component. Both depression and dementia are common features of Parkinson's disease, which, like Alzheimer's, is a degenerative brain condition, and is also a disease, mainly but not entirely, of late middle age onwards. Features of Parkinson's disease can be misleading, as the blank facial expression and the slow response to emotion and conversation may give the impression that the patient is more depressed than is in fact the case. Likewise, they also make it appear that the patient is less intelligent and alert than he or she is. In those patients with Parkinson's disease who are also suffering from dementia, any depression exacerbates the symptoms of the dementia. It is important, therefore, that depression should be treated.

Lewy body dementia should be separated from both Parkinson's disease and Alzheimer's, although it shares features with both. The Lewy bodies, after which the condition is named, are clumps of protein which develop in nerve cells in certain parts of the brain, and are a hallmark of the disease. The Lewy bodies form together with neurofibrillary tangles and plaques in people with this type of dementia; they are also found in Parkinson's disease.

Characteristically, in people with Lewy body dementia, the degree of dementia varies considerably from time to time; a period of dementia may last for days or weeks and then be followed by a phase when the patient becomes very lucid. Unfortunately the patient is often able to remember their behaviour during the earlier demented interval and this increases their distress. These periods of dementia become progressively worse.

Hallucinations are more of a feature of Lewy body dementia than Alzheimer's disease. These hallucinations are often visual and the apparition – person or animal – may be abnormal; for example, it might be footless or headless. These hallucinations are very real but are not usually disturbing to the patients, as they know, even as they are seeing the picture, that it is false. Even so, it is now considered possible that stories originating from those with Lewy body dementia may account for the number of headless ghosts which haunt Britain's ancestral homes.

Lewy body dementia is also frequently associated with some signs suggestive of Parkinson's disease, such as the shake and muscle stiffness. In a later stage of the disease, the Parkinson's symptoms become more marked. Patients with Lewy body dementia also have more black-outs and falls than do those with simple Alzheimer's, and are apt to be more aggressive.

The differences are not academic – there may well be 175,000 people in the UK with Lewy body dementia, and unfortunately if they are treated as suffering from straightforward Alzheimer's, their condition may be made worse. They need different management both in relation to their care and to any drug regimes.

Huntington's disease (sometimes known as Huntington's chorea), a congenital movement disorder associated with progressive dementia, is another complaint bearing a few similarities to Alzheimer's and the other diseases just mentioned. It is a degenerative neurological disease resulting from deterioration of the basal ganglia – concentrations of nerve cells concerned with fine control of movement at the base of the brain. As well as rapid, jerky involuntary movements (chorea) and a change in the appearance of the face so that it becomes expressionless and sagging like that of a bloodhound (caused by a failure of the nerve supply to the muscles of the face) there is increasing dementia and, with it, personality changes.

That Huntington's is a genetic disease is not in doubt, for apart from there being an evident pattern of inheritance, the actual defective gene has been isolated and located in a particular chromosome. The onset of Huntington's disease is usually obvious by the time the patient is forty, but it can occur earlier or later. The traditional belief is that the disease starts at a younger age group in each progressive generation, but the evidence for this is lacking. Dementia increases as the years pass, and the life expectation of those suffering from Huntington's disease is about fifteen years from the time of diagnosis.

Some forms of Alzheimer's disease also have a strong genetic basis. It cannot be denied that having a close relative with the disease – in medicine close or first-degree relatives are parents or siblings – increases the likelihood of a person developing Alzheimer's. The risk of doing so only becomes great if three first-degree relatives are affected – probably because the pattern of the inheritance is not simple. Almost certainly more than one gene may be responsible, and a number of other factors are involved.

Thus it seems likely that the chance of developing Alzheimer's depends on an interplay of genetic and environmental factors such as lifestyle, diet, drugs (including HRT and nicotine) and reproductive history. For instance, it has been shown that women who have had HRT during the time of the menopause score better in the tests for dementia in later life. By continuing this argument, it might be assumed that child-bearing would afford some protection against Alzheimer's because of high levels of circulating hormones, but this advantage would have to be balanced against the lack of time child-rearing leaves for intellectual pursuits.

People who have suffered repeated head injuries, or even one serious head injury, are also more likely to develop Alzheimer's. On the other hand, very few people who take anti-inflammatory drugs for rheumatism and arthritis develop Alzheimer's disease – it is the anti-prostaglandin effect of aspirin, or non-steroidal anti-inflammatory drugs which reduce inflammation, that seems to protect the brain cells. The beneficial effects of modest amounts of alcohol and of such anti-arthritic drugs may account for the intellectual sprightliness of so many gnarled and bent octogenarians who fill the best barside seats in the local pub.

Even in the 1930s, my father, a cautious doctor, had no doubts that aluminium caused Alzheimer's. All our pots and pans were enamel, and he pointed with horror at the shiny, clean inside of an aluminium pan in which he had caught one of his patients cooking fruit. There have been studies which supported my father's view but modern standards of epidemiology and statistics have heavily criticized them, and this theory has been largely, but not totally, discounted. Extraordinarily, the plaques in the brain are rich in aluminium, but the suggestion now is that this is as a result of the disease and is not the cause. Nevertheless a few doubts remain in the minds of some people, and anxieties have been expressed about the aluminium in certain antacid indigestion preparations. Any case against those which contain aluminium hydroxide is unproven, but I recommend to my patients that if they are in the habit of taking large quantities of antacids it might be as well for them to choose those which do not contain aluminium. Research has also shown that there is no association between mercury amalgam fillings in teeth and Alzheimer's.

Harold Wilson was one of the best-known cases of Alzheimer's in the United Kingdom in recent years. It is possible that brain damage from anaesthesia, given during operations on his colon, played a part, but there is a well-recorded family history of Alzheimer's and it is remarkable how similar is the age of onset, as in his case, from one generation to another. Although I had only met Harold Wilson on a few occasions, one day I met him in the

Athenaeum and he wished me good fortune in the forthcoming general election. I thanked him profusely with some surprise as we didn't share political loyalties, but he explained how he thought that the House of Commons should always have some independent, maverick, members. He had liked my earlier contribution to the House, he said, and hoped to see me back. He then added: 'But I shall have resigned as Party Leader because I have no intention of making the same mistake as my mother.' It transpired that his mother had been a prominent local personality and had continued in her various roles as an educationalist despite early Alzheimer's. In a year or two the memory of a lifetime of good work had been overshadowed by stories of her increasing dementia.

There were many rumours as to why Harold Wilson might have retired so suddenly; even fantastic stories that an attachment to the Russian secret service had been uncovered, but I remembered our chat in the Athenaeum and did my best to refute the idea that his retirement had been a sudden decision. Harold's worst fears were realized. Not long before he died, a *Times* journalist went to the Scilly Isles to interview him about some political incident when he was Prime Minister. Harold was as charming as ever but took an hour to dress and when he came through from his bedroom, said, 'Kind of you to come. I remember the man's name, but not what he looks like, and I certainly can't remember any of the details of my last government. My memory is so poor now that it now takes me an age to read a page in a book and I have forgotten the start before I get to the end of it.'

It is fair to say that the Wilson family have always insisted that his dementia was the result of anaesthetic damage. While it is true that anaesthetics cause some damage, more frequently than is realized, it is difficult to see why the mental deterioration would have been so rapidly progressive and at a comparatively early age. It is, however, possible that his major surgery and anaesthesia uncovered a minor cognitive loss which thereafter rapidly developed.

Despite the genetic background of Alzheimer's disease, life-style does affect the age at which it becomes apparent. Those people who are fortunate enough to have had a bright and alert brain when younger, and continue to maintain intellectual interests when older, are less likely to develop early Alzheimer's. It is said that just as people should take half an hour's brisk walk every day, so should they exercise their minds for an equal length of time. Reading doesn't count – they need to do crossword puzzles, accounts or even creative writing. There is something to be said for the Victorian love of letter writing and diaries, and an obsession with the household bills.

Twenty-five years ago, an association between dementia and folic acid was first established; this was confirmed in 1998 by Oxford scientists, who related Alzheimer's disease to levels of homocysteine, which plays a part in the manufacture of the amino acid cysteine in the bloodstream. A healthy, generous intake of folic acid – found in green leafy vegetables, and often added to bread and breakfast cereals – reduces the homocysteine in the blood, and a low homocysteine level is associated with a lower risk of developing not only heart disease and stroke but also Alzheimer's disease. The next step for the scientist is to find out whether artificially lowering homocysteine levels will help to delay the development of Alzheimer's.

Another prophylactic measure is to take a modest tot or two of alcohol every day. Research in Australia has shown that recruits to the Australian army who were moderate drinkers were less likely than teetotallers or very light drinkers to develop Alzheimer's on their retirement forty or fifty years later. One promising discovery was that even those former soldiers who in early middle age stopped drinking retained much of its protective powers. Research in France and Denmark has confirmed these findings, those from Copenhagen being particularly encouraging. Nicotine is known to have an influence in some cases of Alzheimer's, but cigarette smoking inhibits the disease only in a minority of cases, and depends on the genetic make-up of the smoker.

Choice of diet – there is evidence that a low-cholesterol diet may be helpful, as are foliate-rich green vegetables – two or three drinks a day, a lively interest in the world, and intellectual exercise are all prophylactic measures, preventative rather than curative. Recently, drugs have been introduced which may affect the course of the disease. Treatment of Alzheimer's should, however, not only be considered in terms of appropriate medication – changing aspects of lifestyle can also be very beneficial. However, it may only be through medication that the patient is able to stay at home, and be part of the community for as long as possible.

If patients with Alzheimer's are to be looked after in their home surroundings for as long as possible, the impact of the disease on the rest of the family, in particular the husband or wife, must be recognized. One way in which the demands the disease makes on the family may be made easier to bear is the provision of 'respite care' – the availability of short-term in-patient facilities for a patient. Perhaps an even more important measure is to make day-care centres available. These can revolutionize the situation by allowing the family a rest from their 24-hour-a-day caring role and thereby giving them the chance to live some life of their own.

Ruby was a cleaner at a local school, her husband Alf had been a clerk in a timber firm. Ruby lived for her husband, children and house; Alf was devoted to his family, to his firm, to his koi carp and to Norwich City Football Club. Alf was only fifty-eight when his memory started to fray at the edges. It was nothing alarming – he would forget names, telephone calls and what he was supposed to collect from the shops on his way back from the office. At home, it made little difference to his or his wife's lifestyle, but at work it was beginning to cause alarm. Everybody liked Alf but business was business and Alf's bosses were beginning to grow tired of apologizing for his mistakes. When he was sixty his firm decided that they would introduce early retirement and, to nobody's surprise, Alf was the first candidate for it.

Within a year, Alf's symptoms had become socially embarrassing and he was showing the classic signs of memory loss. His topographical sense was appalling – he was unable even to collect the evening paper from the corner shop, or walk the dog, without a good chance of getting lost. He soon lost interest in his hobbies: his once beloved carp were fed by the rest of the family and languished unadmired by their owner; Norwich City was relegated from the Premier League to the First Division and he hardly noticed. His grandchildren were no longer greeted with a hug and a grin, warranting no more than a detached smile – another classic sign: emotional blunting. He also had to be told what to wear and his dressing had to be supervised.

As is so often the case, Ruby accepted the changes in Alf as part of the ageing process but finally even she realized that his change in personality was abnormal and she took him to the doctor. The likely diagnosis was easy to reach, but other causes of dementia had to be excluded. Alf's blood pressure was checked and his cardiovascular system was assessed so that the possibility of multiple small strokes could be eliminated. He had a brain scan (in his case, an MRI scan although a CT scan would have been almost as efficient) to determine the degree of atrophy of the brain, and to rule out cerebral tumours, or, more likely, evidence of strokes.

He had blood tests to exclude simple problems like anaemia, diabetes, renal failure, a very high cholesterol level, or thyroid deficiency. He had his urinary tract examined to make certain that he wasn't suffering from a chronic urinary tract infection. He was questioned carefully to make certain that he was not merely depressed (and to find out if he was possibly suffering from a combination of depression and Alzheimer's). The verdict was that he had Alzheimer's – although confirmation of Alzheimer's is still in fact only available after death (however, a new test involving a complex analysis of the cerebrospinal fluid obtained by lumbar puncture is under trial).

Although Ruby had suspected the diagnosis, being told it was still a shock. She needed to acclimatize herself to the knowledge that her companion of forty years, who had always been so thoughtful and endearing, had already gone. For a family, the development of severe Alzheimer's in one of them is no less than a very complex bereavement, and without the usual support mechanisms of grieving relatives and friends. Alf stayed at home, being cared for by his wife, who, despite the lack of a display of explicit gratitude or demonstrations of affection, devoted her life to his wellbeing. In addition to all the domestic chores, she had to supervise Alf's medication, his dressing and his washing; she had to manage all the finances, and, perhaps hardest of all during Alf's slow death, she had to take all the decisions without the advantages of consultation.

It was a punishing and exhausting regime without even the respite of a good night's sleep as Alf was restless and wandering at night, and Ruby's health, like that of many carers, began to suffer. Those who care for patients with dementia are likely to suffer from depression and from physical ills, hence the need for some regular off-duty period. Fortunately, there was a daycare centre, which gave Ruby the chance once or twice a week to keep up with her old friends and see her family. Without this, she might have lost contact with her grandchildren, who found their grandfather's lifestyle and behaviour incomprehensible. Ruby was perhaps lucky in that her relationship with Alf had been happy and there were good memories to look back on. Life can be a terrible burden for those in whom marriage was only just tolerable when both were fit.

Alf's disease was too far advanced for him to be given Aricept (donepezil), the first of the memory-improving drugs to be licensed in this country. As medication improves, early diagnosis will become increasingly important, as in all psychiatric disease there is evidence that patients do better if florid – very obvious – symptoms are never allowed to become established. Tacrine, Aricept and, more recently, Exelon (rivastigmine), have become available, all of which improve memory in a proportion of cases for a limited length of time. However, the first to be used, Tacrine, licensed in the United States, was not approved for use in Britain as its advantages were usually short-lived and outweighed by its disadvantages – it can be toxic to the liver, and between 20 and 33 per cent of the American patients treated with it developed signs of hepatitis. Other patients taking Tacrine had gastrointestinal upsets and some suffered from a severely lowered blood pressure. None of the three drugs offers a miracle cure but all may improve the patient's condition for a short while and give great hope for the future.

The first of these drugs to become available in Britain was Aricept. Like Tacrine, it acts on the neurotransmitters, the chemical substances released by nerve endings, as and when necessary, thereby allowing communication between the nerve cells of the brain. One of the characteristic changes in the brain following the development of Alzheimer's is a deficiency in neurotransmitters, especially acetylcholine. All three of the drugs are acetylcholinesterase inhibitors: they reduce the amount of cholinesterase (or acetylcholinesterase) – the enzyme which destroys acetylcholine – thus allowing an increase in acetylcholine so the patient's memory is less impaired.

Like the other two, Exelon, the latest of these drugs, boosts the level of the neurotransmitter acetylcholine in the same way. It is claimed to have added advantages in that it improves cognitive function – intellectual ability – as well as memory, and in that, unlike Tacrine and, to a lesser degree, Aricept, it doesn't seem to interact with other drugs or to affect the liver adversely.

Aricept and Exelon are expensive – but it is estimated that at the moment Alzheimer's costs this country over one billion pounds a year. Not only would the patients be happier, but the Exchequer would benefit if they could be kept at home longer. The drugs could therefore be both a humanitarian and a financial investment.

Other drugs to treat Alzheimer's are being developed and undergoing trials, in this country and overseas. Many are of the same type, acetylcholinesterase inhibitors, but the pharmaceutical industry promises that some of those on the stocks act in quite a different way. For instance, springtime visitors to the British headquarters of the pharmaceutical company Janssen-Cilag will admire the daffodils brightening the beds either side of the main drive. The two varieties of daffodils here, however, are no common or garden bulbs, such as delighted the eyes of Herrick and Wordsworth, but have been bred because they are rich in galantamine. Galantamine is not yet a household word, but it has properties which may help to lighten the load of 520,000 British people with Alzheimer's. Research workers have discovered that galantamine has, like the drugs Tacrine, Aricept and Exelon, an inhibitory effect on cholinesterase activity. Cholinesterase is, as mentioned earlier, the enzyme which removes acetylcholine, the neurotransmitter which is in short supply in patients with Alzheimer's disease. If the acetylcholine level can be boosted by removing the enzyme which destroys it, Alzheimer's disease might perhaps be kept at bay.

Galantamine, which is also found in Caucasian snowdrops, is now being prepared by Shire Pharmaceuticals, an independent company allied to Janssen-Cilag. The substance has already completed its phase III trials, carried out in eight different countries. Patients were tested for skills such as memory, word recall and recognition, orientation and comprehension of spoken language. As a result, doctors looking after them were able to form an overall picture of the patients' condition at the beginning of the trial and after they had been given galantamine. Whereas those taking galantamine showed a marked improvement – measured on the scale as a score of +1.7 points – those who only had a placebo continued to deteriorate, and over the six-month period of the study, their score was reduced by 2.4 points. After a year the intellect of those taking galantamine had retained a cognitive level similar to that which they had when they started – there had, in other words, been no deterioration.

One of the exciting features of galantamine is that it is possible that it exerts its influence on the patients' memory and hence on other aspects of their daily life, not only as an acetylcholinesterase inhibitor but also because it may well affect the nicotinic receptors in the brain to make them more receptive to nicotine, which has long been known to have a possible influence on memory and intellectual activity. Genetically lucky smokers are less likely to

develop Alzheimer's – others may merely suffer arterial problems. On the other hand, the arteries of those who take the extract
of daffodil bulbs will remain undamaged and they do not require
genetic good luck in order for galantamine to have an effect. If all
goes well, and galantamine is approved, it may become available
by the beginning of the millennium.

In the meantime, research is proceeding in the use of other
medication – including oestrogen supplements and antirheumatic drugs of the COX-2 variety. COX-2, a natural enzyme
induced by inflammation, may be controllable with drugs known
as COX-2 inhibitors. COX-2 encourages production of prostaglandins which in turn lead to more inflammation. The search has
been to find a product to inhibit COX-2, so that the inflammation
which may be a feature of Alzheimer's as well as rheumaticky
joints is inhibited without at the same time inhibiting the enzyme
COX-1. COX-1 also produces a prostaglandin, but one which pro-
tects the stomach and gut walls, and having less of which can
make patients liable to sudden gastrointestinal bleeds or
perforations.

In Europe vasodilators, which improve the blood supply, are
now prescribed for patients with dementia, but these are not
licensed for use in the United Kingdom and it seems that if they
do have any effect, it is more likely to be in those cases where the
dementia is secondary to a series of small strokes or to narrowing
of the cerebral arteries than in cases of Alzheimer's. No advantage
of using vasodilators in patients with Alzheimer's disease has
ever been demonstrated.

Acetylcholine isn't the only neurotransmitter which has caught
the attention of research workers. Drugs which act on other systems of neurotransmission are also under investigation and the
boosting of those which influence certain receptors – receptors
being protein molecules on the surface of nerve cells which, as
their name suggests, receive the neurotransmitters – may, like
Aricept and particularly Exelon, improve memory and intellectual function.

Professor Nancy Rothwell, at Manchester University, is

investigating the role of interleukin 1, a protein associated with inflammation in Alzheimer's disease. Research has shown that interleukin production is significant in traumatic brain damage – Professor Rothwell's study is to see whether it is equally important in degenerative disease and if it could also offer hope for patients with Alzheimer's disease. If the inflammation in Alzheimer's can be reduced, it is possible that the symptoms might be eased.

In the past doctors have been powerless to alter the course of Alzheimer's. The future is more encouraging but it will be many years before there are any 'wonder drugs' to keep the ageing brain nimble. In the meanwhile, patients with Alzheimer's need skilled care. As more and more patients are being looked after in small private homes, there has been a tendency over the past few years, in order to ensure peace and quiet for fellow patients and the nursing staff, to prescribe heavy doses of the older neuroleptics – antipsychotic drugs – the 'liquid coshes' of a hundred adverse reports. Unfortunately this treatment doesn't even achieve its primary aim – a difficult patient is made even more confused by heavy doses of sedatives and as a result becomes more troublesome, less independent and more incontinent. Research has shown that a large number of patients who have been obstreperous, even out of control, in small nursing homes become quiet and relatively cheerful when they are properly cared for and the heavy doses of drugs have been withdrawn.

There are, however, atypical antipsychotics that are much freer of the liquid-cosh effect and don't leave the patients dazed and confused – feeling, as they always say, 'like a zombie, doctor' – which may ease the situation by diminishing the hallucinations and delusions of dementia without producing bewilderment. However, experience has shown that with kindly, loving care, skilled nursing and withdrawal of all antipsychotic drugs, a great many of the previously unmanageable patients can, if the dementia is not too far advanced, became charming, if somewhat eccentric and demanding, old people.

6

Eating Disorders

The daughter of the obstetrician who delivered me as a baby was the subject of considerable interest in our neighbourhood in Norfolk. Even as a very small child I can remember looking at her figure, so thin that she seemed no more than a skeleton covered by blue skin. Although tall, she can't have weighed more than six and a half stone. My father, a doctor, found it difficult to persuade my mother that, yes, the daughter of our old friend *was* unwell but that any illness which she suffered from was psychological rather than physical. And no, she didn't have advanced and highly infectious tuberculosis, as my mother feared, but anorexia nervosa.

Although anorexia was first described in 1676, ten years after the great fire of London, it was only labelled in the late nineteenth century. In the seventeenth century the condition was rather more poetically known as 'prodigious abstinence' or 'nervous consumption' – the old physicians had noticed, like my mother, a similarity in appearance between someone with severe anorexia nervosa and terminal TB. It was carefully analysed by the Victorians; they were not only interested in appetite in relation to anorexia but were also obsessed by its influence on constipation and the menstrual cycle. Seventy years ago, our obstetrician's daughter was an oddity, and her condition may have intrigued doctors but was not understood by the general public. Twenty years ago there were people who hadn't heard about anorexia, but now it is universally recognized and the Princess of Wales's frank testimony about the influence of eating disorders on a person's life has transformed the public perception of them. Anorexia in medical terminology is a loss of appetite; weight loss may stem from this though it is common to have weight loss without anorexia.

Any young person who has been head over heels in love will testify to the effects of emotion on appetite and the guts. One of my youthful friends finally decided to marry because being apart from his beloved had destroyed his appetite – 'I could do without dinner but when I couldn't eat breakfast either, then I thought something would have to be done.' Food has an importance in emotional life as well as being the means of refuelling the metabolic system. That the digestion can be a barometer of a person's peace of mind is generally accepted; the physical changes which echo different moods are presumably the result of changes in the autonomic nervous system, the system which spontaneously and unconsciously regulates so many of the body's routine activities.

It is not surprising that when someone is in a mental turmoil this should be reflected in their approach to eating. Ever since a baby was fed at the breast, or cuddled over a bottle, nourishment has been associated with love. Many people, even in later life, find the offering of food a simple way of expressing affection and they are able to follow a distinguished precedent – not for nothing was Jesus's departure from an earthly life heralded by a formal supper. It is to be expected, therefore, that anorexia nervosa and bulimia, the best-known eating disorders, are psychosomatic diseases: psychological complaints which can have profound, even fatal, physical manifestations.

Anorexia and bulimia are not the only eating disorders. Pica is the persistent eating of substances never intended as food. It mainly affects children, but it can occur in pregnancy, or even at other times. The patients have a great desire to swallow sand, soil, paint or, more alarmingly, hair. Swallowing hair is very dangerous as it can cause serious obstruction, forming a hair ball, a bezoar, in the guts. Animals, too, but for different reasons, nibble at their hair and they too develop bezoars. (These, when cut out of the beast, are thought in some societies to have magical powers.) Pica is probably psychosomatic but some doctors have disagreed, proposing that it may signify a mineral deficiency. Some pregnant women also have pica, but the desire in pregnancy for unusual foods is more common than for non-foods and women may, for instance, have an overpowering desire to eat oysters or asparagus; this, however, wouldn't be classified as pica, as these are nutritious foods.

Rumination is the ability found in very small children to regurgitate food, rather in the same way as a cow does when chewing the cud. This ability, even if it is not associated with emotional upsets, is undesirable as it can produce severe, and even dangerous, weight loss – the appetite has been sated and much of the last meal has ended up down the child's front. Some paediatricians feel that rumination in a child is a comfort device, and that it may betray insufficient nurturing on the part of the parent. Unfortunately, and not surprisingly, the ruminating child begins to smell rather unpleasant and parental love may be further challenged.

These four eating disorders are classified as psychosomatic diseases. In a psychosomatic disease the patients' psychological problems affect their physical health: the disease is therefore a physical manifestation of a psychological problem. However, in psychosomatic illnesses the extent to which the psyche is involved varies. Few would deny that the extreme wasting of anorexia nervosa is overwhelmingly a psychosomatic problem, but even so there is some evidence that there may be physical factors. Conversely, the extent to which irritable bowel syndrome, or coronary heart disease, for example, are psychosomatic is arguable. Most people acknowledge the role of the psyche in irritable bowel disease but physical aspects such as diet are of fundamental importance.

Anorexia can be a symptom of other psychiatric diseases, including depression. Patients with eating disorders are more likely than similar groups of people to have other members of their family who have also suffered from eating disorders, and are also more likely to have relatives who have suffered from depression. They also tend to have relatives who have problems with addiction to alcohol and other substances, though they do not necessarily have to have been influenced directly by proximity to those people during their upbringing. The families of anorexic patients also have been shown to contain more instances of people with obsessive-compulsive disorder and psychosexual problems. As with many psychiatric problems, the distinction between the inheritance of a genetic characteristic, which would account nature as the most important factor, or the method of upbringing which would emphasize nurture, as well as, indirectly, nature, is unresolved. Almost all the personality disorders are more prevalent in the family histories of patients with anorexia but, comfortingly, they are also more common in those families who show originality, enterprise and leadership. Where would the world be without the Spencer Churchills?

Psychiatrists have never included obesity as a single disease entity in their list of psychiatric diseases as it is regarded as a symptom of a more complex condition which may have its origin in either a physical or a mental abnormality. Those people who grow enormously fat because of comfort eating are all too apparently suffering from a psychosomatic disease whereas in other cases – Cushing's syndrome, for instance, in which there is an abnormality of the adrenal glands, resulting in gross obesity – the disease is entirely physical.

The incidence of anorexia nervosa is now reaching epidemic proportions; few schools are without a case or two and it therefore excites a great amount of public interest which extends beyond anxious parents. There cannot be many people who are unaware that anorexia nervosa is characterized by a triad of symptoms and signs. The triad consists of a disturbed sense of body image with an excessive fear of putting on weight; extreme weight loss; and in women loss of periods (amenorrhoea). Many other symptoms stem from these but their presence is not essential for the diagnosis. Pyschotherapists feel that some anorexic patients may have a voracious appetite, and this concerns them as they fear losing control. They also suggest that anorexia often originates as the result of a difficult early relationship with parents at a time when the acceptance or rejection of food exposes such feelings as anger, or is a means of control.

Amenorrhoea is almost inevitable if more than 15 per cent of body weight is lost, and periods may, but do not always, start again immediately after this weight has been regained. Much research has been undertaken on the relationship between weight and a regular menstrual cycle. Top women athletes almost invariably lose their periods. Before the Moscow Olympic Games I carried out regular medicals on a squad of nineteen women who were going to represent their country in one sport: all were athletically very fit, but only one menstruated. In Australia ballet dancers in training lose weight during the term when their diet is strictly controlled and their exercise is very vigorous. In term time most of the dancers had no periods; during the long holidays, the periods returned. The women attributed this to a combination of being very lean and taking 'too much' exercise. At about the same time, in an experiment at an American university female athletes were given an increased intake of red meat without putting up the total calorie content. After a few weeks of steaks and chops the women started to menstruate, even though their weight hadn't increased.

The reason for the importance of animal protein – meat, eggs, fish and cheese – in maintaining a regular reproductive cycle in women is unclear. During the end of the Second World War the civilian population in Holland was starving, and the crisis was so severe that the Germans allowed the British to drop food supplies for the Dutch. Naturally the food was mainly cereal, starvation was averted, and the population put on a bit of weight, but reproductive capacity was not restored. It is said that only when the war was over and the Dutch dairy and beef industry was restored, and meat again figured in the diet, did women start to menstruate regularly.

Anorexic women and a smaller number of anorexic men are often food faddists. As part of their obsessional interest in food, they tend to regard it not so much as a fuel to be taken three times a day but as an art form, its appearance to be analysed and its ethics discussed. Even when they are eating again they may become vegans, or organic food enthusiasts, with an appetite determined by philosophy rather than palate. When anorexic patients are being encouraged to eat, targets are set for meals eaten and weight gained; but this alone may not be enough – their gourmet soul as well as their weight has to be taken into account. Formerly anorexic people are unlikely suddenly to demolish a plateful of Harry Ramsden's fish and chips, or a two-pound steak, but may be prepared to boost their calorie intake with dishes which wouldn't disgrace the latest TV cook.

This all illustrates the complexity of appetite and choice of diet and is indicative of the reasons for someone's vulnerability to eating disorders. The correlation, for instance, between weight, exercise and the production of female hormones, may act through the pituitary gland which is part of the hypothalamic-pituitary axis in the brain and is the point where the psyche has a profound influence on the physique. The pituitary gland, lying beneath the brain, is the conductor of the endocrine system, the system of ductless glands which produce the hormones, many of which in turn control other glands.

Anorexia is accompanied by changes in the endocrine system. There are therefore changes throughout the whole body, just as there would be if someone was starving to death. Levels of growth hormone produced by the pituitary gland are increased, as are cortisol (natural steroid) levels. There are changes in the levels of some of the thyroid hormones and in insulin production. All of these are presumably compensatory measures designed to enable the body to withstand the effects of starvation and to keep the anorexic person alive and active.

Testosterone levels in men are reduced, which helps to account for their loss of libido and potency, but they remain unaltered in women. These changes are as the result of the anorexia and not the cause. Other psychosomatic diseases also produce endocrine changes and it is not uncommon for patients who suffer from them, but prefer the concept of physical to psychiatric disease, to claim that these comparatively minor variations in their hormone levels indicate that their problems are entirely physical.

Women are over ten times more likely to suffer from anorexia nervosa than men, although the gap between the genders is now closing. The aetiology (origins) of anorexia nervosa has been much studied and various factors which are found more often in the genetic, family, social or early history in patients with eating disorders than in control groups, have been determined. However, it is impossible to say that any one or more of these factors is the cause of anorexia nervosa – they are all merely possible contributing elements.

The classic device to demonstrate a fear of fatness and a distorted body image is to give the woman or, more rarely, man, a mirror and show them pictures of people of much the same age but of varying weights. The patient with anorexia invariably selects someone very much heavier than him- or herself as being the same size.

Although there is a fear of obesity and a refusal to eat food in anorexic patients, there is no fundamental dislike of it, it in fact many are obsessed with cooking. Anorexic people can produce beautiful, mouth-watering meals, even while they starve themselves. One patient, a designer who was a severe anorexic, was a brilliant cook. When I went to dinner with her parents she joined us for drinks before the meal, although she did not have any alcohol, disappeared into the kitchen to work her magic with the menu, and then, wraith-like, appeared with each of the gourmet courses she had created. She never ate the meals herself. In spite of this she led a physically strenuous life: her day started at about 5.30 in the morning, when she went out for a long run, before doing a self-prescribed series of physical exercises at home. After work and before she went home in the evenings she always swam an inordinate number of lengths at the local swimming pool. This obsession with physical activity is a common characteristic in anorexic patients.

Bulimia is always discussed together with anorexia nervosa. Patients with bulimia, like those with anorexia, have the same problems with self-image; they too are likely to fail the looking-glass test. They are also obsessed by all aspects of food, not only its consumption. They, like anorexic patients, may be brilliant cooks, restaurant owners, dinner party hosts or food critics. However, bulimia has been shown to affect people with a slightly different, and rather more complex, personality than anorexic patients.

The Princess of Wales wasn't alone when she was fighting bulimia. Her stories of raiding and emptying the refrigerator will have rung a bell with 5 to 10 per cent of late-adolescent women. People with bulimia stuff and starve. They eat absurd quantities of high-calorie food and then go through periods of totally inappropriate and extreme dieting. Bulimic patients are divided into the purgers and the non-purgers. Those who purge vomit like ancient Roman emperors after over-eating, or they may use heavy doses of laxatives or diuretics (pills to make the patient pass more urine). They will use any medication which will improve the reading on the weighing scales. The non-purgers compensate for their stuffing phases by severe dieting and an inhuman exercise regime. The Princess of Wales did both: after her nocturnal emptying of the larder she made herself vomit but she also followed vigorous fitness routines.

The Oxford Textbook of Medicine, the authoritative work for British doctors, differentiates between bulimic behaviour and bulimia nervosa. Bulimic behaviour they define as occurring when a patient is preoccupied with food and has recurrent bouts of over-eating (stuffing), and then either rids her- or himself of the excess by vomiting, purging or merely heavy dieting. The term 'bulimia nervosa' it reserves for those patients who have a previous history of weight loss, amenorrhoea and an extreme fear of putting on weight as a result of a disturbed body image. Whether purgers or non-purgers, patients with bulimia may also misuse appetite-suppressant pills and, also, in an effort to remain slim, resort to other unsuitable drugs, such as thyroxine, the thyroid hormone which increases their metabolism, as well as diuretics and laxatives, which are favoured by those who purge.

Bulimia, like anorexia, is a problem affecting mainly women. Although only 5 to 10 per cent of the relevant age group are classified as being bulimic, many more will show similar tendencies and have some degree of impulse-control deficit – lack of restraint – when faced with a box of chocolates, pâtisserie or puddings. Comfort eating isn't confined to women but it is found more often in women than in men. Just as being emotionally overwrought may take away the appetite, so may being emotionally deprived stimulate it. Where normality ends and mild non-purging bulimia begins is very often a matter of opinion, but there is no doubt that purging bulimia, even if mild, is abnormal. Bulimia isn't usually diagnosed unless the stuffing is without a good social excuse, like a Christmas or birthday party, and occurs more than twice weekly for at least three months. The guest who finishes off the plate of meringues would be described as greedy rather than bulimic. Even people suffering from bulimia frequently have long periods of normal eating; the resumption of their abnormal habits may be precipitated by some crisis in their lives.

In some instances, there is an obvious physical reason for over-eating. Children are aware that food refusal in early childhood is an acknowledged cause of short stature. They have been told a thousand times to eat up their meat so as to grow as tall as Daddy. Later, through no fault of appetite, they may still be small and such patients may then over-eat because they subconsciously feel that it will increase their height. This form of bulimia is found amongst young adolescents who think they are too short, particularly when their lack of height and development can be traced to emotional deprivation in childhood.

Bulimic patients are more likely to have other psychiatric diseases or conditions that are well-recognized, in particular anxiety disorders, and they are also more likely to suffer from the affective disorders – whether hypomania, mania or depression. Bulimic patients too are more likely than anorexic patients to have symptoms of other impulse-control disorders and it is not uncommon for there to be a history of impulsive theft, alcoholism or drug addiction. The increased rate of theft and drug abuse amongst bulimic patients may suggest that it has origins closely linked to the causes of other impulse-control disorders as well as to the eating disorders.

The causes of bulimia are still uncertain – and this is reflected in the number of theories about its origins. When the cause of the disease is hard to uncover or, in many cases, remains hidden, it is very easy to overemphasize the situations where there is an obvious trigger. There is a multitude of factors – genetic, physical and environmental – which probably contribute in varying degrees in each individual case to the development of anorexia or bulimia. Because in many cases there may be family discord or

211

dysfunction, it is tempting to blame anorexia and other eating disorders on upbringing. This is grossly unfair. It may well be factor in a proportion of cases but even in these instances, th resulting trouble is probably the consequence of a combination of circumstances. If possible, parents shouldn't blame themselve but they should review the situation and see how it can be altere to make it easier for their perhaps complex daughter (or occasionally, son) to slot into adult life more readily.

Part of the case for explaining anorexia nervosa and bulimia i terms of early childhood experience revolves around a discussio of the amount of maternal affection patients were given i infancy. The 'oral character', with its preoccupation with foo drink and smoking, in anorexic patients is considered by man psychologists to point to the possibility of inadequate or inap propriate maternal love in infancy. Others think this too sim plistic, and experts are beginning to shy away from the po Philip Larkin's theory of parenthood ('They fuck you up, yo Mum and Dad') and believe that parents have recently had shoulder too much blame.

Patients with bulimia, their family and their medical adviser long to discover centres in the brain which control appetite and sense of fullness after eating. It would be such a relief for paren who have struggled to give their children a happy start in life t find a demonstrable physical cause. Recent work on animals ha indeed demonstrated that receptors exist which are responsive neurotransmitters which control appetite. Each neurone (nerv cell) in the brain has one thousand connections, connectior which wouldn't work were it not for chemical facilitators, th neurotransmitters. One neurotransmitter has been isolated an has been named the CART peptide. It is possible that som abnormality of these receptors in the brain may account for som causes of over-eating, but far more research will be needed befor the importance, if any, of this work can be evaluated.

The standard medical teaching is that anorexic and bulim patients not only have amenorrhoea, which can precede th weight loss, but that they have a reduced libido. It is said th men with anorexia are frequently impotent. But I was struck when working in the genito-urinary clinic at the Royal London Hospital by the number of anorexic patients who seemed to have a rather more active and varied sex life than the average person. I discussed this with one of the acknowledged experts on anorexia, who suggested that in anorexia in its early stages there was often hyperactivity and that this hyperactivity was extended into the patient's sex life, but that as soon as the weight loss became at all significant their sexual drive disappeared or was severely reduced.

Even when people with eating disorders have lost a dangerous amount of weight they still see themselves as beautiful, indeed their weight loss is an attempt to enhance their beauty as they perceive it. Thus anorexic women will continue to take great pains with their makeup, and are as careful in their choice of clothes, which may be sexily cut, as they are when choosing a hairdresser.

Modern fashion, together with its influence on advertising, may well be an important factor in the present prevalence of eating disorders. A parental wail about eating up Sunday lunch is unlikely to weigh as heavily with an adolescent as pictures in glossy magazines of scrawny infantile figures achieving iconic status. In stylish photographs, there are eminently enviably models, beautifully dressed in designer clothes, pursued by glamorous men, driven in fast cars and languishing in exotic locations – and Mother wants me to have a second helping. Nor does Mother approve of cigarettes, albeit that they help young women to remain slim. Mother, in fact, just doesn't understand what the world is about.

Whatever their cause, both anorexia and bulimia, and the malnourishment which is inevitably their consequence, have a profound and sometimes fatal influence on most of the body's systems. In bulimia, the vomiting and self-induced diarrhoea causes metabolic upsets, the body's blood chemistry is shot to pieces by the loss of potassium and chloride and the system becomes too alkaline. The stomach acids regurgitated into the

213

mouth – where they were never supposed to be – erode the enamel from the bulimic patient's teeth so that widespread decay soon becomes a problem. Likewise, the acidity caused by gastric reflux gives them a husky voice from laryngeal chord irritation, and a chronic sore throat. Very occasionally bulimic patients so overdo the vomiting induction that they rupture their stomachs.

In both of these eating disorders, the patients, as well as suffering from amenorrhoea or impotence, become anaemic, their bone marrow begins to fail and, once the immune system is undermined, their resistance to infection falls. Their bones become osteoporotic and fragile, more from loss of oestrogenic hormones than calcium and vitamin deficiency, and the excessive exercise which anorexic and bulimic patients often take increases the osteoporosis. (It is not always realized that moderate exercise reduces osteoporosis, while excessive exercise increases the likelihood of it.)

Patients with eating disorders are more likely to suffer from upsets in their carbohydrate metabolism – an efficient metabolism is dependent on eating the right proportion of carbohydrate, fat and protein. When this becomes disturbed by starvation, anorexia, bulimia or food faddism, the essential systems of the body may be inadequately nourished and suffer from chemical imbalance; hence an increased incidence of renal failure. Starvation from whatever cause, not unnaturally leads people to feel the cold badly, thereby further lowering resistance to infection. Although anorexic patients may be pleased with their appearance, to most people their lank hair and dry, bruised skin, together with their skeletal appearance, is not only unattractive but deeply distressing.

Anorexia is a potentially fatal disease; but, desirable as it would be to end the present Western obsession with slimness, there is unlikely to be a return to the days when the buxom beauties portrayed by Fragonard or Rubens were role models. Individual victims have to be treated urgently, for the condition has an estimated mortality of between 5 and 10 per cent. Many of the surviving patients fail to make a complete recovery and 30 to 40 per cent show improvement but continue to eat either too little or too much; another 30 to 40 per cent have a more serious outcome and have a distinctly bizarre appetite and lifestyle, and are never able to assess correctly their body image. The remainder show every appearance of having made a full recovery.

In order to understand the rationale of treatment, current beliefs about the role of the family as one of the factors causing anorexia have to be taken into consideration. Even though disturbed family relationships may be only one constituent of the problem, there is still a considerable body of opinion that perceives family upset as the most common underlying cause. This accounts for the belief that many anorexic adolescents cannot be treated with any degree of success within a home environment which has proved dysfunctional. If the patient continues to lose weight when treated at home, or if their weight loss or purging disrupts their vital functions, hospital admission becomes essential.

A standard observation about the home life of anorexic patients is that the atmosphere in childhood may for some reason or another have induced a fear of sexuality. As a result the adolescent girl may subconsciously have wanted to remain anatomically pre-pubertal in appearance – anorexic girls don't menstruate, and are also generally physiologically immature. Other doctors think that the anorexic patient has failed to grow up and is still fighting the tea-table battles waged as a toddler, when they refused their food and attracted an inordinate amount of attention by hurling one plateful after another on to the floor.

Adolescents have to learn to become emotionally, as well as physically, detached from their parents. Parents are always delighted when their children's views echo and reinforce their own parental prejudices, but if this is not to cause conflict in a child it has to be the result of independent thought, and not coercion and moral blackmail. It is thought that many anorexic girls have not learned how to establish an identity of their own, without provoking their parents, and lack self-esteem. Some may have been bullied, perhaps by an over-controlling mother into sharing her approach to life.

The surgery queue frequently includes a domineering, but kindly, woman accompanying a late adolescent, her daughter, emotionally crushed beneath the weight of her mother's personality. Rachel and her daughter Judith were examples of this. Judith was wearing clothes her mother would have chosen, and was thinking the thoughts her mother would like to think that she had thought at that age. She sat passively on her chair while her mother recounted all her symptoms. Rachel had been very pretty twenty years earlier and was still an attractive woman but it was not hard to suspect that she was already unconsciously jealous that as her daughter grew older, she might challenge her mother in the beauty stakes. Her unwitting, over-controlling influence on Judith's emotional development had the power both to repress Judith's individuality and to keep her sexually immature, and therefore uncompetitive.

The study of the father's role in the development of anorexia in a child has not been entirely neglected, and they are not left wholly unscathed by psychologists, who advance the theory that the behaviour of some fathers of anorexic girls may be obsessive-compulsive. The fathers themselves may not be anorexic, or even obsessive about food, but they may be obsessional about other matters, such as their careers. It has been observed that the fathers of anorexic girls often pursue disciplines which require a meticulous approach, like law or accountancy, or they may, like the obstetrician who delivered me, be obsessional. He was intent that his only child, his daughter, should also become a doctor. She did, but she rebelled by becoming anorexic. Obsessional fathers may, unwittingly, drive their daughters to unconscious rebellion, manifested by food refusal.

Some fathers, too, like some mothers, have been blamed for fearing their daughter's burgeoning sexuality. Mothers, it is said, may be jealous of a potential rival; fathers, on the other hand, may fear the emotions within themselves which might be aroused by a nubile, loved but unattainable, woman sharing their house. To keep them pre-pubertal in appearance removes any anxiety that this might engender.

It is easy to forget that men too develop anorexia nervosa. The incidence is variously reported at being between eight and twenty times greater in women. But when men are affected they too suffer from an altered body image and extreme weight loss from an excessive fear of becoming fat. Amenorrhoea hardly applies, but once the condition is established, they suffer from loss of libido and later, in its more advanced stages, from impotency. The deficit in sex hormones probably stems from pituitary dysfunction rather than primary testicular impairment. In this way, it mirrors the effect of the pituitary on the ovary. There is a theory that in men a substitute for anorexia is often over-enthusiasm for exercise, and American psychiatrists have coined the phrase 'obligate running' to describe those marathon freaks, who if they had been female could well have been starving themselves in some, most often, middle-class dining room.

In treating an anorexic patient there are three goals to achieve. The first is for the whole team, not just the doctor, to gain the patient's co-operation, confidence and trust. The second is for the patient to be encouraged and persuaded to eat and regain the weight lost. This may be achieved through the doctor and the patient working together to reach agreed and attainable targets, so that weights consistent with good health are sustained. The course of weight gain is seldom straightforward: there will be scenes and tantrums, efforts made to bargain, and quite a bit of hostility. The staff in a hospital may have to be very much on the look-out for food hiding, surreptitious vomiting, and every other subterfuge which would prevent weight gain. It is essential that reassurance is given by the staff, in whom the patients have confidence, that any weight gained has been rewarded with an improvement in the patient's appearance. It is vital that they are assured that they not only look healthier – which may not concern them – but that they also look more attractive and have a better figure. *The Oxford*

Textbook of Medicine sums up the preferred approach in medical and nursing staff as 'friendly support rather than inquisitorial supervision'.

Finally, the patients need help in understanding the nature of their own problem and why it has occurred. They have to be persuaded to accept their new weight, to reassess their body image and to understand that they will need to be guided gently along paths which will lead them to an acceptance of their own sexual maturity and independence. Cognitive and other psycho-therapy has proved very useful in the treatment of anorexia nervosa; as has family therapy. There is evidence that cognitive therapy is more helpful for younger women, than it is for those who are rather older. A small proportion of women who suffer from anorexia nervosa are middle-aged, and have daughters with whom they try to compete. They don't hope to win the household sexual attractiveness stakes by nobbling their daughter, rather they hope to emulate her by becoming as slim as a young girl; unfortunately they frequently overdo the dieting.

No treatment would be complete without stressing the need to exclude other causes of anorexia or bulimia. Both may be symp-toms of psychiatric disease. The depressed anorexic patients will need treatment of their depression, as well as of their anorexia nervosa or bulimia. Anorexia is a frequent symptom of many different personality disorders. It attracts attention, it causes con-sternation, it reflects an obsession with beauty and appearance – on these occasions it cannot be seen in isolation, but only as part of an overall picture of a disturbed personality.

A terrible medical blunder is to assume that all loss of appetite – anorexia – is a manifestation of anorexia nervosa or some other psychiatric condition. Loss of appetite can be a symptom of phys-ical disease and this must be excluded. Some diseases, cancer of the pancreas, for instance, show loss of appetite as the first indication of trouble, one which may be present long before any other signs or symptoms. Other cancers also induce loss of appe-tite and it is said that sometimes the loss applies only to particular foodstuffs – meat, for instance – and then the patient may be thought of as a food faddist. Likewise, some hardened old soak may suddenly desert his favourite barside stool having lost his appetite for alcohol. Anyone who suddenly loses appetite needs to be thoroughly investigated and if necessary, treated.

So long as families remain small and no longer resemble the disparate, extended families of yesteryear, the major eating disorders are likely to increase. The multitude of brothers, sisters, cousins, uncles and aunts, even bossy grandparents, are no longer there to dilute the intense inter-relationships created by the nuclear family. Furthermore, any tendency to develop anorexia nervosa, or bulimia, is not going to be assuaged by a quick glance through the glossy magazines in a search for role models outside the family. However, there is hope. Anorexia and the other eating disorders are now much better understood and doctors more prepared, and equipped, to treat them.

7

Somatoform Disorders

Natasha was as charming as her name, but despite that, and her pleasing appearance, her obvious kindliness and desire to please, she was what doctors call a heartsink patient. Heartsink patients are the surgery regulars whose attendance fills a doctor with dread. Many of these people are suffering from one of the somatoform disorders, a group of medical conditions where the patient is quite certain that they are ill, as they are actually experiencing physical symptoms even though the most brilliant pathologist would be unable to find any organic disease.

Doctors' hearts sink when they see Natasha and those like her because they know that it is going to be almost impossible to convince them that they are well, and many doctors do need patients to get better to boost their own morale. Also there is always the fear of missing a diagnosis – 30 per cent of patients who have been determinedly diagnosed as suffering from somatoform disorders in fact have genuine disorders.

Patients who have been misdiagnosed tend to suffer from insidious diseases with little to show in the way of signs or symptoms in their early stages. It is a bold doctor, probably a dangerously over-confident one, who can claim that he has never missed an early case of multiple sclerosis, or a minute but lethal brain tumour, and who hasn't dismissed SLE (systemic lupus erythematosus, a connective tissue disorder) as being no more than post-flu tiredness, or has failed to spot hypothyroidism (too little thyroid hormone).

For my own part, I still remember Robert's case with some anxiety. He had had distressing problems at work. A career which once promised a glittering future had slowly dulled, and at fifty he was made redundant. A collection of modern art, displayed in a pleasant Victorian house, two children at university and a bank manager who still offered him lunch, couldn't disguise the fact that, in his own mind, his business career had ended in failure. Robert started to complain of very vague symptoms – he was tired, had ill-defined joint and muscle pains, he was a little bit constipated and experienced some transitory chest pain unrelated to exercise.

All Robert's routine tests were normal, apart from indicating a slight anaemia. However, I suspected he might be ill and he started on a prolonged trip around the consulting rooms of Harley Street. The specialists all thought that he was depressed because of his redundancy, and he was given a variety of pills and potions to relieve depression, but none of these worked. Finally the diagnosis of 'clinical depression' was abandoned and he was told that he was suffering from a somatoform disorder – a term which is derived from ancient Greek 'soma', meaning 'body'.

I didn't see Robert for some months, when he came back again. By now he looked myxoedematous – his skin was dry and thickened, his hair sparse, the outer third of the eyebrows had disappeared and when I tested his knee reflexes, the response was slow: his lack of thyroid hormone was obvious. For some reason, presumably because we were distracted by his obvious business problems, none of us had carried out thyroid tests which would have given the diagnosis immediately. He was prescribed the appropriate pills and he made a full recovery.

The other dreaded mistake is to be taken in by a malingerer. People who complain unnecessarily about their health are too easily dismissed by their colleagues as suffering either from hypochondriasis or malingering. Some people of course do falsely claim to be disabled, sometimes to gain sympathy, sometimes so that they don't have to work, and at other times for insurance money, but this dishonesty is quite different from those who suffer from the somatoform disorders. A patient who complains of the symptoms which together form a somatoform disorder is not intentionally mimicking some disease, but is literally feeling the troubles which are worrying him or her.

The important factor of the somatoform disorder is that those who suffer from it are not pretending to be ill. They really experience the physical symptoms which are suggestive of some actual disorder and, not surprisingly, they are often quite unconvinced when no doctor is able to demonstrate the signs, whether from physical examination or from the laboratory or other special tests which would establish a diagnosis. Often it is very probable that the symptoms the patients feel may have physical origins, but these are more likely to be the ordinary sensations brought on by the body's normal workings, than from any disease process. Examples would be chest pain, too trivial for most to worry about, caused by sitting awkwardly; likewise back pain which happens to be centred over the kidneys; and bowels which are unusually noisy or sluggardly. In many cases the mechanism responsible for the complaint cannot be identified.

The doctor's aim is to be sympathetic to the patient's symptoms and to explain, if necessary repeatedly, that certain people are more aware than others of their body's processes and the innocuous symptoms these produce. The doctor also needs to reassure the patient that some of the bodily functions they can feel or hear, whether it is their tummy rumbling or their heart beating, are quite compatible with good health even if they are more pronounced than those of other people.

Although many patients who visit their doctors do not have any demonstrable disease, very few of them welcome being told that they have a somatoform disorder which lies in the province of psychiatric disease – psychiatric disease, because every function of the body, including the nervous system, seems to be working perfectly and any trouble is therefore assumed to lie in the mind. If the nervous system is relaying normally the sensations of a healthy body, it must be the mind's faulty interpretation of physical sensations which is the root cause of the condition.

The somatoform disorders are classified in the *DSM* as:

Hysterical neurosis, now usually called conversion disorder
Hypochondria, also described as hypochondriasis or
   hypochondriacal neurosis
Somatization disorder, which used to be called Briquet's
   syndrome
Somatoform pain disorder
Body dysmorphic disorder, also known as dysmorphobia
Undifferentiated somatoform disorder
Somatoform disorders which have not otherwise found a niche
   of their own in the *DSM* list

Hippocrates, Plato and the ancient Greeks noticed that while
hypochondria was slightly more common in men, hysteria was
very much a woman's disease. They attributed hysteria, now
known as conversion disorder (in which some inner mental conflict seeks an outlet in physical symptoms), to a disordered womb
('hystero' coming from the Greek for 'womb'). Plato thought that
the symptoms of hysteria were the response of an angry womb,
which he believed to be like an animal frustrated in its procreative
function. In his opinion, if the womb had been happily occupied
bearing a huge family, hysteria was less likely. Other ancients
believed that the womb wandered, migrating around the
body, and causing troubles as it went, hence the multiplicity of
symptoms characterizing hysteria.

Conversion disorder or hysteria is what used to be described
fifty years ago as hysterical neurosis. It is an unconscious adoption of well-known signs and symptoms of disease, which suggest some real physical illness, or disability, whereas in fact
the symptoms are psychological in origin. Naturally, although
entirely subconscious, the greater the patient's knowledge of
medicine, the more difficult it is to distinguish the condition from
malingering, a confusion which is all the more likely as some
patients who are malingering may have an unconscious element
to some of their professed symptoms. Likewise, some patients
suffering from hysteria or a conversion disorder rather overplay
their perceived symptoms. It all makes diagnosis very tricky for

the doctor. As the Greeks knew, the symptoms of conversion disorder can affect any part of the body but commonly the patient
complains of sudden paralysis, weakness or loss of sensation in a
limb, or may have hysterical deafness, loss of voice, blindness or a
fit.

The personality of people who are prone either to malingering
or conversion disorders tends to further confuse the diagnosis as
both groups give misleading medical histories and describe their
troubles in an histrionic, exaggerated way. People with either
dependent or histrionic personality disorders are more liable than
others to suffer also from conversion disorder. There is often an
element of 'gain' derived from the symptoms. The relief of
anxiety, which follows any discussion of the symptoms and their
acceptance by others, is described as 'primary gain', but, beyond
that, patients with these disorders also always have 'secondary
gain'. Secondary gains can range from an avoidance of doing
something the patient would rather not, to potential financial
advantage, as when an insurance company claim is to be sorted
out. This does not imply that the patient is in any way malingering – the advent of the symptoms, and the exploitation of them
are entirely subconscious.

One particular form of somatoform disorder is very common:
hypochondriasis, popularly known as hypochondria. The old
belief was that hypochondriasis stemmed from disorders in the
spleen which lies tucked up under the left ribs, the part of the
abdomen traditionally known as the hypochondrium. To return
to Plato and Hippocrates and the other Greek physicians: they
thought that when the human condition was afflicted by melancholy and misery, the spleen was responsible and that hypochondriasis was a symptom of the depressive state. They were quite
right in their assessment of some of their patients' underlying
mood – then as now, they may well have been depressed.

Hypochondriasis or hypochondriacal neurosis is a symptom of
many psychological disorders as well as the major depressive
states. Hypochondriasis seems to be almost invariably present to

"I'M NOW GETTING TO THOSE UNDER 'M'"

a greater or lesser extent in people with schizotypal personality disorders or with actual schizophrenia, and it may also be found in those suffering from a general anxiety state. In all these instances it may be displayed to such a mild degree that the condition could not be considered severe enough to warrant too much attention. In other cases someone's anxiety about their health is so marked, and even disabling, that even in the absence of a definable disease it must be considered that they are suffering from any one of several personality disorders.

Patients with hypochondriasis are preoccupied with fears of serious disease and confirm their fears by insisting they have only reached their own diagnosis after analysing the symptoms they experience. The difficulty arises because their symptoms in their own mind have been exaggerated and, as in those others suffering from somatoform disorder, they are all too aware of what to other people would be an unimportant pain or discomfort. By definition, a thorough medical examination fails to uncover any serious cause of the symptoms which have been giving rise to such worries. In the hypochondriacal disorder the patient retains insight, unlike one suffering from conversion disorder or hysteria, and is therefore able to believe the doctors when they say that the anxiety may be based on an exaggeration of the importance of the minor symptoms. Doctors need to remember that being hypochondriacal doesn't provide any immunity to diseases – even though a patient may be a hypochondriac, they will, like the rest of us, still catch flu. Only a few people will suffer an accidental death; sooner or later everyone else will, in all probability, develop some potentially fatal disorder.

There is no particular treatment for hypochondriasis, although drugs of one sort or another will occasionally benefit the patient for a time. As well as the short-term benefits derived from anti-anxiety agents, and the longer-term ones occasionally obtained when antipsychotic drugs have been necessary or depression has been treated, the best results have been obtained by kindly understanding and the support of a good general practitioner or physician.

If any underlying psychiatric condition can be sought out and treated there is often a longer-lasting benefit. Only if it is a symptom of a more major problem are patients with hypochondriasis likely to be cured. When hypochondria has no obvious cause, it is thought to be a reaction to any form of longstanding conflict – for instance, of beliefs, in lifestyle, parental influence, sexual orientation or even, more prosaically, in the environment. At various times the condition has been felt to represent hostility, to be a response to failure or disappointment or to doubts about sexual orientation or proclivities.

Somatization Disorder

The French psychiatrist Paul Briquet wrote an epic work in 1859. He described a condition in which patients complained of recurrent and multiple physical disorders. Their troubles, which usually started in adolescence, continued to defeat their doctors' diagnostic powers, year after year. Dr Briquet thought of this as a form of hysteria, and it was later named Briquet's syndrome, now known as somatization disorder, one of the somatoform disorders.

Patients with somatization disorder are 'regulars' in the surgery or out-patients' queue, and, like Natasha, mentioned earlier, are archetypal heartsink patients. They have, in their opinion, been ill for many years. Somatization disorder is found far more frequently in women than in men; indeed is described as being rare in men. It is most commonly found in the teens or twenties, although its progress varies. In general it can be described as being a chronic disease, for which sufferers are frequently admitted to hospital for a plethora of examinations and investigations.

Like all the somatoform disorders, the severity of somatization disorder is influenced by external factors. If, for instance, Natasha's mother were to fall ill, her family to go bankrupt or her dog die, it is a reasonable bet that Natasha herself would suffer from some vague symptom – breathlessness, ill-defined indigestion or heart pain – which in other people, if it occurred, would not in their opinion have warranted further investigation. Somatization disorder is chronic but the symptoms may vary from time to time – it is as if the musician is playing the same instrument with a limited repertoire of tunes.

The body's systems are not all equally at risk of becoming the site of the latest anxiety. As somatization disorder is usually a disease affecting women, worries often centre on the menstrual cycle, but the gastrointestinal tract, heart or lungs are also potential areas of concern. Long experience has shown that patients with somatization disorder are therefore particularly liable to complain of shortness of breath, lumps in the throat, loss of memory, vomiting, difficulty in swallowing, painful limbs, difficult periods and a wide variety of unpleasant sensations in the sexual organs or rectum.

Patients with somatization disorder are frequently depressed or anxious, and they may have a variety of personality disorders – in particular histrionic personality disorder or anti-social personality disorder. The patients' problems become of

227

overriding importance to them; they find it hard to think of anything else – thoughts about their condition preoccupy their mind and totally disrupt their lives as well as very often the lives of those around them. Naturally they are always seeking a cure and are prepared to accept the advice of any plausible physician who offers them hope. A physical diagnosis is what they are desperate for – something that would restore their lost self-esteem by making their chronic ill-health acceptable to themselves, as well as to their families and colleagues. And that is a diagnosis, which, in some ways unfortunately, the doctor can only rarely give them.

Intriguingly and controversially, it has been said that the features of somatization disorder could account for some of the symptoms of chronic fatigue syndrome, or ME. Consistent with this theory would be those feelings of depression, which are not always associated with the classic symptomatology of major depression, and which many, but by no means all, chronically fatigued people experience. Although disputed, it is the opinion of the Royal Colleges of Physicians, Psychiatrists and General Practitioners that the best method of treatment is regular exercise from an early stage in the disease. Patients are encouraged to get out and about and discouraged from lying in bed in a darkened room all day. Some of the patients with somatization disorder and/or chronic fatigue syndrome, will respond to the antidepressant Prothiaden (dothiepin), preferably taken at night as it induces somnolence.

In general, the doctor should try and discourage the patient with somatization disorder from going from one consultant, and from one type of medical care, to another as they anxiously seek a physical diagnosis and a cure. When treating patients with somatization disorder the doctor must try not to make things worse by reinforcing a person's belief in their existing symptoms or encouraging them in their conviction that they are ill, but neither should the doctor ever ridicule them or become irritable with their inability to get better.

Somatoform Pain Disorder

A further condition, somatoform pain disorder is almost a sub-class of somatization disorder, concerning as it does only one particular apparent symptom which is causing unfounded fears in a patient – that of their pain. Even so, it is classified separately in the *DSM*. In this condition the patient is not so much preoccupied with a plethora of symptoms inexplicable on medical examination, but by the presence of pain, for which no physical cause can be found. As in other conversion or hysterical disorders, pain is a symptom which often provides some physical or emotional advantage. Although the motivation is entirely subconscious the pain can enable a person to escape from some duty or activity, which would otherwise be troubling them. In others, the pain, in some cases, may be the only way in which the patient receives the attention they feel (perhaps subconsciously) they need.

Very often in somatoform pain disorder the psychological link between some emotional disaster and the start of the pain is quite obvious to everyone but the patient, who resolutely refuses to agree that their symptomatology could be based upon some psychological catastrophe or loss. These patients are frequently depressed and nearly all are emotionally disturbed. Quite often, because of the depressive component, characterized by loss of self-esteem, they show some improvement with antidepressants. The choice of antidepressant is important – those such as the tricyclics, which have an anti-anxiety component, are preferred, and from time to time anti-anxiety agents, for instance, benzodiazepines, which have no antidepressant action may be helpful, albeit prescribed for a short time.

Patients suffering from somatization pain disorder tend to take larger and larger doses of painkillers and although there is no evidence that this makes any difference to their symptoms, it certainly increases the risk of their becoming drug dependent. As in all cases of apparent somatoform diseases there is always the danger that a physical cause of the pain may be overlooked or, in some cases, even though a cause has been observed, the degree of pain from which a patient is suffering may be underrated. Pain is always subjective and doctors, perhaps by their very nature hardy creatures, may well have a higher pain threshold than is usual. As a result, the pain from a genuine illness such as an arthritic hip may be dismissed as being no more than evidence of somatoform pain disorder and essential painkillers withheld. These patients, not unnaturally, will resent having to persuade the doctor that their pain is at an unacceptable level and may have to endure invasive and pervasive questioning, interpreted as being as impertinent as unnecessary.

Dysmorphobia

Few, if any, people are satisfied with every aspect of their bodies. No one can be happy with every feature handed out by the genetic lottery spun at the time of conception. Most people learn to accept their flaws, some may even turn them to their advantage. In others, a real or imagined imperfection rules every moment of their lives and dominates their thoughts, from when they wake until when they sleep. This single-minded obsession with their allegedly faulty appearance is known as dysmorphobia or body dysmorphic disorder.

The term 'dysmorphobia' or body dysmorphia was first used over a hundred years ago, in 1886, to describe someone's own feelings, however unjustified, that they are ugly or have a physical defect. It can be a symptom of many different disorders and is reasonably frequently found both in major depression and in schizophrenia. The patients are often obsessive, and even if they do not have an obvious major depressive disorder are slightly depressed.

Whereas many of the somatoform disorders cause doctors considerable diagnostic worries, the body dysmorphic disorder does not present any problem of diagnosis, but does raise questions of treatment. The essential feature of dysmorphobia is the preoccupation with the appearance of one particular aspect of the patient's body. The object of the anxiety may be slightly out of the ordinary, but very often the doctor is unable to detect any abnormality. In any event it is not the abnormality which leads to the diagnosis of dysmorphobia, but a patient's obsession with it.

The more exposed the part of the body causing the anxiety, the more likely it is to be seized upon by the sufferer as the reason for the preoccupation. Patients are therefore particularly concerned about any abnormality of the face, in particular the teeth and nose or any bumps or lumps on jaws or foreheads. There are worries about wrinkles, drooping eyelids, spots, shadows under the eye, facial hair, the appearance of hands and feet, and women, of course, tend to be self-conscious about breasts. Some women may feel embarrassed because they have 'too small' breasts, sometimes, less often, because their breasts are in their opinion so large that they excite comment and wolf whistles. It is easily overlooked that men, too, can be worried about their breasts, as some men are born to be big-breasted, and others have them thrust upon them by their doctors' pills and potions. Men are also legendarily concerned about the size of their penis, the overwhelming majority because they think it is too small, but an appreciable minority because they perceive it as being too big. At the genito-urinary clinic it was always a matter of interest that the amount of anxiety about penile size bore little relation to actuality and that no use of the tape measure to assess length or girth would calm the patient's fears. Many men worry about their faces as well, and about their physique – they may consult the doctor about the former and spend hours in expensive gyms working complex machinery to try to perfect the latter.

It is difficult to decide which patients are unnecessarily over-anxious about some aspect of their appearance and need psychological treatment, and which ones have some case for being concerned about the way they look and should have surgical treatment. If the anxiety is entirely delusional and a woman's breasts, for example, are an absolutely normal size or another's nose would grace a calendar, most doctors would feel it a mistake to recommend plastic surgery.

Patients who have these extreme and groundless anxieties should have psychotherapy and, in particular, discussion of their relationships with other people. Some patients with body dysmorphia have difficulty in establishing a comfortable rapport with those around them, and some of them may subconsciously find it a relief to attribute all their problems to their hated physical characteristic. In other cases, this imagined flaw may genuinely be the cause of their social unease and once its imperfections, however trivial, have been corrected, they may blossom with their newfound confidence.

Some patients cease to dwell on their imagined infirmities once any co-existent depression has been treated. If the dysmorphia is a symptom of schizophrenia, or one of its associated diseases, or of a major depressive state, it may be treated with antipsychotic drugs or antidepressants, as the case may require, and sometimes with good effect.

However, not everybody who complains of an unsightly aspect of their appearance is suffering from dysmorphobia. They may be self-conscious about some defect, and who can blame them. If someone, for instance, does have bags under the eyes or a very large nose it is not for the patient's doctor to determine how they should feel about this and to declare that the patient's anxiety is a symptom of their preoccupation and hence of dysmorphobia.

Dysmorphobia frequently begins in adolescence. Many adolescents spend hours in front of the mirror, peering and playing with their acneform spots, but often this can be dismissed as no more than normal teenage behaviour. Some adolescents, however, do become obsessed with some feature, which quite frequently revolves around their sexual development.

Celia is typical of patients who worry about their breasts and was only fifteen when she started to become preoccupied with their development. As she matured, she attracted wolf whistles and stares from many, she thought most, of the men she passed in the street or shop, and walking past a building site became a misery. Going into her class was a blush-making ordeal for her as she occasionally heard muttered remarks from male contemporaries about the size of her breasts. The unwelcome attention concentrated Celia's mind on her breasts, they became her overriding preoccupation, and the all-pervasive thoughts interfered with her exams and her social life, and exacerbated any depressive state she may already have had. She became convinced that she was ugly and resorted to overeating. Plastic surgery proved the answer, although Celia did not opt to have it done until she was over twenty. She has never regretted the operation and can now walk down the street with confidence.

As medicine improves and plastic surgery becomes ever more sophisticated, it is increasingly important that those patients with conspicuous physical peculiarities should have the very best advice and treatment.

Not all patients with somatoform disorders visit their doctor with several symptoms which fit a well-known pattern. Many patients, no less heartsink, complain of a single symptom – such as inexplicable breathlessness, or difficulty in swallowing. These symptoms can be classified as undifferentiated somatoform disorders. The same designation is given to those who have a clutch of symptoms for which no physical cause can be found.

Psychotherapists believe that people unconsciously express feelings through somatic symptoms. A baby, before it can talk, communicates feelings through his or her body and this pattern may be carried on into adulthood. So, for instance, if a person was experiencing sadness, they would become ill instead of expressing it more conventionally. Psychotherapists find these patients difficult to treat, but if they are strongly motivated they may gain an understanding of their feelings so that they can 'give up' their somatic symptoms.

8

Orgasmic Disorders

Just as the silicon chip has revolutionized material life since the Second World War, so has a small blue multifaceted pill, Viagra, transformed people's attitudes to the previously taboo subjects of sexual arousal and even the quality of orgasms. Tabloids, broadsheets, magazines, even those speaking with the dulcet tones of BBC Radio 3, have been absorbed by Viagra (sildenafil) and its effect on sexual potency and orgasmic response. They have also dealt with such rival products as MUSE, Viridal Duo and Caverject, which have to be inserted or injected. These are misnamed 'rival' as in selected cases they may complement Viagra's action in improving potency, and hence sex life.

The influence of Viagra on women's sexual response is still being investigated but there are unconfirmed reports that it not only improves genital blood flow, and hence engorgement and lubrication, but also has an effect on the libido. It would be difficult to understand why there should be any gender difference in the physiological or psychological response, and it is now claimed, although no scientific evidence has been produced to support it, that it may even improve libido in men.

Splendid news for those with a wide group of mild to moderate physical problems causing sexual problems, and, so far as Viagra is concerned, great news for those whose desire is strong but whose sexual inhibitions blight otherwise normal instinctive responses. Sexual inability, whether talked about or not, is responsible for much unhappiness and may also be symptomatic of many different psychiatric complaints.

There are twelve different types of sexual dysfunction listed in the *Diagnostic and Statistical Manual of Mental Disorders*, but the divisions between them tend to be somewhat arbitrary, and the causation is often very similar. The *DSM* heads the list with hypoactive sexual desire disorder, which is usually referred to as a loss of, or absence of, libido. It may be a persistent state or can be recurrent. The doctor needs to decide what would constitute normal sexual activity for somebody of their patient's age, gender and race. Moreover, the patient's usual sexual drive may be inhibited by some transient circumstance – they might, for instance, have recently been stricken with some personal tragedy, or threatened by bankruptcy, in which case it is unlikely that their libido would be very high.

Loss of sexual desire must therefore be causing marked distress, or difficulties with partners, before it can be classified as a disorder. Likewise it should not be symptomatic of some other psychiatric disease. Depressed patients, schizophrenic patients, anxious patients and those who are suffering from various somatoform disorders are all liable to lose enthusiasm for their sex life. Similarly, alcohol, or other drug misuse, can, contrary to popular belief, diminish desire as well as ability.

The next disorder is sexual aversion disorder. Whereas hypoactive sexual desire is indifference, in sexual aversion there is a desire to avoid sexual contact with a partner but this, however, is only considered a disorder if the feeling of aversion is causing distress.

If, despite sexual desire, and with no obvious aversion to sexual activity, the woman finds that she is unable to obtain adequate lubrication for sex, and there is no outward and visible sign in her genitalia of sexual excitement, she is said to be suffering from female sexual arousal disorder.

The diagnosis 'impotence' is now unfashionable. It is referred to instead as 'erectile dysfunction', which is defined as an inability to attain or maintain an erection rigid enough for satisfactory sexual intercourse. In only a small number of cases is erectile dysfunction a result of psychological causes – usually there is a physical reason, possibly medical, such as diabetes, arterial disease, damage to the spinal cord or to the nerves lead-

ing from it to the penis. This may have occurred as the result o
surgery.

In female orgasmic disorder, some women will have no physio
logical sexual response but the majority will initially have the
normal physical and emotional changes associated with sexua
arousal, but which are not always necessarily followed by ar
orgasm. This is despite being stimulated in the way which woulc
have triggered one in the majority of women, or perhaps in the
way in which they would have achieved one when masturbating
Other women are only able to achieve an orgasm when stimu
lated by a partner, and in yet others, orgasm is only possible with
penile, rather than manual, stimulation.

A woman's orgasmic response varies according to her age, anc
what is a normal response is inevitably her subjective opinion
which may or may not be confirmed by the doctor she is consult
ing. Although male erectile problems are more obvious, anc
receive more publicity than women's problems, both gender.
have troubles with their sexual responses which can cause untolc
problems. In both sexes orgasmic disorder may be related to
physical changes associated with ageing, or to problems in the
partner.

Two other sexual problems which can have a psychologica
basis are also troublesome to women. Vaginismus is caused by

"MAYBE WE'RE A LITTLE INHIBITED"

involuntary spasm of the pelvic muscles, in particular the strong muscles of the inner thigh, so that the legs are, as it were, fiercely held together, but even more importantly, by spasm of the pubo-coccygeus muscle which closes the vaginal opening. Vaginal penetration then becomes difficult or impossible; the muscle spasm may become so marked that even the back may become arched. Although penetration may be prevented, many women who suffer from vaginismus have normal orgasms. The disorder is subdivided into different types, depending how long it has been present and whether it is constantly present or only a problem with certain men or in specific situations. Vaginismus is one of the conditions for which it is possible to give a very good prognosis. With understanding, education and a step-by-step approach, well over 90 per cent of women achieve normal intercourse.

Dyspareunia, painful intercourse, is a more difficult problem as it may well be due to a physical cause – indeed, it is very often the result of some pathological condition of the female genitalia or pelvis. It is divided into either deep or superficial dyspareunia. Deep dyspareunia is felt in the pelvis and is more likely than not to be organic in origin. If it is the result of pelvic disease, the pain is worse during intercourse. These complaints lie in the province of the genito-urinary physician or gynaecologist. However, in some cases no physical cause can be found for the pain and it is assumed that there is some psychological reluctance to have intercourse, which is often amenable to psychological treatment.

Superficial dyspareunia is caused by a sensitive vulva or vagina, and the pain occurs on penetration. This may be because of lack of lubrication, because of some tension or because of local disease. Sometimes no obvious cause can be found, but even in these cases it is a mistake to assume that it is necessarily of psychological origin. Symptoms in this latter group can prove intractable. Both types of dyspareunia may be either primary – where there has never been pain-free intercourse – or secondary, where there has. This difference is important in assessing the likelihood of a psychological cause.

One of the more common problems for men is that of premature ejaculation – ejaculation which occurs with minimal physical sexual stimulation, or, in some instances, with no physical contact at all, or, if penetration is achieved, more quickly than the partner would have wished. A concept taught by an earlier generation of psychoanalysts was that premature ejaculation was the result of a man trying to punish a woman of whom he was frightened, by denying her sexual satisfaction. Not unnaturally, opinions of this sort caused considerable stress in partnerships.

Premature ejaculation or a very short excitation phase are often found in healthy, active, well-orientated males – and those with no animosity against their partners. I was once consulted by a member of a First Division football team – not a group of men famed for their psychological frailty – and was able to help him with his problem. About a month later the footballer returned with half a dozen of his colleagues, all of whom had the same trouble, and all of whom responded to simple advice – and a prescription for Seroxat (paroxetine).

Premature ejaculation is not at all unusual among young, sexually active men, even those with a voracious sexual appetite; and often the novelty of a new partner makes it even more likely. However, sometimes premature ejaculation may be a manifestation of some deep-seated anxiety, and some men may have premature ejaculation with one partner, but not with another. Fortunately there is now a whole group of drugs readily available, the SSRIs, many of which have as one of their side-effects the capacity to delay ejaculation. Seroxat, the medication I prescribed for the footballer, is particularly useful.

The *DSM* includes three other categories, catchall situations, in which actual sexual dysfunction cannot be classified, but where there is reason to suppose that a patient's psychological state is causing them problems with their sex life. One such condition is the problem experienced by some people, either male or female, in which they have perfectly normal sexual organs and reflex responses, but have no erotic response or imagination.

Before any treatment can be determined, the doctor needs to

talk to the patient in some considerable detail, and the patient needs a thorough physical examination. Even if the doctor is certain from the patient's story that the cause is psychological, it is important that the patient should be examined, as otherwise they will always feel that the diagnosis has been hastily made, without giving due weight to detail. It is surprising, for instance, how many patients are unaware that a wide variety of drugs will affect the sexual response, and even diabetic patients, who have been regular attenders of a diabetic clinic, are unaware that total impotence, or erectile dysfunction, in middle age is very common.

One man's case was particularly tragic as his whole life had been ruined by both urinary tract incontinence and erectile dysfunction. I listened to his story and he told me that it all dated from the beatings he received from a sadistic headmaster while at a boarding school. He thought the incontinence, and therefore presumably the impotence, could be related to the time when the headmaster's aim was not as good as usual and the cane struck the small of his back. On examination it could be seen that the man, now in his thirties, had a congenital bony abnormality of the lower spine and thus an inadequately protected spinal cord. I suspect that the spinal nerve was damaged by the headmaster and that my luckless patient had paid the price ever since.

Education is the answer to many cases of sexual dysfunction. In one clinic where I worked, a doctor treated cases of dysfunction, in particular impotence in the male and anorgasmic response in the female, with a psychoanalytical approach. In the rather more down-to-earth room next door we tried simple education – the facts of life and sexual behaviour presented in a simple, straightforward manner. These patients did very much better. It is surprising how many people have little knowledge of the anatomy and physiology of the sexual response, and what they can achieve when they understand its intricacies. When people are young and hormones are racing, a lack of expertise may pass unnoticed. As they grow older, when libido is waning, and long-term relationships have settled into a comfortable routine, problems may arise.

Both partners have to learn about the other gender's sexual response, what is normal for a particular age group and what can be done to enhance stimulation. Quite apart from any direct benefit derived from the advice proffered by a doctor, there is also the advantage that the partners will start talking candidly to each other. It may well be that the union between the two is satisfactory and that neither partner wants sex, but both feel that they should in order to oblige the other. The number of cases in which both sides have 'confidentially' told me that they are attending only to please the other, and that they want to continue with a sex life only to please the other, is legion.

The Masters and Johnson technique, first pioneered in the 1960s to help a pair who were suffering from some form of sexual dysfunction, is still much advocated. In it the couple initially learn to relax with each other and enjoy close bodily contact without any intention of having sexual intercourse. Only later, when confidence is gained, do they attempt coitus. Anorgasmic women are usually initially treated by encouraging them to explore their own bodies themselves, before they attempt to achieve successful intercourse with a partner. Most doctors treat sexual dysfunction with a combination of education and Masters and Johnson type behavioural therapy.

Increasingly, hormone therapy has been used in an attempt to stimulate sexual response. If male hormone levels are low there is sometimes a satisfactory outcome. I had one patient who had a long-lasting, and apparently happy, relationship with his wife, but the relationship was entirely aphysical. This man, who had very low levels of testosterone, also had a long-standing girl-friend, who lived in California. Once or twice a year he came to me for testosterone treatment, so as to restore his potency before he left for America. His fortnight's holiday over, he gave up testosterone supplements, the level in his blood fell and his impotence returned until the process was repeated in preparation for his next transatlantic trip.

Impotence in men can sometimes be related to the expertise of their partners – Thai women, for instance, are famed as lovers.

Sex to the Thai woman, so I hear, is an art form but one to be undertaken light-heartedly. It is seen as a natural skill to be prac- tised adroitly and sensitively, but without necessarily any great emotional intensity. In my particular role in medicine I see patients from all over the world and have listened in awe as some of the most world-weary travellers have told me how their impotence vanished in the massage parlours of Bangkok.

These patients' conclusions would seem to confirm the opinion of a neurologist for whom I once worked. He maintained that there was no such problem as impotent men, only incompetent women. He was wrong. I suspected he was wrong at the time, but was too junior to suggest it. He, however, was teaching the then standard view that over 90 per cent of cases of impotence were the result of psychological difficulties. Recent research has shown just how mistaken he was: over 75 per cent of three million British impotent men have a physical problem, which is no more to do with their psyche than spots in measles or the yellow hue of jaundice.

Impotence may largely be a problem of older men but it shouldn't be forgotten that younger men may too frequently have erectile dysfunction. This is more likely to be the result of psycho- logical troubles than physical ones. Men of this age group who are sexually insecure frequently find that they lose their erections easily, even if they initially achieve one. Sometimes it is because they are too concerned by their own performance, for sex has to be like breathing or marching; so natural that it happens spon- taneously. Once someone thinks about their breathing they hyperventilate: once they worry about their erection, they lose it.

'Erectile dysfunction' is not just a euphemistic way of referring to impotence. There is a grain of common sense about this as not all impotence is complete. Its onset when the cause is physical is often gradual – erections are not quite as hard as they were, are more transient and certainly less reliable. In younger men when the cause is more likely to be psychological the onset may be, and often is, sudden; and is likely to return as quickly, given a sympa- thetic woman – and perhaps a few of the magic blue Viagra pills.

Although the official definition of erectile dysfunction is consistent, or recurrent, inability to attain or maintain a penile erection rigid enough for satisfactory sexual intercourse, many men wouldn't think that this is a sufficiently wide definition. They have noticed the insidious march of time, but they don't think they are impotent, they wouldn't be classified as impotent by this medical definition, but they are not what they were, and they would like to re-experience the first fine careless rapture of youth.

Note the word 'some' in the description of the patients who tell me of the rejuvenating powers of the Thai courtesans. Most men who are partially impotent, or impotent, are suffering from some organic disability. The women may help them to muster their failing resources but they cannot provide a new arterial system, replace leaky valves, top up diminishing hormones or repair diseased or divided nerves. The degree of disability varies, both from person to person, and from time to time. Just as the ex-athlete in middle age may no longer be able to run even a four-minute mile, he can still, despite his increasing arthritis, make it

"AND CAN I GET A SKILLED WOMAN ON PRESCRIPTION, TOO?"

o the gate if a bull is after him – it is all a question of the incentive
being strong enough. Likewise, the declining sexual athlete may
no longer be assured of a strong lasting hard erection on demand.
However, provide the right incentive – for instance, a latter-day
Marilyn Monroe – and some of the forgotten ardour of youth will
rise phoenix-like in the flames of passion.

Doctors are by nature inquisitive and they have been using all
the paraphernalia of modern science to explore the secrets of the
connubial bed. With the help of the latest techniques in neuropharmacology, neurophysiology and the study of the arteries leading to the penis, and the veins from it, and of the female genital
tract, they now know not only what turns somebody on, but how.
They can measure blood flow accurately, follow the actions which
cause the erogenous zones to swell, however minutely, can plot
the ever-increasing number of drops of fluid gathering on the
vaginal wall, and record the changes in heart rate, respiration and
the tension in the pelvic muscles. No secrets are hidden.

Men and women may be different anatomically, and certainly
have very different psychological approaches, and needs, in
lovemaking, but erotic foreplay has the same function in both
sexes and the physiological sexual response is remarkably similar.
In both sexes spongy erectile tissue fills with blood, and its flow
away from the area is restricted. In both sexes during foreplay
there is vasocongestion, and an increase in the production of a
viscous fluid; in the man this may have the role of cleaning the
urethra ready for the sperm; in the woman it is an aid to lubrication. In both cases the neuropharmacology, the influence of the
nervous system on the chemicals produced in the genitalia, is the
same.

Likewise, in both men and women the mechanism of orgasm is
the same: the muscles of the pelvic floor, together with those
around the genitalia, contract involuntarily and rhythmically. As
the neurophysiology and neuropharmacology are the same in
both, it is not surprising that the preparations which are the basis
of the latest treatment of impotence, in particular Viagra, not only
help men but women in whom the same conditions are mirrored.

Given a good partner, Viagra enhances the physiological sexual response in both.

The sexual response, male or female, in part relies upon physical stimulation and in part is determined by the psyche. Up to the point of orgasm, the response can be turned off by a misplaced remark or action, by conscious or subconscious fears, guilt, anxieties, or of course by the appearance of a small child, or a mother-in-law as she brings in the morning tea.

Doctors can now provide three great innovative remedies for many men who are impotent. Some authorities, however, feel that whatever the cause of the trouble, they need to have an average, or slightly higher than average, blood testosterone level and that this testosterone should be in a form readily available to the tissues. Care is needed as cancer of the prostate is testosterone dependent – we don't want to see queues of Don Juans waiting for a place in the urology wards.

The great breakthrough was the discovery that prostaglandins like Caverject can be injected into the penis to produce an erection. Even if a man is not physically stimulated, this will produce a firm erection. However, an artificially induced erection may not always be of the standard type, for sometimes there is a 'Concorde' effect – a soft tip, but hard shaft. The second advance was the introduction of MUSE, a small soft wax-like pellet which can be inserted into the urethra; this is neither as difficult nor as painful as might be supposed. Unfortunately it doesn't produce such a hard erection as an injection, and it may often be even less uniform. One man commented that after MUSE his penis looked like a serpent which had swallowed a rat. In other cases the erection tends to soften if the man lies down, a problem which demands a sound knowledge of the *Kama Sutra* if union is to be achieved. Whatever its disadvantages, with MUSE a majority of impotent men achieve an erection good enough to effect penetration.

Finally, Viagra. Unlike the injections, or MUSE, the man who takes Viagra, it is still usually assumed, must be turned on sexually if it is to have any effect. Viagra will enhance sexual response but not create it; a man still needs a full complement of testoster-one flowing through his veins, a sexy partner and an intact, even if inefficient, genital apparatus, if success is to be achieved.

As with any bit of machinery, oiling the works, which is what Viagra does, won't be adequate if the machine is broken. Viagra, with a skilled woman, only helps in a comparatively small number of cases in which there is severe arterial disease, venous leak or disease to the nervous system from diabetes. Disappointingly, it is only very occasionally successful following impotency from pelvic surgery – usually a radical prostatectomy or large bowel surgery – or spinal disease.

In this more enlightened age, the millennial man is beleaguered. Women are laying siege to his most sacrosanct preserves: the boardroom seat, the club, the bed, even his boxer shorts. An insecure man's self-confidence is increasingly undermined. The man is no longer necessarily the principle bread- (or bed-) winner. Even worse, once in bed, women now have other men with whom they can compare his performance; this can be a nasty thought for most men, indeed all men except for the most narcissistic. For the impotent it can be crushing.

However, men shouldn't despair, whether they are sexually insecure or suffering increasing erectile dysfunction as the result of ageing. Research has shown that a surprising number of women – the majority – rate cuddling, massage and sexual stimulation, either orally or manually, as being more important in the enjoyment of sex than penetration. Interestingly, only 25 per cent of women achieve orgasm with penile penetration alone, whereas 90 per cent do so when it is associated with loving, tender and venturesome foreplay.

How can a woman help the failing man – short of cashing in her diamonds and buying a regular supply of Viagra or MUSE? It goes without saying that men's penises needs as careful handling as do their tender superegos. If a woman is too demanding, too physically assertive, the inevitable result is that the male response will shrivel away. This will happen whether the man is twenty-five or sixty-five. The young woman with an uncertain partner has to combine a sympathetic approach with an abundance of sexiness – if both the man and the woman are inhibited, there may well be a shambles.

A sensitive woman, whatever her age, who has an older partner must accept that her partner's genitals are beginning to age, as inevitably as his hair is greying. If she is able to maximize the best of what remains of his manhood she is a lover to treasure. One fifty-five-year-old man told me that his wife always picked up his penis between her finger and thumb, 'like a dirty and rather smelly dish cloth'. Not unnaturally the effect was not very stimulating. Interestingly, they had been married for over thirty years, had a very happy relationship together in every other way and the wife never knew that her reluctance to fondle him wasn't absolutely standard. Indeed it may well have been for people who were brought up in her particular pre-war era.

After middle age the tables are turned and women, whether they have a regular partner or not, but particularly if they do, have to become the sexual instigators, otherwise their sex life soon dies. More often than not, older men lose their capacity to have spontaneous erections – a coy way of saying that they need physical stimulation before they can perform. The changed role needs tact and skill on the part of the woman, for the days when candles on the dining-room table, a sexy scent and a gin and tonic already poured to greet a returning middle-aged urban warrior would be enough to ensure a passionate evening, are over. A hands-on approach is necessary.

Homosexual men, of whatever age, seem to be less troubled by impotence than their heterosexual contemporaries; perhaps this is because their inhibitions appear to be less, and their spirit of adventure greater. However, when older, they, too, suffer from exactly the same degenerative diseases which can affect the genitalia, and exactly the same considerations apply to them, and they too must pray for an understanding, sympathetic and considerate lover. Women's sexual desire, particularly if they take HRT, whether homosexual or heterosexual, doesn't usually diminish with ageing unless they are depressed. Desire is supposed to level off after middle age, but it may increase. The female genitalia may shrink after the menopause, but this is nothing which cannot be put right with HRT whether in pill form, in patches or as a locally applied cream. HRT often improves a woman's libido, and a return to her pre-menopausal bodily scent may work wonders for her sexual attractiveness. When a woman's sex life peters out, it is usually because of her partner.

With a well-orientated regular partner, a supply of Viagra, MUSE or a few injections, is there any role for a counsellor? In at most 25 per cent, probably only 10 per cent, of men, impotence is entirely psychological and some form of psychotherapy may well help these. 10 per cent of women are anorgasmic – they too could be helped; and 3 per cent of women have vaginismus, finding male penetration painful if not impossible. The overwhelming majority of these are comparatively easily cured by explanation, reassurance and discussion, and, of course, evidence shows that some of the psychologically sexually dysfunctional may also be helped by Viagra.

9

Paraphilia

Although sexually deviant behaviour – that is to say, deviant from the rules of the culture in which the paraphiliac lives – has been described in literature and history for hundreds, if not thousands, of years, it is only in the last hundred and twenty years that it has been carefully studied. Freud gave a great boost to interest in sexual behaviour, and he saw paraphilia as an arrest at some point in the usual psychological development of a child as he or she grew to sexual maturity. Although Freud is no longer venerated as a psychological oracle it is agreed that people with deviant sexual behaviour have never learnt to achieve satisfactory sex with people who share the same cultural beliefs.

The paraphilias are those peculiarities of human behaviour which in less sensitive times used to be called sexual 'perversions'. In the past these habits filled the columns of the tabloid press on a Sunday, before their editors became obsessed with the marital irregularities of politicians. The ever-useful reference, *The Diagnostic and Statistical Manual of Mental Disorders* includes nine different types of paraphilia. It is politically correct and also classifies sexual dysfunctions and gender identity disorders. The modern indices no longer, of course, include homosexuality, which is now considered normal behaviour.

Disappointing as it may be, the variations in most people's sex lives are not great and the repertoire of their sexual tricks is limited by what psychiatrists call 'normal arousal activity patterns'. These patterns vary, of course, from one culture to another, but whatever the culture, to deviate from it is likely to prevent the normal reciprocal affectionate relationship which a good sex life engenders. A paraphilia is a sexual disorder in which a patient is sexually aroused and responds sexually to some object or situation which is outside the cultural norm. The other sexual disorders, such as erectile dysfunction (impotence), frigidity, and premature ejaculation are disorders of sexual functioning and may or may not have a psychological basis.

The nine types of paraphilia are: exhibitionism, fetishism, frotteurism, paedophilia, sexual masochism, sexual sadism, transvestic fetishism, voyeurism, and paraphilia not otherwise specified.

Exhibitionism

Exhibitionists are motivated by an intense desire to expose their genital organs to a stranger, usually in the hope that the stranger will be upset by the sight. Some specialists divide exhibitionism into whether or not the sufferer has an erection and masturbates as part of this ritual. It is claimed that in 80 per cent of the cases the penis is flaccid and the exhibitionist does not masturbate. He – it is more frequently a man – is driven by a desire to expose himself but after he has done it he is usually riddled with guilt. Doctors Smith, Sell and Sudbury in their textbook *Key Topics in Psychiatry* suggest that most of these people belong to an introverted, inhibited and immature group of patients. In the other 20 per cent of cases the exhibitionist takes a sadistic pleasure in shocking the woman, and feels no remorse. The authors have noticed that these patients have a very much worse prognosis than those who feel guilty, and that many of them have other well-defined personality disorders.

Exhibitionists are the 'flashers' who feature so regularly in barside conversation. The flasher can achieve sexual pleasure, even if he does not masturbate; he achieves a relief of tension merely by showing off his genitalia. Exhibitionism is much less common in women than in men. Women often like to expose their bodies, but, despite changing mores and fashion, are still selective about the parts they will show to strangers. Even in primitive communities in which the breasts are always left exposed, the women almost invariably wear a thong to cover their genitalia. In the Western world breasts, but usually not nipples, have been exposed from time to time, but provided it is within the cultural rules of the time, this could not be described as exhibitionism and it is unlikely that the women have derived any sexual pleasure from it as a male flasher would. Women who expose themselves hope to attract and please other people, like a bare-breasted model on a catwalk, or a nude model in a girlie magazine, but not disgust them, as a flasher hopes to do.

Exhibitionists display one or two odd characteristics, including a habit of repeating their actions very exactly, so that they are liable to be apprehended by the police with remarkable speed. Exhibitionism is common amongst children, both boys and girls, and both seem to derive sexual pleasure from it. In adult life the desire for exhibitionism usually disappears and exhibitionism, even in those who are prone to it, becomes less demanding as they become middle-aged. It is also seen in mentally retarded people of all ages: 5 per cent of cases of indecent exposure are committed by people who are either psychotic or retarded. Very old men are another group who are liable to offend when they reach their second childhood. Not very long ago a highly respectable octo-genarian, who was still working part-time, went into a West End showroom, sat down and exposed himself to the surprised owner. Fortunately, she was able to see this aberrant behaviour for what it was and merely told him to do up his trousers.

Exhibitionists frequently show no other signs of severe psychi-atric disease, although if their self-esteem is eroded by a depres-sive illness, or by some overriding anxiety, they may become more outrageous. Old-fashioned psychologists have taught that exhibitionists suffer from castration complexes and their exposure is therefore an attempt to seek reassurance. Other sur-veys have attempted to show that they are sexual inadequates who may be impotent or have some other sexual dysfunction. It can be a symptom of loss of inhibition.

When I was in general practice I was called by a patient to view her male neighbour's behaviour. The neighbour, also a patient of mine, was a man of the utmost probity, a greatly valued local government officer, married and with two children. As I peered through his neighbour's net curtains, I saw him in his back garden, all too obviously exhibiting himself and masturbating in front of anyone who cared to look out of their window. So out of character was his behaviour that a full neurological examination certainly seemed worth while – something which, as I was his doctor, I was able to engineer. The examination revealed that he had a frontal lobe tumour, and it was this that was affecting his behaviour.

Harry, on the other hand, was a very typical exhibitionist. Although physically attractive to women, well-dressed, articulate and a keen cricketer, he was sexually inadequate. This is possibly because he had a very socially ambitious and dominant mother, who not only ruled him but smothered him with affection. He was never able to develop his own independent manhood, having learnt to see women as the dominant sex. This view was reinforced by his father who, far from being a suitable role model, was a workaholic who in his own home was an unobtrusive and subservient figure. Harry continued to live with his parents in the Home Counties long after his contemporaries had moved on to a flat-sharing life, which did nothing to improve matters.

Harry was a good salesman, but despite a ready charm, a reasonable salary and, his pride and joy, a seductive car, he was never able to maintain a long-term, normal relationship. For all his barside jollity after a cricket match, he was a very lonely man. He would telephone his mother after work from kiosks some little way from their house so that she knew when to put the supper on. Before making his telephone call, he would wait in the car, until he saw a woman approaching the telephone box, and then nip in front of her. While making the call he would catch her eye, smile and then as he came out he would expose himself. This gave him a great thrill. Not unnaturally, as the telephone boxes were always within a small radius of his own home, he was soon picked up by the police.

Although the women were shocked by this emotional assault

he never made any attempt to assault them physically in any way. In this manner, too, he was acting like most other exhibitionists, for, contrary to popular belief, they do not usually indulge in sexual assault, receiving all of the satisfaction they need from their flashing. However, it would be a mistake to assume that these people are necessarily an otherwise benign presence in society: it has been found that 12 per cent of people who are convicted of such crimes of violence as murder, aggravated burglary and rape, have had a previous conviction for indecent exposure.

The chance of recovery depends on the patient's underlying personality and the pattern of their exhibitionism. As mentioned earlier, those men who do not have an erection and do not masturbate, and are therefore less sadistic, have a better prognosis than those who do. Furthermore, the men who want to expose themselves to children of either sex do not respond to treatment as well as those whose victims are adult women.

Treatment is often unsatisfactory. If there is any other underlying psychiatric problem, such as schizophrenia, or an affective disorder, in particular mania or hypomania, which might be exacerbating the exhibitionism, this is treated. Otherwise the patient, should he genuinely wish to change, is treated with psychotherapy which is directed towards improving his sexual self-esteem and his sense of manhood. One-third of all sexual offences that come before the courts concern exhibitionism. Most of the offenders are placed on probation, and in a very high percentage of cases the shame engendered by the publicity of the court appearance is enough to prevent them reoffending.

Fetishism

Fetishism is defined as a recurrent intense sexual urge, which must have been present for at least six months, in which arousal is obtained by practices involving the use of a non-living object – the fetish. Long before the term 'fetish' was used to describe an object useful in someone's sex life it meant, in earlier societies, an inanimate object which was worshipped for its magical powers. Men who are fetishists – for it is confined to men – find it difficult to achieve sexual arousal and fulfilment without the presence of the fetish, which may play an important part in any sexual act.

Fetishists may be either homosexual or heterosexual. It has been suggested, by Kinsey (who wrote a report on human sexual behaviour) and others, that this male exclusivity is because men respond far more to sexual stimulation provided by sight, smell and feel, whereas women have in the past been supposed to be aroused by amorous gestures, touching and kindliness. Kinsey or not, this pattern of behaviour is changing with gender evolution and it may well be that the new generation of women reaching sexual maturity will be as turned on by sight, smell and feel as their male counterparts, and possibly in future they too will become fetishists. Time will tell.

Common objects which achieve the power of the fetish in this day and age are such things as gloves, handbags, shoes, women's underclothes, fur rugs and of course rubber goods. It is thought that the origins of fetishism go back to childhood, when the male child was sexually aroused by the sight or feel of his mother's or sister's clothes. Whatever its origins, fetishism itself does not usually make itself manifest until the male reaches adolescence, when the fetish becomes an important part of the masturbatory, or later coital, ritual. Sometimes in middle age when sexual drive and ability are failing, these rituals are not only important, they may be essential, to sexual fulfilment.

Thirty years ago the condition of partialism was not separated from other fetishes. Now it is considered in its own right, albeit that it may be to some extent be a fetish. Partialism is not over-concerned about an inanimate object but is the preoccupation some men have with some particular part of a woman's body. This is an exaggeration of the male characteristics which form the basis of the ribald jokes about whether a male is a 'breast man' or a 'bottom man'. For other men it is a woman's legs or hips, or even lips. Whereas a fetish is often an obvious substitute for a woman, partialism is very much an integral part of the woman herself.

To a limited extent, fashion utilizes both fetishism and partialism. Clothes may play upon some men's love of plastic, rubber or fur, and their design might emphasize one part of the body in preference to another. There is a thin divide between the aesthetics and paraphilia, but the tricks of fashion are usually tongue-in-cheek.

Since fetishism requires some degree of imagination in order to achieve the desired fantasy, it has traditionally been taught that men who are fetishists tend to be introverted rather than extroverted. Since fetishism itself also indicates an obsessional trait in someone's character it is not surprising that in my days as a junior doctor I was taught that they usually had other obsessional traits and tended to be meticulous, pernickety, fastidious and overly neat and tidy. Fetishists were also reputed to be great collectors – whether of stamps or of train numbers (because of their obsessional nature), or of thousands of pairs of shoes or drawers full of women's underclothes (because of their fetishism) was not made clear.

Mr Christopher Jones was headmaster of the local grammar school and much respected. One day his wife telephoned to say that she was concerned and asked for a home visit. She led me upstairs to the bedroom, took a suitcase from under the bed and opened it with a flourish. It was filled with women's underclothes. She then opened one of the two small drawers in a bedside chest; it was stuffed with photographs of shop windows, all displaying women's underwear. Mr Jones could only achieve sexual intercourse if one of these garments was within his vision, and he much preferred it if he was able to wear one of them. It was not enough that his wife should wear sexy underclothes – he had to have his own. I advised Mrs Jones that any sacrifice she had to make was rather minor and that she was lucky to have such a well-established marriage. She looked doubtful; but women from a younger generation seem to take fetishism in their stride.

Fetishism is very common. Perhaps one of its most frequent manifestations is over-attachment to a particular scent. Some scents invariably attract some men's attention, but whether this mild fetishism dates from childhood, and perhaps the mother's scent, or from some early girlfriend, is unknown. Other men have very bizarre fetishes. One very rich sixty-year-old tycoon found that he could only counter his increasing erectile dysfunction if he made love to his younger wife on his library floor – in this way he was able to look at his big-game trophies hanging on the wall while he had sex with her. Another man, although younger by thirty years, was only able to have sex out of doors, but whether it was the freedom this produced or the feel of the groundsheet beneath him he never knew.

" I PREFERRED IT WHEN YOU JUST HAD TO **LOOK** AT THEM "

Fetishism is treated in the same way as exhibitionism. If it is associated with some treatable psychiatric condition, this is dealt with; if it causes offence to a partner, psychotherapy designed to increase the patient's sexual self-esteem can be instituted.

Frotteurism

Frotteurism is the habit of rubbing genital areas against the body of a complete stranger. It is a crime usually committed in, say, a crowded underground train during the rush hour, while in a queue pushing through a turnstile, or in any place where people are penned together. Frotteurism is essentially a male habit and the man usually chooses a woman's buttocks to rub against, although other parts of the body may be touched. For the habit to be defined as frotteurism, the intense urge must have existed for at least six months and the transgressor must find that the action produces sexual arousal. In the typical case the man who indulges in frotteurism feels guilty about his impulses, and the anxiety which they cause frequently results in distress, both at home and at work. As the crime is one of indecent assault the courts can take a hard line in cases of frotteurism, and frequently hand out a prison sentence for such behaviour. The convicted men, it is often found, have led socially isolated lives, and are so shy and sexually inadequate that they have failed to make normal social friend-ships with women. Treatment is difficult but psychotherapy in one form or another may help.

Paedophilia

Paedophilia has become a scourge of modern society. It is unlikely that there is any sudden change in the true incidence of this paraphilia, but a greater openness in society, coupled with improved communications, easy transport, and the breakdown of protective family life and small communities – so that anonymity is that much easier – have increased this offence to epidemic pro-portions. Fear of paedophilia can also create its own problems and be very destructive to a child's proper development and future sexual relationships.

As it is recognized by the courts, paedophilia is not the same as it is defined by psychiatrists in *DSM-IV*. Psychiatrists have determined that paedophilia should only be diagnosed when the person's sexual attraction to young pre-pubertal children is either the only way in which they can achieve sexual relief or, if not their exclusive form of gratification, it is the repeatedly preferred one. Conversely, the law, as one would expect, considers that an isolated sexual act with a child represents paedophilia and does not accept that from time to time the child may be acting as a substitute for an adult who, for some reason or another, is not sexually available.

Psychiatrists determine in their definition that someone suffering from paedophilia should have had recurrent and intense sexual urges and sexually arousing fantasies for at least six months which involved some sexual activity with a pre-pubescent child. As is widely known paedophiles can be either heterosexual or homosexual, but, contrary to popular belief, heterosexual paedophiles are twice as common as homosexual ones. Ten per cent of paedophiles are bisexual. Homosexual paedophiles are more likely to be recidivists, for those men who are attracted by boys are the most likely to offend repeatedly, despite the deterrence of prison or help through psychiatric treatment.

A study of paedophiles in Sing Sing prison in New York, by Dr B. C. Glueck, reported that a high proportion of homosexual paedophiles showed evidence of severe psychiatric disease and many were frankly psychotic, with marked impairment of reasoning and judgement. The study found that these people had great difficulty with all human relationships, but their relationships seemed to them to be most successful when they were with young boys. Interestingly, whereas 50 per cent of homosexual paedophiles want to have an orgasm when with their victim, only 6 per cent of the heterosexual paedophiles wanted to pursue their urge to its climax. Heterosexual paedophiles are also much more likely than homosexual paedophiles to commit the offence within their own household and family, often when under the influence of excessive alcohol, whereas homosexual paedophiles are more frequently the marauders on the common, in the woods, or lurking by the playground.

Research by Doctors J. W. Mohr, R. E. Turner and M. B. Jerry, in *Paedophilia and Exhibitionism*, published by the University of Toronto Press in 1964, found that paedophilia was not committed with equal regularity throughout life. There were peaks: the first in adolescence, when paedophiles tended to be emotionally, socially and sexually retarded; the second in middle age – this group were often unhappy, maladjusted, had had difficult or unsuccessful marriages and had sought relief with alcohol. The third age of paedophilia was in old age. The elderly paedophile was often lonely, turned to children to relieve this and away from adult heterosexual relationships because of increasing impotency and a fear of sexual failure and any subsequent judgement.

Paedophilia can affect either sex, but is much more common in males. Surprisingly, most paedophiles are not aggressive and do not use any force in furthering their sexual activities, which are much more likely to involve fondling and caressing than penetrative sex. Paedophiles may do no more than talk about sex to children or young adolescents – but that in itself can be damaging. Others exhibit themselves or, as well as stroking the genital organs of the child, encourage the child to touch theirs.

Every policeman knows that although paedophilia is found in every class, race and age, there are particular types of man or woman most likely to indulge in it. The classic picture of the paedophiliac is of an inadequate, usually unobtrusive, mild man, who is frightened of his contemporaries, whether male or female. Psychologists have taught that the typical paedophile has a well-developed castration fear and a dread of being 'engulfed' by a mature woman. The amount of credence which can be given to these deep psychological explanations is uncertain but psychiatrists do claim that many men who are paedophiles are obsessed with having what they visualize as a small penis. It is possible, and frequently stated, that they might therefore prefer the sexual

Paraphilia

company of children who would not be critical. There is always a danger that discussion of paedophile motivation may allow the paedophiles themselves to seize upon the points raised as justification for their own behaviour, but so important is this crime and so severe its consequences that efforts must be made to understand its motivation.

The older generation of psychologists also dispute whether paedophiles are narcissistic, and are in part attracted by children because in a child they see their own gilded youth. Another explanation is that they are masochistic, because many paedophiles have a very intense sense of guilt about their behaviour, they may loathe themselves for their actions and the more they repeat these actions the more they feel absolutely worthless, useless and degraded – the emotions which masochists crave.

Other explanations which have been offered are that the paedophile with very low self-esteem has been conditioned to, or has conditioned himself, to expect to be rejected by women or men and therefore seeks the company of children. It has also been suggested that the paedophile brought up in an unhappy household with either absent or conditional love in his childhood initially takes an interest in children in the hope of giving them a better life, with more kindliness, than he himself enjoyed. In some of these cases, those who hold this theory maintain, the affection gets out of hand and is expressed physically.

It is certain that the majority of paedophiles have had an unhappy childhood and that many were brought up in dysfunctional families. There is genuine evidence that many adults who are paedophiliac were themselves assaulted in childhood. The exact importance of this is hard to quantify as paedophilia is often incestuous and therefore the perpetrator has the same genetic make-up as the child: when the child grows up and he too becomes a paedophile, is it an effect of nature or nurture? The evidence of childhood assault as a cause for later paedophilia, which is sound, has also been undermined by the claims made about repressed memory, and hence the vexed question of the existence of false memory syndrome.

Apart from these generalizations, there are particular groups who may exploit children sexually. These include the mentally retarded, people with antisocial personality disorders, those with schizophrenia, and sufferers from organic brain disease such as a cerebral tumour or any cause of dementia, whether senile or otherwise. Sexual aberration can be the presenting sign or symptom of many different psychiatric conditions. A very similar story to that of the exhibitionist who cavorted in his garden is that of a certain respectable minor civil servant. He served his country arduously and meticulously by day and lived a worthy life with his wife and three children when off duty. His neighbour came to see me complaining that he was behaving very oddly when he was watering his garden – he was using the flowing garden hose to simulate his penis as he played with it in front of his neighbour's young children. The story seemed so out of character that, as with the exhibitionist, we sought a neurological opinion. It transpired that this man, too, had a cerebral tumour and his behaviour had been the only symptom from it. Sadly, although surgery and radiotherapy cured his paraphilia, the treatment came too late, and he died soon after.

An isolated incident of child sexual assault can occur when the adult is undergoing some temporary period of stress and tension. This may have induced a marked degree of transient depression, or of heavy alcohol consumption, and it is found that such a situation may frequently account for occurrences when the sexual assault has been uncharacteristically perpetrated by someone who previously has had a well-balanced personality. Periods of marital disharmony, bereavement or other causes of loneliness may also induce depression and can lower the resistance of a man or woman to an urge which they had either not acknowledged, or if they had, had previously kept in check.

The child is always in physical as well as emotional danger from the advances of paedophiles. The paedophile who suffers from gross personality disorders may also be sadistic, or may attempt to hide evidence by killing the child. A few paedophiles may also indulge in necrophilia – people can suffer from more than one paraphilia.

Sexual Masochism

Leopold von Sacher-Masoch (1835–95) was an Austrian writer who, because of the subject of his novels, gave his name to masochism. Masochism is the opposite of sadism, although both conditions are now thought of as being interrelated and are often discussed together. Masochism may have been defined by Leopold von Sacher-Masoch but it existed long before he published his books, and indeed, in some societies it was so acceptable that it was considered spiritually praiseworthy. Von Sacher-Masoch drew attention to a strange habit which was falling into desuetude – the saintly who indulged in this practice of course didn't think of it as a sexual pleasure but as a means of subduing the flesh and acquiring humility.

In their textbook *Psychiatry*, Professors Ian Gregory and Donald Smeltzer draw attention to a little-known fact that it was English women throughout the seventeenth and eighteenth centuries who were the great practitioners of sado-masochism. At this time there were groups of women, usually married, who met, not as they would today for coffee or to play bridge, but to practise flagellation for the good of their souls. Some presumably enjoyed doing the whipping, some being whipped, but as so often happens in sado-masochism the roles were probably reversible. Flagellation – in the form of ritual beatings of one sort or another – has until very recently always been an recognized part of life in British boarding schools, and it is arguable whether or not it was more damaging to the schoolmasters than to the boys. It has also been practised in convents and monasteries throughout the world, throughout history and in a wide variety of different religions.

The pleasure which a masochist experiences can extend to sexual gratification and a relief of sexual tensions and revolves around feelings of being humiliated, reviled and dominated. Humiliation is the essential feature, but even so it is a myth to think that the 'punishment' may only be token – I have seen patients who have been severely damaged, and in one case a patient of mine was all but left for dead. He was an aristocratic homosexual, who enjoyed being beaten by the 'rough trade' he picked up in those pubs which cater for such needs. On this occasion the beating had got out of hand and the patient was more than a little relieved to be able, once he had recovered consciousness, to reach the door of my clinic. Other masochistic patients I have had have been left so raw, red and bleeding, that they have been unable to wear clothes or lie on their backs for several days after their sexual activities.

Pain is not the only humiliation and degradation which masochists ask to suffer. They pay to be bullied, sometimes bullied into the most foul activities (which they find every bit as disgusting as the normal person). Masochists dress in clothes which make them look vulnerable and absurd. They may ask to be led around in leg irons or with a collar around their neck. Others seek to dress as schoolchildren and pay some ferocious woman to be the schoolmistress. Many prostitutes make a speciality of catering for masochists.

As the distinguished psychiatrist Dr Anthony Storr has explained in his book *Sexual Deviation* (Penguin, 1964), masochism in a lesser degree can be seen in many everyday aspects of life. He suggests, for instance, that the woman who goads her man until he finally strikes back, whether verbally or physically, may be masochistic. The same observation has been made before, when it has also been proposed that this accounts for the perverse pleasure a minority of women experience in being abused. These women may have also learnt that after the man has given way to his temper, which they have enjoyed, they are then able to revel in the abject contrition subsequently displayed by their partners. The seeds of later heterosexual masochism are thought to date from an early upbringing by women and men who were overly demanding, dominating and, on some occasions, physically violent to their children, even if they did wrap up their behaviour as 'just chastisement'.

Sexual Sadism

Sadism is the other aspect of sado-masochism. Sadism is also an eponym, named after the Marquis de Sade (1740–1814), another man who wrote extensively on his own paraphilia. The Marquis de Sade served several prison sentences for his urges and was even sentenced to death after two prostitutes who took part in his orgies died from the cantharides (Spanish fly) with which he had laced their drinks. Spanish fly is a highly irritant substance and the theory was that if it was excreted in small quantities it would stimulate the external sexual organs of the woman, thereby driving her to hitherto unparalleled excesses. Spanish fly is in fact highly dangerous and toxic: there has never been any reputable evidence that it works as an aphrodisiac, while there have been numerous reports of fatalities after its use. The Marquis was later released, more as a consequence of his social position than because of any belief in his innocence. However, like most paraphiliacs, the Marquis did not learn his lesson. Some time later another woman died from blood loss after she had been subjected to his sadism, and he was reincarcerated. Finally he died in a mental hospital at the ripe old age of seventy-four, having paid for his brutal sexual tastes with a total of twenty-five years in jail.

When sadism, like masochism, exists in isolation and is not merely a symptom of some more extensive personality disorder, it is also thought to date from childhood upbringing.

British boarding schools have always been regarded as the typical breeding ground of sado-masochism, but until recently flogging in one form or another was part of the penal code in a great many institutions, military and civil. Physical chastisement is not confined to the privileged classes, whether at home or institutionalized. When working as an inner-city doctor, which I did for well over thirty years, I was constantly surprised by the amount of physical violence parents displayed towards their young children. The level of assault would have left even the old-fashioned public-school master gasping in astonishment. Little wonder, therefore, that children grow up seeing some association between love, as it was normally displayed by their mother or father, and physical pain.

Minor inflictions of pain during sexual intercourse are not considered abnormal. These practices are described in euphemistic terms as 'love bites', affectionate pats and 'love smacks'. Men or women (usually men) proudly display the scratches down their backs as indicators of the frenzy to which they can drive their partners, little realizing that it is one of the ways in which the partner derives his or her pleasure. The level of this behaviour is often determined by unspoken agreement. The point at which these practices can be described as sadistic is to some extent decided by the culture of the community. The desire to inflict any appreciable pain or to receive it, whether at one's own hands or at someone else's, seems to most people to be quite extraordinary, but listening to accounts of it is a regular part of the daily life of a doctor working in genito-urinary medicine. Initially I was dumbfounded by the wide variety of injuries which people sustained in the pursuit of sexual fulfilment. Their violence extended far beyond that of corporal punishment and involved deliberate mutilation. From a psychiatric point of view the greater the degree of violence, the more likely that the perpetrator is suffering from other mental disease as well as paraphilia. Sadism as part of the sexual drive can also be a feature of psychotic behaviour.

Transvestic Fetishism

Transvestism is the recurrent urge felt by a man to wear a woman's clothes in order to become sexually aroused. Some women prefer to wear men's clothes or female clothes styled in a male way, but they do not obtain sexual gratification from doing so. As in other paraphilias, the condition must persist for at least six months before it can be diagnosed as part of the patient's psychological make-up. A popular and accepted belief is that transvestites are essentially heterosexual and that their cross-dressing only serves to increase the excitement they feel when making love to a woman. Most of these men, however, have extensive female wardrobes and are apt to dress in these clothes when alone. In the privacy of the genito-urinary clinic I have, however, asked many transvestites what they fantasize about when cross-dressing and when masturbating by themselves and most have told me that they envisage making love to another man even though they may not do so in reality.

I once asked a celebrated drag queen, who made no secret of his bisexuality, about the standard teaching that transvestites were fundamentally heterosexual. He told me that he had never yet met a transvestite he could not seduce. This may have been an exaggeration, even a boast, but it certainly shows that it is possible not to be dogmatic about such intimate aspects of life and it is probable that even if most transvestites, as they would be appraised by the general public, are heterosexual, a greater proportion than is believed are bisexual. Some authorities insist that transvestism should only be diagnosed as a paraphilia when the person is heterosexual and that in other cases some other term should be used to describe their sexual behaviour.

Cross-dressing is frequently a secret habit, unknown to anyone other than the transvestite and their sexual partner or partners. This characteristic has been lampooned in the media by the exploitation of the caricature of the pinstriped, bowler-hatted, club-tied traditional man who underneath his Jermyn Street shirt is wearing a bra and knickers. Cross-dressing is a comparatively common feature of early childhood and it seems very likely that the origins of transvestite behaviour lie there.

One possibility is that a son was a disappointment for parents who were hoping for a daughter. This thwarted desire is sometimes not only betrayed by a mother's tendency to dress the child in feminine clothes or colours, but even by the choice of name. The mother is frequently the dominant parent, and more emotionally demanding than the father; and if there are daughters, the household is predominantly feminine. Transvestite behaviour is only one of the results of this background. Within the last year or two, a detailed study of the outcome of cross-dressing by small boys under the age of five showed that a very high proportion, in this series a majority, were homosexual in later life. Whether their interest in feminine clothes was an early sign of latent homosexuality or whether the availability of the clothes, the background and emotional temperature of the household determined their later sexual proclivity must be uncertain.

Voyeurism

Voyeurism is the paraphilia in which those who take part in it derive intense sexual satisfaction from watching the object of their desire, usually a stranger, while they are, for instance, undressing, undressed, going to the lavatory, or making love. The classic voyeur derives sexual excitement from watching only, and therefore does not assault or expect to have any physical contact, other than in their fantasies, with their unsuspecting quarry. Unfortunately, a small minority of voyeurs may have other psychiatric diseases or personality disorders as well, and they will occasionally attempt to realize their fantasies and attack the person they have been watching. Reading accounts of criminal proceedings in rape or sexual assault cases will often reveal that the perpetrator of the crime started his aberrant behaviour as a voyeur and had been spotted peering through windows.

Like sadism, voyeurism is a question of degree. Psychiatrists maintain that since interest in the naked body has existed since Adam and Eve, everybody displays sexual curiosity to a greater or lesser extent. The general public, however, is well aware of the difference between the peeping tom who creeps around housing estates at night looking for a crack in the curtain, and the page three reader. Some essentially timid men derive the whole of their sexual gratification from being peeping toms. They may achieve orgasm just from the excitement of viewing, or they may masturbate at the same time. However satisfaction is achieved, it, by definition, leaves the sufferer feeling guilt-ridden and miserable. Voyeurism is only defined as such if the person has had these tendencies for at least six months, acquiesces in them and regrets their actions later.

Voyeurism is another paraphilia which is blamed on the early influence, even the unwitting, sexually evocative presence, of the sufferer's mother when he (voyeurs are usually men) was very small. The adult voyeur is thought to look back with longing to the days when he was a child, and was totally cared for by his beautiful and exciting mother at whom he could look but would not have been allowed to touch sexually. Voyeurs are usually sexually inadequate, and it is claimed that a considerable proportion are impotent when with women, or suffer from premature ejaculation.

Treatment is difficult. Part of the pleasure of voyeurism is its secretiveness; furthermore its practitioners are usually introverted and shy. These two factors prevent them from disclosing any anxiety they may feel about their voyeurism to their doctor, and their shadowy life often saves them from being apprehended by the law. Although guilt-ridden after indulging in their fantasy, voyeurs rarely seek help unless ordered to do so by a court. Voyeurism is in many cases the only way in which they can obtain sexual satisfaction so they are reluctant to seek treatment in case it removes the only sexual pleasure they have. They may be aware that psychiatrists are unable to guarantee that they will be able to boost the patient's self-esteem to the point where they can have a normal relationship with a woman.

Paraphilias not otherwise specified

The approved list of psychiatric conditions in *DSM-IV* describes a further group of paraphilias as 'paraphilias not otherwise specified'. At the time of drawing up the list, these were considered of only limited numerical importance. One of these paraphilias, telephone scatologia, the sexual gratification that some men derive from making obscene or frightening telephone calls to women, is very much more common than previously thought and its true seriousness is now understood. Laws and penalties have been introduced which reflect the extent of the anxiety and fear, quite apart from the nuisance, which this use of the telephone engenders. The telephone authorities have established various high-tech devices which enable the police more readily to arrest and charge perpetrators of obscene calls, and the courts now frequently send them to jail. Just as porn films may satisfy limited voyeuristic tendencies, so may the telephone chatlines which are now available. These provide an intimate conversation with an anonymous partner of your choice, but the law forbids the discussion to be obscene.

Necrophilia, making love to the dead, is also classified as an otherwise non-specified paraphilia. Although cases of this type achieve great notoriety when they are uncovered, this paraphilia is very rare.

Bestiality is defined as the use of an animal as either the preferred or the exclusive object of sexual desire. The concept of this form of sexual activity seems so bizarre that it is assumed to be very rare, but there are reports that sexual relations of one sort or another with animals are not as uncommon as is usually supposed. The traditional belief is that these paraphiliacs are usually mentally retarded, perhaps rural workers with access to animals who live in lonely isolation on remote farms. Some may conform to this stereotype, but whatever their background they do tend to be lonely people who find it more difficult than most to make normal sexual relationships.

Some instances of bestiality seem to be motivated by an aggressive and bizarre sexual drive, often in people who are, if not mentally retarded, suffering from some other psychiatric disease. In others this behaviour seems to be an outlet for misplaced and aberrant affection and the animal is acting as a human substitute. The choice of animal can sometimes be related to pets of childhood. The act of bestiality has been recorded as a symptom in both depressed and psychotic patients, who have found love and acceptance from a treasured pet and allowed the relationship to go too far. Bestiality (although zoophilia is now the preferred term) can affect either men or women.

In one case of mine a woman, although she would have been horrified to be described as a paraphiliac, had trained her horse to lick her nipples and breasts. Since this patient also had boy-friends, whom she loved as deeply as her horse, she would not have been defined as suffering from bestiality. Unfortunately, the horse did not understand the limits to which it was expected to go in displaying affection and one day took a large bite at her bosom. The X-rays (mammograms) of the resulting damage are still frequently used as a lecture exhibit by one of Britain's greatest experts on mammography. They are always introduced by the assertion, 'few of you will be able to guess the cause of this woman's X-ray findings'.

In another case, a severely depressed woman was so besotted by her horse that the psychiatrists believed that she was deeply in love with it, just as much as if it were a human and that there was a sexual component to this love. She was admitted to a hospital in Scotland, but pined so badly for the horse that it appeared that her depression would never lift. Eventually her psychiatrist had to capitulate and the horse was sent for and stabled near the hospital. I suggested that this was only going to cure part of her problem, but he rightly replied that her depression was life-threatening, and that the need to lessen her excessive love of the horse was less urgent. When the patient cheered up her reliance upon the horse became less.

A few months working in a genito-urinary medical clinic teaches the most callow doctor that the human sexual response and need is, if not infinite, extremely varied. To most people, two of the less comprehensible paraphilias are urophilia and copro-philia. Urophilia is the achievement of sexual pleasure through an interest in urination. Likewise in coprophilia defecation is a similar paraphilia. In klismaphilia, sexual excitement is aroused by having enemas.

In the past, when the law took a greater interest in what happened behind closed doors, cases of paraphilia were more frequently heard in court. It was a very unwise doctor who promised that treatment would 'help' and a very naïve bench of magistrates who ever believed that what was needed was 'medical treatment'. Usually patients show very little desire to change their habits, they may not understand why they have these atypical desires, which most people cannot comprehend, including their doctors, but to them they seem perfectly acceptable.

As in any personality disorder if there is no desire to change, it is unlikely that psychotherapy will help. Some younger people with paraphilia may, as they grow older, find pleasure in a more orthodox sex life. Psychiatrists have studied paraphilias and tried to relate them to other personality disorders. Some obviously have a sadistic component and these may be part of an antisocial personality disorder. Others, particularly in those who experience many different forms of paraphilia, may be a symptom of a borderline personality, of which bizarre sexual practices can be a feature.

In some paraphilias there is an element of compulsive behaviour; very occasionally this may be helped by treatment with SSRIs, which are particularly useful in this condition. Likewise, if the patient's paraphilia becomes a problem when it is made worse by the exacerbation of some other condition, treatment of that condition may help.

10

Drugs

Jack Straw, as Home Secretary, experienced every parent's night-mare when the telephone rang and he learned that his son was to be exposed as a drug dealer by a Sunday paper. The way in which the Straw family dealt with the crisis won plaudits from all other parents but the incident still has the power to make them shudder. Lying in bed awake at three o'clock in the morning, worrying lest their son or daughter should become involved in the heroin, cocaine or some other illicit drug scene, anxious parents can now think: if this could happen to the Home Secre-tary's son, why not to mine?

There is nothing new about drug taking and it has always attracted people from a variety of backgrounds, but in the main it used once to be only the occasional Eastern trader, merchant seaman or literary aesthete who took more exotic substances. The milieu frequented by Jack Straw's son was very different from the erudite setting of such famous earlier drug takers as Thomas De Quincey and Samuel Taylor Coleridge.

Thomas De Quincey only became famous after the publication of his *Confessions of an English Opium Eater* in 1821, although he started taking opium while an undergraduate at Worcester Col-lege, Oxford, where he went in 1803. However, recondite as these writers' interests may have been, it didn't stop them coming to grief as a result of their addiction, which, in Coleridge's case, was probably instigated and encouraged by medical practices then current.

In the 1930s drugs were back amongst the intellectuals, but there wasn't much of it around in Brixton or Hackney. Later, Aldous Huxley wrote two seminal books, *The Doors of Perception*

(1954) and *Heaven and Hell* (1956), which presented drug taking in a romantic light as a rite solemnized by the Aztec Indians as a means of attaining a spiritual experience. A decade or two later Huxley's opinion was proselytized by the pop music movement, and was invoked to endorse the use of such drugs as LSD. Drug taking had been through an unsmart phase in the early fifties and sixties. Most drug users were poorly educated drop-outs, and although there were occasional more sophisticated heavy drug users, they tended to be wayward sons and daughters of the rich and famous, who had perhaps found comparison with their parents too hard to bear. By the late 1960s, drug dependence had become unfashionable, rather passé and downmarket, only later to be revived, so that now it is becoming a greater social problem than ever before in the country's history.

In Norwich there is a former dispensary practice, originally funded by the city to care for those too poor in pre-NHS days to join a medical insurance club. In 1966 I took over this practice, by now an integrated part of the NHS, with a full complement of standard patients. Historically, however, it was still my role to look after the dispossessed, the homeless, the destitute, and a posse of drug users who at the time were not looked after by the NHS psychiatric services. While I was in the practice drug use became much more widespread and began to rise in the social scale. The down-and-out psychiatrically disturbed patient was rapidly being joined by middle-class drug takers, many of them the victims of dysfunctional homes. This was the period when the old established order with its traditional family unit was crumbling.

Once again, in the 1980s and 1990s, drug taking became front-page news. No longer confined to inner cities, and subcultures, it has become widespread. Little wonder that parents have read, and been told by their younger friends or their own children, that these drugs are now readily available and that they are taken by otherwise well-orientated people. They will certainly not be reassured by their children's and youthful acquaintances' confidence that the younger generation do not necessarily become addicted, but use drugs from time to time with no greater consequence than would follow from a hard weekend's drinking.

Who is right? The local drug enforcement agencies, the Church, the doctors and the social workers, or the people who use them themselves? The answer lies between the two. Just as heavy social drinkers run a risk of becoming alcohol-dependent, so will drug takers be in considerable hazard of becoming drug-dependent. Not all drug takers will become addicted, but neither do all heavy social drinkers lapse into alcoholism; yet the risk is there, and it would be a very strange parent who did not worry about it. One of the problems is that those very drug users who are most likely to gain maximum relief from occasional use are also those who are most likely to become dependent.

The breezy and unassailable confidence of the younger generation that they are invulnerable and will never become addicted betrays some naivety but it is music to the ears of the current drug dealers. They cut the cost of heroin, or even initially give it away; they have cynically improved its quality; they sell it under bland names which conceal its real nature and market it in 'user-friendly' packaging, so that it can be smoked like a cigarette. In some areas it is now as cheap to become high on heroin as it is to be stoned on cannabis. The objective of the pushers is to form a large pool of recreational users. They of course remain callously indifferent to the fact that some of their customers will inevitably later have problems of addiction.

The dramatic after-effects of taking drugs – whether sudden death from Ecstasy, stroke or heart attack from cocaine, or HIV infection, hepatitis B and liver failure from heroin injected with contaminated needles – are the rarities which make the headline story. These stories would be sensational enough just because they so often involve young people, who have collapsed just because of their inexperience – they have perhaps not realized the dangers of Ecstasy. On other occasions the person who has been 'found out' or has come clean, as in a recent case of a presenter on a children's television programme, is a media figure, in which case the newspapers and television give even more publicity to the drama. These disasters obscure the greater danger, and the one which should be stressed more in anti-drugs campaigns: the slow erosion of intellect, personality, mood, friendships, family life and wealth which accrues to those who may only be habitual drug users and not addicts.

There is also the seldom-expressed observation that people with some co-existent psychological defect, which has perhaps been kept in check or may have gone unrecognized since youth, will have their susceptibility exposed by drug taking. Regular drug taking does compound many of the psychological and personality problems from which those who take drugs already suffer. A widespread survey in the United States shows that all psychiatric disorders are found more frequently in those who misuse drugs, including cannabis. These drug users are also more likely to have an antisocial personality disorder, to be depressed, anxious and/or suffer from mania or hypomania. These troubles may either precede, or follow, drug use – that is to say, it may be a symptom of some other problem, or it may actually cause it.

In some cases of personality disorder, or even psychiatric disease, the drug taking may act as a crutch, which enables a person to walk confidently through life, but as time goes on the crutch has to become stronger and stronger. Users develop tolerance. In other cases, the drug precipitates an acute psychotic breakdown. In the 1970s this phenomenon was frequently denied by drug users, social worker and some doctors, despite the clinical observations of those who were looking after drug takers. It is now a well-accepted danger, and in those families where there is a history of psychiatric problems, the question as to whether to take recreational drugs including cannabis is not a matter of philosophy or morality, but entirely of medical practicability.

Several of Harry's family had had schizophrenia or schizotypal personality disorders; he was a very bright boy, who won scholarships throughout his early academic career. Apparently happy and well-orientated, he opted to go to a Canadian university, where he did no more than experiment with drugs – cannabis and acid. After one session, Harry had an acute

"IF THEY DO CHANGE MY PERSONALITY
HOW MANY SHOULD I TAKE TO CHANGE
IT BACK AGAIN?"

psychotic breakdown, a total loss of the power of rational
thought, so that his days were ripped apart by delusions and
hallucinations. Despite the best treatment, he didn't recover and
was sent back to England, where he continued to deteriorate. For
many months he occupied his days by dressing in a breastplate,
holding a sword aloft, and walking round and round his sitting
room, like a tiger pacing a cage. After many years he made a
partial recovery, but he never regained his academic ability, and
is now only able to do unskilled jobs around the family farm.

Harry's is not an isolated case. Among other examples I have
come across was Peter, the inhibited and quiet son of a local

parson, who had never taken drugs. He went out to celebrate the passing of an examination with a group of friends, smoked large quantities of cannabis, Lebanese 'Black', had an acute paranoid psychotic breakdown, and when I last saw him was still, many months later, incapable of work.

Peter and Harry are comparative rarities in everyday life, but, in common with many doctors, I can think of many other cases like them. A real hazard of soft drug taking is that the personality changes it wreaks are insidious and subtle, while the social advantages to those who lack confidence are obvious and immediate. Most people are short-termist: they want to be an immediate social and sexual success, they see the pathway to this being lit by sharing a joint with their contemporaries or, increasingly often, by sharing a 'line' in the loos. Most young drug takers fortunately have a family history and a genetic make-up which will not lead to sudden breakdown – and any pitfalls which will have to be circumvented in years to come are problems for another day.

What parents want to know is whether their child is likely to become a drug misuser. Doctors have pondered as to the characteristics of those who are likely to become very rapidly physically and psychologically dependent and haven't produced firm answers. In addiction, as opposed to psychological dependence, the desire to take the drug is so overpowering, because of the body's adaptation to its use, that if the drug is withheld the person suffers withdrawal symptoms. The various characteristics of drug addiction and physical dependence on drugs are now accepted. Those who are addicted show some or all the following signs and symptoms, listed in the *DSM*:

A psychological compulsion to take the substance

Loss of control over the amount taken, and the times when taken

Physiological withdrawal state – that is to say, the person suffers certain well-recognized symptoms if deprived of the drug

    Evidence of increasing tolerance to the drug so that larger and
      larger doses are needed to achieve the same effect

Progressive neglect of alternative pleasures or interests as a
    result of substance abuse and persisting with drug
    taking, despite evidence that it is doing harm, whether
    psychological or physical. This is very similar to the plight
    of the alcoholic who becomes obsessed by all matters relating
    to alcohol and, above all, where his next drink is coming
    from. To an even greater extent people who have become
    drug-dependent plot and plan how they are going to score
    next, how they will obtain the money to pay for it, and to
    achieve this limited end are prepared to sacrifice their whole
    day. As time goes on, fewer different drugs are taken. Some
    doctors claim that although eventually there may be
    increasing dependence on one particular drug, this does not
    stop the user taking other substances, including alcohol, to
    enhance it.

Apart from those who become physically and psychologically addicted, there are many others who become 'habituated' to drug taking and emotionally, if not physically, dependent on drugs. Drug taking becomes an essential feature of their routine, without it they feel insecure and lost, even if they only need this crutch once or twice a week, or even less.

    Meg was kind, pretty, clever, she had a university degree, was employed as a civil servant and ran her local tenants' association. However, she had a secret. Meg admitted on one occasion that whenever she went to a party she took 'E' (Ecstasy). When asked why, she was totally honest. She felt that she was too shy and boring, but with E she could scintillate. The confidence the drug gave her not only enabled her to enjoy an evening but to be confident enough to be attractive to men. In short, she felt she had become 'interesting'. There are many like Meg whose use of a drug is understandable – but whose wisdom is questionable. How can it be other than dangerous, given that the supplier is likely to be as untrustworthy as the quality of the drugs being peddled? Furthermore, the individual response to drugs can vary enormously, and in the same person, from time to time, depending on the circumstances.

Habitual drug users range from clubbers taking their E on a Saturday night to the party-goer who regularly smokes cannabis, through to the rich and successful who may use cocaine, or even heroin after a dinner party. Drug taking, particularly heroin use, has become an epidemic and, despite widespread denunciation, has now a controversial symbiotic relationship to the fashion industry, each feeding off the other, with a destructive effect on society.

Mikhail was a refugee from the former Yugoslavia, where he lived in a fishing village and was quiet and orthodox. At a party he met a model agent who immediately signed him up. There was a demand for tall, gaunt young men with bony pale faces, hollow eyes and long dark hair. So successful was Mikhail that he had an offer to work abroad. Mikhail asked his agent why he had been chosen and why he was doing so well. The agent replied frankly, 'You look like a heroin addict – this is what the fashion industry is after.'

The unexpected and puzzling feature of the drug-taking scene is why so few people who take drugs, comparatively speaking, do become addicted, rather than why many are able to take drugs relatively often without becoming dependent on them. Drug taking is no longer regional nor confined to any one class, or age group, nor is the use of any particular drug restricted to any one social group. Anyone's child may become a drug user and their background will not determine the nature of the drug.

It is interesting that it is comparatively easier to induce addiction in animals, who have little control over their responses, than in humans, who have a more highly developed central nervous system and greater control over their reactions. The contrast between the effect of drugs on humans and animals illustrates that the ability to discipline natural responses is innate in most human beings and can be fostered. Whereas animals do not have the capacity to recognize the dangers which drugs offer, a human

278

reaction has to overcome another danger – that of peer pressure. The ritual and paraphernalia attached to drug taking is part of the pleasure of being accepted into a peer group, in some cases the essential part. The drug ritual, sharing a joint or even a needle, is an easy way to make immediate social contact, so easy that any friendships made in this way are also of course likely to dissolve equally quickly, with or without acrimony.

There is evidence that taking drugs during adolescence is particularly likely to lead to dependence. The adolescent is still in his or her formative years, and their ability to cope with difficult social situations is not yet fully developed. They may lack confidence in their own opinions and lifestyle and are therefore more likely to be subject to peer pressure. It has been suggested, although the scientific evidence is scant, that there is even a neuro-psychiatric difference and that the neural pathways in younger people are poorly formed, which enables them to experience the 'pleasurable' sensation, the 'rush', more rapidly. Another factor in determining the response to any given dose of the drug is the expectation of what it might achieve. Those who expect to get a high after taking a drug are likely to do so, even if the dose has, unknowingly, been cut. Likewise it seems possible that a disappointing experience is as much determined by the state of mind of the individual before they take the drug as it is by any lack of quality of the drug.

The 'bad trip', which can occur after taking acid (LSD), is usually a reflection of the user's psyche or even mood before taking the drug, rather than any difference in the composition of the acid. Acute psychotic breakdowns in vulnerable people are very much more common after taking acid than after taking other drugs, in particular, cannabis. With cannabis the effect may be dose related and it is more likely, but not inevitable, for there to be a gradual onset of the symptoms.

William was the easygoing, likeable son of a successful family. He was the traditional gentle giant, who had done well at school. Once he left school, however, he was an academic under-achiever, too sensitive and introverted to brave the emotional minefield of university. A few years after school he was introduced into the drug-taking world by a great friend. He started by smoking cannabis, later took acid, Ecstasy and, whenever he could afford it from his salary, cocaine. For the next eight years he drifted through life, seemingly quietly content, but his only highs were as the result of drug taking, when his mood was described as over-excited and too tactile. His personality steadily deteriorated and he started to show features of paranoia, and in consequence aggression. The paranoia became extreme – he was convinced that there were hostile elements in society out to get him. Finally he sought escape from them by committing suicide. After his death it became apparent through letters he had written, but never posted, that he had had delusions of demons for at least two years.

Parents frequently ask their doctor, and each other, how to tell whether their child is using drugs. The Health Education Authority provides some excellent booklets giving the facts and figures on commonly available drugs. The booklets are very readable, detailed without being heavy, and are not judgemental. Some have obviously been written with the primary objective of imparting information to young drug users without alienating them. Another booklet deals with the parental question, 'Is my child on drugs?'

It is not easy to spot drug taking or substance abuse. Many of the early symptoms of drug taking – moodiness, sullenness, irritability, and loss of appetite – are standard features of late adolescent life. The Health Education Authority warns parents to be on the look-out for a sudden loss of interest in previously enjoyed hobbies and sports. Academic work may wane and there may be an unexplained change in friends. Although these are features of early drug taking, so are they very often the features of growing up, and a greater interest in the opposite sex, even if as yet unrequited, is only to be expected. Unusual sleepiness, loss of money or household possessions, unexpected smells or evidence of drug-taking paraphernalia, stained clothes or marks on the son or daughter's body are much stronger evidence, but even then it is as well not to jump to conclusions.

Substance abuse still tends to be an inner-city problem in deprived areas. Men are much more likely to sniff glue, butane gas and other solvents than are women. The choice of household object which can be sniffed is legion and includes such things as hairsprays, air fresheners, gas and a host of glues, particularly those used in model making. Domestic cleaning fluids and industrial degreasers are also used. One rather frightening figure is that more young people die of solvents than from heroin.

Inner-city youth may be the predictable solvent-sniffers, but there is another, different group – doctors. Many have, over the years, fallen prey to the temptation to sniff chloroform, ether and other anaesthetics, which have a relaxant effect like a strong drink. Usually this wears off quite quickly but the person can be left feeling sick and drowsy. Just as solvents have a rapid action, so may they cause death rapidly, sometimes almost instantaneously.

The Straw family could have been an illustration in the Health Authority's booklet of how to behave when you suspect or discover that your child is using drugs. They maintained their support for their son and openly expressed their love and concern for him even as they accompanied him to the police station. They were not too proud to seek advice and to persuade their son to do likewise.

As in any branch of medicine, the best treatment is preventive. Children crave their parents' interest and love, provided that the love is not controlling. Most modern parents work long hours, and the national and domestic economy demands that the majority of mothers have to go out to work as well. This not only deprives children of their company but can dilute the amount of attention which can be given to them when they meet up in the evenings. The travails of the day have not only left the workers physically tired but emotionally exhausted, with few reserves to enable them to appear ever-listening to the children.

In my days of looking after drug users I was struck by how in some families a hectic life with scant time at home with the children seemed to cause little damage, whereas in what appeared at first sight to be a very similar household, there was mayhem amongst the children. In time I realized that the difference was that in the better adjusted family, when the parents had to be absent, they always made it quite plain to the children that they would far rather be with them than busying themselves with office affairs. Interestingly, the Health Education Authority makes the same point: 'Show, and say, you care. Children need to feel valued and cared for even when they have done something that they know you will disapprove of.'

The clue may well be to hit that fine line between being too liberal and too authoritarian. Most adolescents are proud, are alienated by bullying and are not impressed by preaching and lecturing. They will listen with interest (or perhaps sometimes boredom) to your shock-horror stories but won't feel that they apply to them. What has to be achieved is an easy relaxed relationship with the children so that they can talk about drugs at the same mealtimes as they discuss, say, football or music, and with no more embarrassment.

If the worst fears are realized and a child is taking drugs, the best course is to persuade them to go to a local drug advice service. At most of these the advisers will be splendidly reassuring and will provide sound advice, delivered in a detached, non-alienating way. If the child really is in big trouble, they will institute the necessary assessment and care.

It requires determination and a great deal of objectivity to give up drugs whilst feeling low and battered from their side-effects, and with former friends and lifestyle lost. A drug user who has become clean may relapse if he or she has exposure to drug-taking paraphernalia or meets up with friends from the drug-taking days. It takes strong character in someone who has renounced drug taking to remain in the same environment and continue to forgo drugs. Ideally, those who have stopped taking drugs should change their group of friends, even if it means moving to a different place, or at least a different part of the same city. The price of loneliness, for a short while, is a small one to pay to be freed of the compulsion to take drugs.

Not all young people start on drugs to boost a low self-image and lack of confidence. Boredom can be a potent cause. When seeking new friends and a new environment, this should be borne in mind. I once saw two cousins, both drug users, who were of the same age and had grown up almost as brothers, attending the same schools from the age of seven. Both had good brains, but little application, and both were bored. One cousin accepted the advice to seek adventure and challenges which would broaden his character and, at the same time, would replace the thrills of scoring and the comradeship of the drug takers with comparable but constructive excitement. He found a job in a war-torn, bandit-ridden country and lost his drug habit. His cousin failed to make the break, moved from one drug-taking community to another, until finally he vanished without trace, having been last heard of in a notorious Far Eastern drug ghetto.

11

Children's Disorders

Attention Deficit Hyperactive Disorder

When in practice in Norwich I always dreaded a call to visit Mrs Williamson. It was, however, one better than having Mrs Williamson and her son, Tim, visit the surgery. Tim suffered from what was then called hyperkinesis, and is now known as attention deficit disorder or attention deficit hyperactive disorder (ADHD). Tim was always 'on the go'; he would not sit still, and rushed around the surgery waiting room, annoying the other patients, tearing down the notices and fiddling with the windows. Once in the consulting room he would play with the equipment, open the drawers and scatter the papers on the floor.

Each home visit was a revelation as to the essential goodness of people and the capacity some parents have for patience and forbearance. In his own environment, Tim jumped from chair to chair, sofa to table, hung from the window and door frames, knocked over the vase of flowers, spilling all the water, and constantly interrupted the conversation. The tolerance displayed by Tim's school was as amazing as Mr and Mrs Williamson's kindliness. The way in which the teacher managed to look after, and teach, the rest of the class with Tim among them, never failed to astonish me. Tim was said to be of slightly below average intelligence, but was certainly not seriously retarded. His failure to learn could be attributed almost entirely to his impulsiveness, his hyperactivity and above all his inattention.

Forty years ago, when I started in medicine, the disorder was universally known as hyperkinesis (which only means over-activity), thereafter hyperkinetic syndrome, hyperkinetic reaction or hyperkinetic brain disorder. It then became ADD – attention deficit disorder – in an effort to persuade doctors and educational psychologists that the essential feature of the disease was an inability to concentrate on a particular task for any length of time, rather than that of hyperactivity. The syndrome has recently been renamed attention deficit hyperactive disorder (ADHD). This, while acknowledging the hyperactivity, still gives greater prominence to the attention deficiency, which is considered the most important feature of the condition. Indeed, attention deficit disorder may exist without any hyperactivity at all. The attention deficit often persists into adult life even when the over-activity and restlessness have disappeared.

'When I was a child, I spake as a child, I understood as a child, I thought as a child: but when I became a man, I put aside childish things' (I Corinthians 13:1). This biblical observation applies as much to a child with ADHD, and very probably learning difficulties, as it does to the well-orientated, quiet scholar. With maturity the childish manifestations of the disorder wane – the adult who has been troubled with ADHD in their early years does not leap from bar stool to bar stool, once old enough to visit the pub. They may remain restless and agitated, but even that is less of a problem than their inability to concentrate for any length of time on a constructive course of action.

Impulsiveness and inattention are integral aspects of ADHD. Impulsiveness is usually obvious. Children with ADHD are those who act without thinking and are therefore constantly causing damage to property and to themselves; they are the children who get stuck at the top of the tree, fall down the cliffs or into a swimming pool; they are the children who break their grandmother's prize Ming jar and then pull down her curtains. They need constant supervision and don't fit easily into a team. Not for them the long, patient wait in the pavilion before they can go out to bat, or the suspense until it is their turn to tell the class about their weekend activities.

Children with an attention deficit are equally hard to entertain and to educate. Their attention for any particular task is short-

" HE IS JUST A LITTLE HIGHLY STRUNG"

lived; long before the point of the story has been reached they are fidgeting and squirming in their seats; the sight of a van drawing up to the school gates completely distracts their mind from the object of the lesson. Hence the need to sit these children in the most boring part of the classroom where there are not many other children whose eyes they can catch or windows they can look out of.

The current edition of *The Diagnostic and Statistical Manual of Mental Disorders-IV* now breaks up ADHD into three different types. Anomalously, although the symptom appears under the name of the disease, someone doesn't have to be hyperactive to be diagnosed as suffering from ADHD. The *DSM-IV* classification includes the adverb 'predominantly' in ADHD types 1 and 2 thereby showing that some degree of a mixed picture is the rule rather than the exception. The types are defined as: those where there is predominantly inattention; those which are predominantly hyperactive; and the combined type.

Tim characterized the combined type and was a severe case; perhaps unusually, however, he seemed to be entirely free of unpleasant characteristics. He was never unkind, never bullying, was honest and, within the limits of his impulsive chatter and attention-seeking, very polite. He said 'please' and 'thank you' even as he destroyed your possessions and habitat. He was likely to greet anyone he knew with an unaffected hug and kiss. Like many children with ADHD, he did not respond readily to treatment: neither the highly controversial and paradoxical stimulant medication – which advocates the use of Ritalin, one of the amphetamine group of drugs, in order to make the child more amenable to normal society – nor to its alternative, behavioural therapy, which introduces parents and child to a behaviour modification programme.

A few years ago, any medical conference where the treatment of ADHD was on the agenda could be guaranteed to cause uproar and discord amongst the doctors. Disagreement was not surprising as for forty years doctors had been waging war against amphetamine misuse. It thus seemed inconceivable that distinguished paediatricians should suggest that a group of stimulant drugs known to cause problems of dependence, and readily misused – amphetamines include such notorious drugs as speed and purple hearts – should be prescribed for a disturbed and vulnerable group of children. Nobody doubted that the children's problem was a very real one but its treatment divided both paediatricians and lay experts in a way achieved by few other medical problems. The controversy is still a recurrent source of newspaper comment.

The conflict over the use of amphetamines also stems in part from disagreement about the origins of the illness. Those paediatricians who think that it is the result of enzyme deficiencies, food hypersensitivity, maternal deprivation, or even fluorescent lighting in schools, hospitals and public transport, naturally think it is wrong to prescribe powerful drugs when all a patient with mild symptoms may need is a few more cuddles and a little less Coca-Cola while watching the television. Coca-Cola is frequently blamed for hyperactivity in small children, possibly as a result of its additives, and so is television, because its flickering light is considered to be a dangerous stimulant. TV, therefore, is suspected of being more damaging to the psyche than can be accounted for by the violence of the programmes on offer.

Many a parent is convinced that ADHD is only an unfortunate reaction to E-laden junk foods. If, they argued, children could be separated from crisps, Coke, sweets, bright orange fizzy drinks and weirdly coloured puddings, their over-boisterous child would be a quiet and well-behaved member of the classroom, always ready to walk in a crocodile. There is some evidence, which is rather scant, that some children do react to certain foods, but those who are food-sensitive can only account for a small section of what is a considerable problem. How child psychiatrists wish that banning sweets would give my patient Tim, and all those like him, as good a chance as his neighbour of developing normally.

Were Tim's problems the result of a distinct condition, from whatever cause, or was his behaviour merely a precursor, or early symptom, of some psychiatric problem such as – always the worry – schizophrenia? When the paediatricians in conference had emphatically expressed their views on the treatment of ADHD, they could then turn to each other, and dispute quietly about whether attention deficit hyperactive disorder can exist without evidence of other psychiatric disease or personality disorders. The argument continues as to whether hyperactivity of patients with ADHD is merely the extreme end of a spectrum of behaviour – perfectly normal children, for instance, may be timid introverts, or extravagantly wild extroverts. How many apparently over-the-top noisy members of an extrovert family have been unnecessarily labelled as suffering from ADHD?

Other doctors suggest that ADHD could be a response in a vulnerable child to an unfavourable environment – lack of attention when an infant, for instance, or, conversely, outrageous spoiling. Parents shouldn't judge themselves too harshly. ADHD like many other disorders is almost certainly multi-factorial and the home environment they provided might have been absolutely perfect, if other circumstances had been different. Even if the child had minimal attention from busy parents there is always the possibility that this was only a minor factor, and that the ADHD was the result, for example, of minimal brain damage whether from a genetic cause, birth injury or intra-uterine damage or disease. Finally, there are those who insist that, at least in some cases, ADD or ADHD is a distinct disease, the nature of which has yet to be fully explored and understood.

Unlike the debate about the difficulties of treatment, or its causes, ADHD's symptoms are readily recognized. ADHD affects boys ten times as often as girls. It is rarely formally diagnosed before the age of four, but parents will often comment after the diagnosis has been made that their child, when still a toddler, was hyperexcitable, 'a real handful', who was never able to concentrate for a moment. The extent of the problem is usually evident before children are seven, and by the time they are eight to ten years old, they have usually joined the queue in the Child Guidance Clinic. ADHD is the commonest single cause of referral to a child psychiatrist.

Affected children show a varying combination of symptoms typifying inattention, hyperactivity and impulsiveness. Like Tim, they don't listen and frequently ask the same question time and time again. They lose all their belongings; Tim frequently returned from school with his uniform incomplete and his satchel contents – ruler, rubber, pencils, crayons, the lot – scattered around the district. Children with ADHD are forgetful, easily distracted and find sustaining interest in a single subject for the entire length of a formal class an impossible objective. Their concentration is constantly wandering, and as they neither listen nor pay attention to detailed instructions, they fail to carry out any allotted task competently, not only because they are often unaware of what they are supposed to be doing, but also because they failed in the first place to take in how to achieve their objective. Not unnaturally their lives are utterly disorganized. It takes them very little time to realize that, regardless of intelligence, they will not do well in anything that requires concentration. They therefore steer clear of those tasks which would necessitate confrontation with authority, thus avoiding failure and thereby a further loss of self-esteem.

Associated with attention deficit, although by no means

invariably, is the hyperactivity, which has to be distinguished from boisterousness. A child's behaviour is defined as hyperactive when it has reached the point where the intensity of the physical activity interferes with his or her life, whether at home, school or at play. Children with an attention deficit hyperactive disorder are impulsive and impatient. They cannot wait their turn when asked in the class for an answer. The concept of holding up their hand before shouting out to the teacher is totally alien to their make-up. At home, they might start a household task designed to help their mother with huge enthusiasm, only to lose interest in it within a matter of minutes. They are forever straying into other people's space, and generally being intrusive. They are the children who are forever tugging at a visitor's or doctor's jacket, or at their parents' sleeves while they are trying to talk to the teacher. Parents are too frequently subjected to a level of wear and tear which would have tested St Luke; not surprisingly, family relationships are put under enormous strain if a husband and wife never have time to enjoy a quiet chat.

Very often the children don't appear to be unhappy, or to be perturbed by the chaos they engender, but inevitably their approach to life excites varying degrees of irritation or antipathy. Given this background, and the ensuing isolation, it is not surprising that many develop other behavioural problems, all of which can contribute to a fundamental lack of self-esteem.

Not all forms of hyperactivity are related to ADHD. Hyperactivity is associated with many cases of mental retardation, and in these children it may have been present since birth. In other cases, the child whom neighbours, and grandparents from one side of the family at least, consider seriously hyperactive may be absolutely normal and only displaying extreme extrovert behaviour which might be a family trait or a characteristic of certain races. A sad example of this, which had a long-term influence on a whole family, was illustrated by the problems which beset a patient of mine who had married a local woman while engineering in Africa. Posted back to Britain, the engineer settled with his wife – an intelligent woman but with little formal education – and their two young boys in the Cotswolds. Their children were clever, as was to be expected with such bright parents, but the teachers had never dealt with African children. The children were very active and curious but had a short attention threshold, and by Cotswolds standards were too extrovert, over-pushy, and did not understand the concept of other people's space with which English children had grown up.

The school was certain that these two children were suffering from ADHD and insisted that they saw a child psychiatrist. The parents were offended, but the more the father told the education authorities that his children's behaviour was in accord with the cultural norm of their birthplace, the more he was accused of believing in racial stereotypes and of being racist. A man who had spent many happy months living in his wife's African village, he was much distressed by being described as racist. So far as he was aware, his only offence had been to explain that, from his own experience of living in Africa, there were cultural behavioural differences between black and white children, that the level of activity and impulsiveness in children considered socially acceptable differed from country to country – as it does to a lesser extent between one family and another.

The father became increasingly depressed, was unable to work, and, despite antidepressants, it seemed that he might become suicidal if the situation couldn't be resolved. His wife, meanwhile, having initially begun her English life with high hopes and, having been so well accepted into the community, now simply sat miserably hunched in a chair. All her vitality had been undermined by the lack of understanding of her children's behaviour, which to her was no different from that of all their African friends. Finally, the engineer retired from his firm early on medical grounds and the whole family decided to return to Africa, where their children would be understood, and their intelligence treasured. There, the engineer found an undemanding job and, when last heard of, the family was very happy.

*

Not all children who suffer from ADHD have a below-average intelligence. One cause of hyperactivity which is rarely discussed is the unrecognized possession of an extremely high IQ. The intelligent child whose intellect isn't stimulated, and is therefore not developed, is liable to become bored and disruptive. The child may have a limitless curiosity, to the point of being intolerably inquisitive; they are always on the move during the day but even so may be loath to sleep at nights. They refuse to eat, won't stop talking and, as would be expected, are impulsive. In medical practice, when a parent or grandparent talks of an over-active child, it is a safe bet that the child is either very much above average intelligence or is appreciably less bright than his or her peers. Further, just as children with ADHD may be either under- or over-intellectually stimulated, so may some with a vulnerable predisposition have too little or too much physical stimulation – games, whether rough-and-tumble with Dad at home, for instance, or even some organized activities at school can increase their excitement level.

It is not unknown for a difficult but clever child with a low attention span to be misjudged, sometimes with dire consequences. Anna was a case in point. She was a bright little girl, whose sharp brain helped her to dominate the toddlers with whom she went to playschool. When her family moved away from my practice area they kept in touch. One day Anna's mother telephoned in great alarm to say that her daughter had just been designated ESN, or 'educationally sub-normal' (the term now replaced with 'learning difficulties').

It seemed that Anna's attention span at school was very short, she was forgetful and disorganized, never still, disruptive and, despite doing very badly in formal tests, never ceased to want her point of view to be the first to be heard. I remembered Anna when she had been the brightest of her group of toddlers and unless she had developed some rare regressive neurological disease, a diagnosis of mental retardation seemed most unlikely. I recommended that Anna should be sent to a private school where there is more opportunity for individual stimulation, as I was convinced that she was not only clever, but very clever. Fortunately, her parents were in a position to be able to do so. About three years later Anna won a county scholarship to a prominent girls' boarding school and from there to Oxford. The subsequent career of this formerly 'educationally sub-normal' pupil can only be described as brilliant.

There is a familial tendency to develop ADHD, but doubt has been expressed about its genetic nature, as it is more common in socially deprived areas, and environmental factors, together with possibly below-standard antenatal and natal care, could confound the statistics. It has even been suggested that the higher rates of lead in the atmosphere in crowded inner cities could contribute to the disorder. However, twin studies, including the study of twins brought up in very different surroundings, have shown that there is a true genetic factor – that the familial tendency is not entirely environmental and susceptibility to ADHD can be inherited.

The long-term future after having ADHD in childhood has been poorly mapped, but it is known that many of these children grow up to be hard-working, successful and admirable citizens with enough concentration to hold down demanding jobs. It is known, however, that inattentiveness is more likely than hyperactivity to persist into adult life, and naturally any mental retardation is unlikely to lift. These people will be more likely than their contemporaries to become regular out-patients in the psychiatric department and, regrettably, will even have an increased tendency to appear in the police courts. There has been great discussion as to whether ADHD is the forerunner of any specific personality disorder but although there is evidence that children with ADHD are more prone to have a record of antisocial behaviour later, no other personality disorder seems to be associated with ADHD. There is, however, a higher incidence of both depression and schizophrenia in adults who have had ADHD in childhood.

ADHD may sometimes be a symptom of depression and

anxiety – which could herald more serious psychiatric disease – or even be a manifestation of depression or anxiety in a young child. Attention deficit hyperactive disorder can also be the first sign of more serious mental disease in later life. When talking to parents whose children developed schizophrenia in late adolescence, not all of them had, as is usually supposed, memories of their child being the classic loner.

The standard picture of the pre-schizophrenic childhood personality is said to be that of an introspective child not mixing with the others playing in the centre of the playground, but looking on from the edge. So it is surprising how many parents of schizophrenics noted hyperactivity as being one of the most striking memories of their children's earliest years. The sister of one schizophrenic patient told me how sad it was now to look along her mother's bookshelves and read the titles of those reserved for the mother's secret, night-time reading away from the curious eyes of her family. The books on child care bought when her brother was young were on hyperactivity, but by the time he had become a late adolescent, the titles had given way to ones about coping with schizophrenia.

Ironically, hyperactivity may be an unexpected consequence of inappropriate medication for the condition, as for instance when some children, in particular those who are mentally retarded, are treated with benzodiazepines like Valium. These preparations can have a paradoxical effect on behaviour so that rather than being quieter, the child becomes out of control. Small doses of alcohol may cause similar disinhibition. The symptoms diminish altogether once the child no longer has the benzodiazepine or other tranquillizer.

One fifteen-year-old hyperactive boy of limited intelligence was becoming increasingly disruptive. He was cared for in a special residential school but the time was coming, the headmaster said, when they would no longer have the facilities to cope with his behaviour. The zenith of his unruly conduct was reached during his school's expedition to a local cathedral city where the staff were unwise enough to take the party into an antiquarian bookshop. This part of the afternoon, presumably arranged so that the teacher could have a good browse, was a catastrophe. The hyperactive boy had a splendid time rummaging through valuable books, scattering them around the shop, peering into every nook and cranny and finally being irritable when restrained. Close questioning revealed that in an effort to control his agitation and hyperactivity he was being given huge doses of Valium (diazepam). When he was taken off his tranquillizers and given a mild antidepressant, his behaviour reverted to its previous level of tolerable over-activity.

Temporary hyperactivity in a child, whatever the intellectual state, may be stimulated by difficulties in any relationship with those in authority, whether parents or teachers. Hyperactivity in these cases is usually no more than evidence of unhappiness. For a child to be happy he or she should be in secure surroundings, confident of the love and care of those in charge. If the child becomes aware, or believes, that he or she is regarded by those people who are looking after him or her as nothing more than a nuisance, it is a perfectly rational response to indulge in attention-seeking.

There has been much discussion over the influence of diet in the aetiology of ADHD. Earlier in the chapter, claims that certain foodstuffs are the culprits were touched on. To pinpoint these, particular groups of foods have to be excluded from the child's diet. However, the clinical symptoms noted by parents and related to the omission of certain foods have been difficult to reproduce in controlled trials. Such foods as sugar, gluten (in wheat and most other cereals but not in maize), fizzy drinks, citrus fruits and dairy produce have all been excluded with, parents claim, an improvement in their child's mental health. Even if firm evidence of food allergies as a common cause of ADHD is scant, most doctors are prepared to accept that hyperactivity is one of the symptoms of food intolerance and that it may occur without any classic physical symptoms of sensitivity such as migraine or joint pain.

Cynics who reject what they consider only anecdotal evidence claim that the chief advantage of manipulating the child's diet is that it encourages the parent to take a close interest in the child, who responds to this by behaving better. Many people have an idealized view of parenthood; few parents are good with every age group and there are times in a child's life when, in retrospect, both parent and child would admit that they had little in common. However, a discussion about the child's diet creates an intimate link, and a parent likes to feel useful, while the child likes the attention.

The first line of treatment of attention deficit hyperactivity disorder is behavioural therapy. Only when this has failed should there be recourse to drug therapy. In the long term, doctors who do not approve of drug therapy advocate introducing measures to prevent hyperactivity and attention deficit. These are mainly concerned with better antenatal care, improved delivery and a more relaxed, hands-on and cuddly approach to the baby. Too often this is a case of locking the stable door after the horse has bolted, and a discussion about what should have been done is little help to the parents of a child who never sits still and seems to need the minimum of sleep.

When a child first develops symptoms of attention deficit, with or without hyperactivity, much can be done to help by providing parents with a schedule aimed at modifying their child's behaviour. A carrot-and-stick approach is helpful. Like all children, the ADHD child must learn to be responsible for his or her actions: one who does well is rewarded for socially acceptable behaviour with treats and privileges, but if the child has been quite impossible, the parents shouldn't show anger but should withhold treats and withdraw those hard-earned privileges. The ADHD sufferer begins to learn that there are benefits to being better behaved. This occasionally helps and increases the child's accountability for its own behaviour.

At school, the smaller the class and fewer the distractions, the better such children flourish and the more they concentrate. The best of all is a one-to-one teaching system, coupled with playtime in a group. When the class cannot be reduced below a certain size, the ADHD child should be at the front of the schoolroom and away from the window.

If this behaviour therapy fails, and a child over the age of six and under ten is obviously out of hand and suffering – having through its behaviour alienated parents, teachers and playmates – most doctors would recommend giving the amphetamine Ritalin (methylphenidate) a trial. As remarked earlier in the chapter, the use of stimulant medication would seem paradoxical, just as it is paradoxical that use of sedatives such as Valium sometimes makes the situation worse, whereas antidepressants can improve the condition.

Those who recommend amphetamine treatment are keen to explain how the stimulants calm the hyperactivity, reduce impulsiveness and improve the concentration and thereby the attention span of the child. They are also keen to explain that in children amphetamines may have fewer serious side-effects than the old style tricyclic antidepressants, which would only have helped if the hyperactivity was concealing depression.

A few years ago, people were shocked to learn that in some parts of America between 3 and 5 per cent of primary school children were having drug treatment with stimulants for ADHD. The proportion is very much higher today. Ritalin is the usual choice, but if it is not effective it is sometimes considered worth while using some other amphetamine; many cases, however, will not respond to any amphetamine. As described, the prescription of any amphetamine, milder relatives of speed, the drug which causes so much mayhem in clubs, to treat a clubber's younger brother or sister who is suffering from ADHD, has not unnaturally caused considerable dismay, and an occasional outcry in the popular press. In addition, amphetamines may minimally stunt growth in children and can induce epilepsy in vulnerable patients. However unpalatable though, it is an inescapable fact that the amphetamine group of drugs, if drugs are to be used, are the ones which are most likely to benefit children with ADHD.

Autism

A five-year-old with an angelic countenance, but the temper of Mephistopheles, is playing by himself, slowly and continuously banging two toy buckets together. A care assistant tries to hold his attention but he neither looks nor smiles at her, he is only interested in being allowed to play with his buckets and to keep an eye on his carefully hoarded collection of shells. The little angel, who even tiptoes around like an angel, is autistic. He has had some ability to speak for about a year, although his speech is bizarre, repetitious and hard to interpret. He is one of the luckier autistic children who may benefit from education.

Until 1943 the lonely autistic child, much more often a boy than a girl, was not distinguished from other children with severe mental handicaps. In 1943 Dr Kanner drew the attention of his colleagues and the rest of the world to these strange children. There are about thirty autistic children born in every hundred thousand births; twin studies show a genetic link but it is not a strong one. They were often more beautiful and graceful than their contemporaries, but appeared to live in a world of their own. Many had seemed to be perfectly normal babies until at some time, usually at about a year, but always before two and a half years old, they started to develop strange characteristics and to regress. They rejected the loving kindness given to them by parents, and were so unresponsive that they didn't even look at them – refusing eye contact is one of the characteristic signs of autism. The autistic child often takes no more interest in a parent than it would in some stranger who happens to be visiting the house.

As in any medical problem where doctors don't know the answers, there is controversy over the cause, or causes, of autism. In some cases there is certainly a genetic origin: it is found more often in both twins when they are identical than in non-identical twins, and more than one case appears in the same family than could be accounted for by chance. The controversy becomes particularly acrimonious when other possible causes are discussed.

Forty years ago, argument raged over the likelihood of brain damage at birth being a factor; even now it is agreed that it may be secondary to brain damage, such as could be caused by meningitis or encephalitis, in infancy. In the early days psychologists blamed a cold and distant mother, a theory now disregarded – but even greater extremes of emotional deprivation are a possible factor – and some doctors believe it can be induced by any severe physical or mental trauma.

Autistic children live in a world of their own. Even if they were beginning to talk when autism set in, what speech they had is lost as the disease becomes established. They neither talk to other humans, make eye contact or return facial and other gestures – the smiles, nods or glances which make up non-verbal communication. Even if they don't become attached to the humans around them, autistic children become very attached to their physical surroundings and often to some particular object. They have a marked resistance to any change so that even moving a piece of furniture, or setting the table in some slightly different way may precipitate a rage. They like their food to be very similar – not for them the gourmet-cooking mother – and a change in the menu may provoke a crisis. Their games are repetitious, too, and the autistic toddler may sit beside an upturned toy truck and spend hours spinning the wheels. Moods can vary quickly and not always for any obvious reason. Anger, anxiety, fear or suspicion may erupt in what had hitherto been a normal day.

Looking after autistic children is never easy. Unusual behaviour, including hyperactivity, coupled with the lack of emotional response, is very discouraging to parents; the rages and, often in adolescence, seizures, increase the difficulty of caring for them. Drug treatment – at various times major tranquillizers or, conversely, amphetamine-type drugs have been advocated – has little place in the care of autism. Behaviour therapy is accepted as the treatment of choice and parents are taught to continue this in their own homes if the child is living there. The psychologist's aim is to find out what makes the child more disturbed, and to train the parents, or those who are looking after the patient, to avoid these triggering actions. Speech therapy is helpful but even with the best will in the world, the majority of autistic children need to attend special schools and many will respond better to residential care.

It is difficult to estimate the IQ of an autistic child but it can be done. An IQ of less than fifty is very discouraging and there is little hope of any form of fulfilment in life. Most of the children who develop fits in adolescence have IQs of about this level. About 50 per cent of autistic children by the time they are adult have learnt to speak well enough to carry on a reasonable conversation. About one in six autistic children has an IQ which is compatible with standard schooling and later employment. The occasional child has a high IQ and I have certainly come across one case who, although diagnosed as autistic as a child, later completed his A-levels and went on to university. However, his father told me that, although of high intelligence, his emotional detachment, his obsession with routine and his difficult personality hadn't changed. Other autistic children have had phenomenal memories, or occasionally a remarkable aptitude for art or music.

Parents take heart – many perfectly normal toddlers may show one or two of the features of autism. Not every infant who battles over the toy bus from which he or she will not be separated, or spends entire days in an endlessly repetitive game, is likely to become an autistic child.

Asperger's Disorder

In 1998, when Angela Browning was a high-flying politician, the biggest headlines she made were not from any political gambit but from deciding to curtail her career so as to have more time to look after her son Robin, who has Asperger's disorder. Her action benefited not only Robin but all the other people who are suffering from Asperger's, which is still an under-recognized condition although it is three times more common than autism (to which it is very probably related).

In the year after Dr L. Kanner described autism, Dr Hans Asperger, in 1944, wrote about and defined the disorder which now bears his name. Interestingly, Dr Asperger was quite unaware of the work of Dr Kanner, but both agreed that children who are now diagnosed as autistic or as Asperger's sufferers did not have a pre-schizophrenic condition but did have to endure 'lifelong social isolation and conspicuous eccentricity'. They have many characteristics in common, but not all, and Asperger's patients tend to be of much higher intelligence.

Asperger's syndrome, rather to the chagrin of those who have it, or care for those with it, is frequently described by the popular press as 'the mad professor's disease'. The term may be derogatory but it demonstrates that people with Asperger's often have nothing wrong with their IQ and no serious language problems. A substantial minority of doctors believe that Asperger's syndrome is comparable to high-level autism – autism associated with an average or near-average intelligence. The children (and adults) are abnormally solitary, they avoid eye contact, fail to understand facial expressions and use inappropriate ones themselves. They are insensitive to the feelings of others, are aloof and distant and, not unnaturally, fail to establish any empathy.

If their intelligence is unimpaired they may display all the characteristics of the so-called mad professor. Prickly and defensive when criticized, distant, and with a rigid behavioural pattern, they may have an inventive mind capable of highly original thought, and they have a habit of accumulating vast amounts of knowledge about limited subjects. People with Asperger's who are less bright may still have the ability to work out seemingly intricate sums in their head and make calculations which would defeat many an academic.

Robin Browning, it appears, has an uncanny ability to remember birthdays, parliamentary majorities and can translate dates into days of the weeks in a flash. However, he hasn't the temperament to keep a job and like many people with Asperger's needs a very well-routined life. Interrupting a daily regime can lead to much unhappiness, even violence. Some years ago I was involved with the care of a family in which the thirteen-year-old suffered from Asperger's disease. If he didn't have his meals to the absolute second, if his table placing was at all out of order and different from usual, there would be a dreadful and violent rage.

The first case of Asperger's I came across I can only diagnose in retrospect. It was a boy at school with me, friendless and detached, with few, if any, social skills. He languished around the bottom of the form, interested only in butterflies and moths. His knowledge of these was encyclopaedic. He managed to learn enough physics and chemistry to go with his biology so as to pass into a university, and has indeed become a 'mad professor', recognized as an eccentric, at an American university. His knowledge of butterflies is now respected worldwide.

Although the earlier idea that Asperger' disorder was related to schizophrenia, or even a schizoid personality, has been abandoned, it is thought that there may be a genetic aspect to its development, possibly linked to that which determines the likelihood of autism. Research has shown that Asperger's and autism are not found in greater numbers than would be expected in

"AND JAMES WILL CONFIRM THE ANSWER FOR US
BY USING BASE 'e' LOGARITHMIC TABLES"

families with a susceptibility to schizophrenia. The generally accepted view now tends to reject suggestions that Asperger's is the result of upbringing or unfortunate experiences.

Behavioural therapy, of the same type as is used to treat autism, is helpful in those cases of Asperger's where it is needed. The condition, as Hans Asperger said, is a lifelong one – there is no cure, as such, but if the IQ is reasonable the obsessional interests and strange abilities may be encouraged so that in some cases when the child is an adult, they can become the foundations of employment. Behavioural therapy not only helps those with Asperger's but also their families to adapt to it. A twelve-year-old boy has recently been diagnosed as having Asperger's – and this came almost as a relief to his parents who didn't know what could be wrong with him. Unfortunately, the boy is a very easy target for bullies, and even gets harried by the local children in the street, who clearly latch on to his slight oddity – the possibility of a child with Asperger's being bullied is one that parents must always be aware of.

Four Common Problems of the School Years

Four conditions in which there either is, or parents think there is, a psychological component, are bedwetting, soiling (anal incontinence), truancy and school refusal. These problems can assume disproportionate importance in a family and as they are comparatively common, deserve mention even though they are as likely to be treated by a paediatrician as a psychiatrist.

Most children are dry at night by the age of three but one in ten are still wetting their beds when they are five. If a child is bedwetting by the age of seven, an expert opinion should be obtained. The current view is that the most likely cause of enuresis, bedwetting, is that the nervous control of the child's bladder has matured more slowly than is usual. There is certainly a strong family history in many cases, and indeed it is one of the most consistent findings.

Search for an organic cause for bedwetting such as a recurrent urinary tract infection, congenital abnormalities of the urinary tract or diabetes, are usually fruitless although they must not be excluded.

The assumption that persistent bedwetting is indicative of emotional turmoil in the household is widely held but is hard to reconcile with the findings of various research projects. These have shown that there is little association between unhappiness in childhood and bedwetting up to the age of five; thereafter there is a relationship between the two but it is thought that the unhappiness is more likely to be secondary to the distress caused to the mother, and the mother's punitive response to the continuing problem.

If a child is still bedwetting by the age of seven or eight, he or she will become increasingly disturbed by it, as they feel different from their contemporaries and a failure. In one respect, through no fault of their own, they have failed to achieve one of the most simple physical goals, an inadequacy which can so easily become a talking point in the family. Already downcast, it is not surprising if their sense of self-esteem is further eroded if they are humiliated, rebuked and derided by angry, over-worked and overwrought parents who have been driven to distraction.

Various methods of training may be employed by parents and doctors, including a system of stars or rewards for dry nights, which are carefully marked on a calendar; the use of a bell, placed in the child's bed, which rings once it becomes wet so that in time the child is able to anticipate urination and bell-ringing, or finally the prescription of desmopressin which is available in a spray form, Desmospray, or in tablets, Desmotabs. Desmopressin is an analogue of vasopressin, an anti-diuretic hormone produced by the pituitary gland, which therefore restricts the secretion of urine. Desmopressin treatment is effective in 80 per cent of cases, but unfortunately the patient may relapse after it is discontinued.

Whereas bedwetting is likely to be the result of late maturation, faecal incontinence after the age of four should be regarded as abnormal. Unfortunately it tends to produce an even more unsympathetic response from contemporaries, school staff and parents, than does bedwetting and therefore the loss of self-esteem experienced by the child is all the greater. A cycle is very easily produced whereby the emotionally disturbed child dirties its pants, excites extreme displeasure and revulsion from all around him – it is more often a him than a her – and thereafter becomes even less accepted. As with enuresis or bedwetting, it is necessary to exclude any organic cause for the problem, the simplest of which may be extreme constipation, so that fluid motions flow past the obstruction.

Parents should be recommended to seek specialist advice early so that the degree of emotional disturbance may be reduced to a minimum. The initial treatment is of an entirely physical nature and advice is given as to diets, bowel training, and, if necessary, mild but regular laxatives are prescribed so that the rectum is kept empty. Many, however, will need skilled psychiatric care from a child guidance clinic.

Truancy

The distinction between school refusal and truancy is not always understood. Truants are apt to be the bad boys (or less often girls) of the class. They come from disturbed households with no great love or understanding of the advantages of learning, with a lack of care from their parents, and they do badly at school.

School refusal, on the other hand, affects anxious depressed children, boys and girls equally, who do well at school when they are actually there. The family background is often over-emotional, smothering rather than loving, and very often parents will have emotional problems, too. A distinction has to be made between the child who is having a bad time at school, perhaps being bullied by pupils or staff, and the child who is so tied to its mother's apron strings that he or she can't bear being away from home. School phobia may not necessarily be the result of a continuing problem but may possibly have stemmed from one unfortunate incident.

Help should be sought early on, to deal with either truancy or school refusal. Treatment will depend on the cause, and will certainly involve careful co-operation between the child, the school and the parents.

12

Suicide

For thousands of years, society's approach to suicide has varied. In Roman times suicide was an honourable death, preferable to being caught by an enemy, which was in itself a disgrace. Other forms of disgrace for ordinary citizens would also be assuaged by suicide. In ancient Rome, only those who were citizens were granted the privilege of suicide – slaves were not allowed to kill themselves as this was far too great a waste of labour and there was the assumption that a slave's honour was unimportant.

The Japanese approach to war and suicide is not so very dissimilar to that of ancient Rome. In Japan, death was traditionally considered unimportant when compared to honour; now that the Japanese Samurai are no longer active warriors, it is the students who fail exams, or financiers who are vanquished on the Stock Exchange floor or in the bank board room, who choose to die rather than shame their families.

The Christian Church in the Middle Ages, and later, regarded life as sacred and that therefore taking any human life, even one's own, was a mortal sin, so serious that damnation was inevitable, as shown in Dante's *Inferno*, where a particular circle of hell is reserved for suicides. Until recently the Church forbade burial of a suicide victim within consecrated ground – but an exception was made if insanity was so obvious that the sinner could not be blamed for the sin.

In the eighteenth and nineteenth centuries an interest in humanism became intellectually respectable and lessened the influence of the Church. At the same time the Romantic movement found drama in suffering and suicide. There was the

assumption that a manic-depressive temperament was usually an
integral part of an artistic personality, and honed writers' and
painters' talents. The solid Victorian citizen already regarded the
artistic community as living by different laws: a godless, immoral
and amoral lot in whom suicide was merely the extreme and final
example of their sinful and indulgent lifestyle. Suicide in the
Victorian era, and up until the Second World War, was such a
disgraceful act in normal society, where honour was not concerned, that it cast a permanent slur on the family and on the
place where it happened.

In my own childhood I remember occasional suicides among
the people who lived in the local villages and were patients of the
practice. For years as children we were hurried past the barn
where some luckless labourer, driven by poverty and the hopelessness of depression, had hanged himself from a beam. Even
now, when I visit a neighbouring house I can hear the shocked
voices of my parents as they discussed the death of the Colonel,
who lived there in great state. One day he found that his money
had disappeared. He completed a morning with his accounts,
took out his First World War revolver and shot himself so that he
fell over the desk, still covered with his ledgers. The Colonel
received a poor press; bankruptcy could be disgraceful, but so
was suicide.

On the other hand, sexual transgressions could be even more
disgraceful than suicide. King George V was amazed when a
prominent politician, and one of his friends, Lord Beauchamp,
opted to emigrate when it was discovered that he was a homosexual. The king had no time for talk of extradition and trial; the
regal opinion was that in these circumstances a gentleman
should have shot himself. Lord Beauchamp had failed to do the
'honourable' thing and conceal his terrible secret.

The Victorians thought it essential, whenever possible, to bring
a verdict that the suicide had been carried out when the 'balance
of the mind' had been disturbed. Even thirty years ago, similar
verdicts were nearly always returned. Many of these were given
by kindly coroners, aided and abetted by the medical profession,

who wanted to spare the family the disgrace of suicide and the risk of being buried in unconsecrated ground.

However, the current lack of the 'balance of the mind being disturbed' verdicts may not represent a toughening in the approach of the coroner's courts to grieving families but may reflect a changing pattern in suicide. It seems that more suicides are now being committed when the person is technically in their right mind but have found circumstances overwhelming. The weakening of the power of the Church has also undermined social taboos over suicide.

Within the last twenty years or so, with changing socio-economic conditions and loosening family bonds there is, indeed, some evidence that mental disease is becoming a less important factor than before. A retrospective diagnosis carried out in 1974, enquiring into the behaviour and background of victims, and quoted in *Psychiatry* by Dr C. Smith, Dr L. Sell and Dr P. Sudbury, showed that twenty years ago 90 per cent of people who committed suicide were reported as suffering from psychiatric disease, and something under one-third had seen a psychiatrist. In 1994, using the same techniques, it was estimated that only 50 per cent of successful suicides had been committed by people who were psychiatric cases.

Other sources are contradictory and suggest that at least 70 per cent of suicide victims have a treatable psychiatric condition. Any discrepancies may well, in part, be due to differences of definition, and opinion as to what constitutes a treatable psychiatric condition and a sound mind. How, for instance, would an anti-social personality disorder be classified? The antisocial person's neighbours would certainly have seen him as a psychiatric case, but the law and the psychiatrists might well have thought him untreatable and suffering from a personality disorder rather than a definable psychiatric disease. Under legal rules a person can suffer from a diagnosable personality disorder but still be of sound mind in the eyes of the law.

Even so, suicide is still widely, and rightly, regarded as a symptom of psychiatric disease; to attempt to justify it on rational grounds, other than for the minority who believe in euthanasia, is alien to present cultural beliefs. Part of the British Government's Health of the Nation targets, which were announced in 1992, and were readopted by the Prime Minister, Tony Blair, aim to reduce the suicide rate by 15 per cent by the year 2000 by improving psychiatric and social services.

What is the profile of the patient who is likely to commit suicide? The doctor's job is to try and sort out the one patient who will commit suicide from the nine who are merely going to discuss it. This can only be done if a rapport is established and the doctor has an understanding of the patient's thinking. Contrary to the widespread misconception that people who talk about suicide will rarely, if ever, commit it, over two-thirds of suicide victims have previously discussed their general intentions and nearly half have given details of their plans. Even so, fortunately, the number of people who even make a suicide attempt is very much smaller than those who have considered its possibility. However, once one suicide attempt has been made, another is more likely.

Having established whether patients have had any suicidal ideas, it is important to establish how well-founded these are. Every doctor has his own series of questions to evaluate the risk, if risk there is. The first question to ask is whether someone is seriously contemplating suicide or whether they only feel that they might just as well be dead. If suicide is in their mind, it is as well to ask how they intend to do it. Those in whom the risk is great have usually decided on the method and are often prepared to divulge this. If they have a plan, have they put any of it into operation – like buying the rope or hoarding the pills? One patient I asked this said, 'Yes, I have indeed made preparations.' He then led me to his car in which there was a rope on the floor behind the front seat. Once the severity of his depressed state had become apparent, he was prescribed the necessary treatment and in fact responded well to antidepressant tablets. His life had previously been one of stress and strain, but when he recovered, he decided to sell his business, fortunately in a boom time, and

" SO BUYING A DOG TO CHEER HIM UP
DIDN'T WORK TOO WELL"

settled down at an early age to a reasonably happy, semi-retired life.

Some doctors are shy about discussing suicide with a depressed patient, not so much because they do not want to plant the idea, but because they are afraid of offending the patient by thinking that they might be so irresponsible as to do so. I have been asking questions about suicidal intent regularly for forty years – no patient has ever expressed resentment or anger over them, and, although it is possible that they may have felt some transitory irritation, they never showed it.

In the journal *General Practitioner* Dr Tony Coates, a consultant psychiatrist, has described four myths about suicide:

Suicide is a rare event – not so, the number of deaths from suicide is at least equal to those killed on the roads.
Assessment of suicide risk is only for the expert – not so, any doctor can assess suicide risk, given the necessary time and support.

Suicide is caused by social factors – not so, while factors such as
   unemployment are important, an overwhelming majority of
   suicide patients are suffering from treatable psychiatric
   illnesses.
*Focusing on thoughts of suicide (by discussing it) does more harm
   than good* – not so, there is no evidence to support this.

Do patients always intend to kill themselves when they apparently attempt to? The term 'parasuicide' means deliberate self-
harm which could be construed as a suicide bid. These bids may
be intended as suicide attempts, or may simply be gestures
designed to attract attention to the patient's misery. The British
are particularly prone to parasuicide and, since 1733, suicide itself
has been known as the 'English malady'. Foreigners attribute this
to our 'gloomy' climate and what they see as an uninspiring top-
ography. Parasuicide is twice as common in women than men.

Cricket is quintessentially English but we don't always win the
Test matches. Suicide may be the English malady but, thankfully,
the number of suicide bids far outnumbers the actual successful
attempts. The usually accepted figure is that there are ten unsuccessful suicide attempts for every one which ends in a death. On
the other hand, there are many suicides, which are designated, for
one reason or another, as accidental, and in other cases an open
verdict has been returned. There are very few doctors who have
not had their doubts about car accidents in which no other vehicle
has been involved, and in which the patient who has been driving
has in the past expressed feelings of quite severe depression and
even threatened suicide.

Every year ten million people throughout the world attempt
suicide, and a number equal to the population of Edinburgh succeed. In the United Kingdom there are 4,000 suicides every year,
and experts estimate that 70 per cent are committed by patients
who are depressed. Although suicide is commonly associated
with poverty, it is not confined to the shanty towns of the Third
World or the inner cities of developed countries. In fact, those
who are most at risk of committing suicide are affluent members

of the professional classes who set themselves high standards difficult to achieve. In general, suicide becomes more likely at either end of the social scale. It has been said that the risk of suicide varies inversely with income: the richer the patient the more likely they are to kill themselves. But unemployment and extreme poverty may also lead to a higher than expected incidence of suicide. There is a limit to how far suicidal patients should be stereotyped, for of course people from every income group and every social background may be driven by feelings of hopelessness to take their own lives.

The well-orientated heroes and heroines practising their useful occupations, who so delight television viewers watching *Dr Finlay's Casebook, All Creatures Great and Small* or *Emmerdale,* are ironically the very people who have jobs which make them more likely to commit suicide. The real-life James Herriot tragically killed himself. It would seem he was exemplifying this point, although there was evidence that he had suffered from depression for much of his life. Some occupations carry with them an increased suicide risk. After due consideration has been given to those with known psychiatric disease, the unemployed, the ill, the divorced and the bankrupt, statistics show that doctors, vets and farmers are at greater risk than the rest of the population.

A doctor, perhaps, should be particularly concerned if a colleague says that he or she is contemplating suicide. The average suicide rate for male doctors is double the rate for the average man. If the suicidal doctor is a woman, the situation is even more disturbing. Female physicians are four times more likely than comparable women to kill themselves; this is the only group of women who are more likely to commit suicide than men, perhaps because their medical knowledge converts suicide attempts into actuality. In general, very many more suicide attempts are made by women than men, but men are much more likely to die from suicide.

It is difficult, even when one has taken into account the usual obvious reasons – such as death, debt, divorce and disease – to predict who may commit suicide. Any of these disasters of modern life may precipitate it but rarely does suicide result from a single factor. The death of a loved one is bearable if there is also a devoted family; likewise debt can be tolerated if there is an understanding partner to share the problems it brings. People who are lonely are particularly likely to commit suicide on a festive occasion – Christmas for instance, or a national holiday, when everybody else appears to be enjoying themselves. Other people take their lives on the anniversary of the death of someone close to them. Very often suicide is then partly as the result of satisfying a desire to join – in heaven, one hopes – someone who has died earlier. Married people are least likely to commit suicide, with the divorced or widowed at greatest risk. The risk for those who have always been single comes between that for the divorced and widowed.

One type of person contemplating suicide can be particularly confusing – the patient whose abject misery is transformed into misleading 'smiling depression'. Some patients become more cheerful when they have finally decided upon a life plan – to end their own life.

Mary had had a very difficult life both at home and in her work. She was admitted to hospital as an emergency, as her family thought that she was very severely depressed, but when she came into the surgery she was smiling, quick-talking and appeared to be relaxed. All the classic signs and symptoms of depression were discussed – sleeplessness, loss of appetite, feelings of hopelessness, etc. and then finally the consultation turned to suicide. The doctor asked her if she had ever contemplated suicide, and if so by what means she would carry it out? Or, if she hadn't thought of suicide, had she ever thought that she might be better off dead? 'I don't want to frighten you, doctor,' she said with a smile, 'but I planned my suicide yesterday afternoon; an overdose of pills, it is to be, accompanied by plenty of alcohol.' After her talk with the doctor, she never looked back. She found a new job and a boyfriend and has remained cheerful.

A previously depressed, well-known social figure attended the usual round of Christmas parties, where she was once again her old cheerful self – family and friends were delighted to see that she was back on form. She spent an apparently happy and relaxed Christmas with relatives, returned to her own flat and committed suicide on New Year's Eve. What was unexpected was the discovery that the suicide as well as the Christmas festivities had all been planned in the first week of December when the suicide note had been written.

It is when suicide is committed on holiday that the resulting grief is particularly devastating. Holiday suicides are comparatively common because the sufferer has felt that all would be well if only he or she had a holiday. Having started the holiday, and feeling no more cheerful, the last ray of hope is extinguished. One of the lessons I was taught by my psychiatric mentor, Dr Spencer-Paterson, was that severely depressed patients should never be allowed to go away until after they have cheered up with the prescribed medication. A time away from the stresses of work and domestic responsibility can play an important part in convalescence, but going away to unfamiliar surroundings, having to cope with travel and the irritations and disorientation of other people's customs and lifestyles while pretending to be cheerful and well-socialized could undo all the benefits of treatment. A holiday should therefore not start until after recovery is well established.

It should also always be remembered that one of the times when a depressed patient is most at risk is when they are beginning to respond to therapy. When in the depths of despair they may be too inert and despondent even to rouse themselves sufficiently to implement their suicide plans.

Suicide is more common in the spring and early summer than at other times of the year, possibly as a response to an inability to feel 'the joys of spring' which are affecting everyone around them. This seasonal variation has a different origin from that affecting patients with seasonal affective disorder (SAD), where depression reaches its nadir in the darkest months, whereas, by early summer, the evenings are lengthening.

Even feminists haven't attempted to deny, or alter, the gender

315

differences in suicide. Men and women kill themselves in different ways. In general, very many more suicide attempts are made by women than men, but men are much more determined when killing themselves. Deaths from suicide are between two and three times more common in men than women. Gas fires are no longer a fashionable or dependable means of self-destruction, but men – who still prefer to gas themselves – will now use the trapped exhaust fumes from their cars. Women prefer pills – overdosing as a female method of self-destruction is more common than all of the other ways which might be chosen put together. Women are nearly three times more likely to drown themselves than men, but very rarely shoot themselves. Dorothy Parker, American writer, humorist and depressive, said wryly:

> Guns aren't lawful;
> Nooses give;
> Gas smells awful;
> You might as well live.

If only suicidal people were all as resigned and analytical as Dorothy Parker. Apart from the young psychotic men who all too frequently choose to jump in front of a train, or cast themselves off a tall building, women more than men tend to opt for an horrific way to commit suicide. Possibly they may want to enhance the revenge effect – the 'they'll be sorry when I have gone' motivation – or possibly a gory end is a final gesture of contempt of their own body, a symptom of self-hate. When I was at Oxford, a ward sister, the girlfriend of one of my tutors, committed suicide by taking an overdose. Although she had access to a large number of hypnotic drugs, which would have ensured a peaceful finish in perpetual sleep, she took a drug which gave her a tortured end. When talking about her death, the tutor told me that when I had qualified I would be surprised to find how many people choose a painful, uncomfortable or physically destructive end. His words have proved to be right.

Even though suicide as a cause of death in young men is second only to road traffic accidents, old, solitary men, who are lonely, unaccustomed to household chores and less likely to have close family ties than elderly women, are more likely than any other group to commit suicide. Retirement leaves many elderly men comparatively impoverished and without the community of the workplace, or the boost to their self-esteem which may be provided by the respect of colleagues. However, the proportions are changing. The rate of suicide in young men, those under thirty-four years old, has increased by 50 per cent in the past thirty years – whereas that of young women has halved.

In all age groups, but predominantly in older age groups, downward social mobility and loss of status are contributory factors to suicide in both sexes. In some older people the suicide may be determined by their desire not to be a nuisance, coupled with a feeling that they have had their life and that their own disabilities are now a trial to themselves and an inconvenience to others. These motives may be misplaced, but in their own way are unselfish.

Other aged people, who are perhaps invalids, commit suicide because the pain they are suffering for twenty-four hours a day has eroded their determination to keep going. The older patient who suffers from chronic illness or has recently had surgery is more likely to commit suicide. However, not all suicides in the elderly are altruistic or rational – even more frequently than others, older people kill themselves in order to exact the final revenge. A depressed patient blames family or friends for their unhappiness and this is the way to get back at them.

When a sufferer is terminally ill the question of euthanasia arises. A patient's judgement may be clouded by depression, and all doctors have seen patients who have lived for many months, or even a year or two, after their mood has been lifted from thoughts of euthanasia by antidepressant treatment. The desire for euthanasia is often provoked by not realizing that good medical practice, unfortunately not always readily accessible, is now available and palliative treatment may be prescribed in quantities designed to ensure a bearable, if not continuously comfortable,

317

illness and a peaceful end. This may involve the withdrawal, as well as the supplementation, of drugs. So long as the motivation is the patient's comfort rather than that of ensuring death, all authorities agree that if the patient dies slightly earlier than would otherwise be the case, no ethical, or criminal, offence has been committed by the doctor overseeing the patient's care.

The motivation for suicide has caught the interest of psychiatrists down the ages. Many of those who do commit suicide are suffering from serious psychiatric disease; 10–15 per cent of patients with depression and a similar percentage of those with schizophrenia commit suicide. Of those people who commit suicide and are known to have a psychiatric disease, up to 70 per cent have symptoms of depression, up to 12 per cent have schizophrenia and up to 27 per cent have alcohol dependence. Many patients obviously have symptoms of more than one condition.

Suicide is always a risk with any depressed patient, whatever the cause of the depression. Therefore, as would be expected, most suicidal people have other psychiatric problems, of which depression is one of the symptoms. These include such conditions as alcoholism, drug dependence, schizophrenia and its related conditions, or one of the personality disorders. Whatever the underlying disease, feelings of hopelessness in a depressed patient are a particularly ominous sign.

Patients who have been diagnosed with an affective disorder causing depression are thirty times more likely than their apparently normal neighbour to commit suicide. There is always, therefore, a risk of suicide in any patient who shows evidence of the so-called 'core' symptoms of depression – feelings of hopelessness, loss of self-esteem, no sense of pleasurable anticipation, withdrawal from friends and family, insomnia, weight loss (or occasionally gain), and irritability. Depressed patients may be adept at hiding their true feelings, particularly in traditional Britain where the trailing of emotion is not only culturally unfashionable but considered bad manners. So clever are the devices used by some depressed patients to conceal the depth of their feelings, and so insidious can the growth of depression be, that those nearest to them who have forgotten what the patient's former mood was like, may miss the gradual change entirely and ever thereafter feel unnecessarily guilty if disaster follows. When a patient suffers from psychosis, the suicide may not only be an expression of the feelings of hopelessness or depression, but as the result of the clarion call of the auditory hallucinations or delusions. The voices can be very demanding.

Schizophrenic patients are particularly prone to suicide, which it can be difficult to pre-empt. This is partly because in schizophrenics, and patients with a schizotypal disorder, moods vary much more quickly than in patients who are suffering from depression resulting from an affective disorder. It is now considered that the oft-quoted figure of 10 per cent of schizophrenic patients will die by their own hand is an underestimate. The type of schizophrenic patients who are most likely to die in this way are newly diagnosed, young, male patients in whom depression is a major symptom. The younger schizophrenic patient is very likely to have employment problems and have considerable insight into the difficulties their disease is going to cause. Fearing a lifetime of psychiatric illness and recurrent employment problems, they opt for suicide. Very often the decision is taken on being discharged from hospital, when they have confirmation that fitting back into society is going to be more difficult than they had assumed when in the hospital ward.

Hypochondriacal patients may commit suicide, whatever the underlying nature of their disorder. Disease doesn't have to be clinically proven to prompt suicidal thoughts. Patients may commit suicide not because they are terminally ill but because they think they are, and believe that their end will be painful. Alcoholics and drug addicts commit suicide, not as a direct result of their addiction but rather as a reflection of their unsatisfactory lifestyle and the feeling that they will never be able to drag themselves up from it.

Suicide in Children

That the happiest days of your life occur in childhood is every parent's dream, but sadly is not every child's experience. Even if home life is free of tension, which is unlikely, schooldays never are. And sometimes the tension becomes too much for a child to bear. Depression occurs in all age groups – contrary to popular belief, children do become depressed, even though the symptoms may not be the classic ones associated with the condition in adults, and symptoms in younger children are not necessarily the same as those in adolescents. 5 per cent of teenagers are seriously depressed, as are 2 per cent of children before adolescence. Because depression in these age groups is often masked – some do not complain or even show any characteristic symptom – these figures are certainly an underestimate.

All children may at some time be edgy, or even frankly difficult; tearful, antisocial, rebellious and truant. It could be a sign that they are depressed; equally it could be that they are over-tired or 'going through a bad patch'. Like adolescents the world over, they may refuse to take part in any family or school activity, or they may seem unusually sensitive and irritable. Differentiating between the normal rebellious stage of adolescence – the behaviour indicative of a desire to leave the nest – and adolescent depression may be exceptionally difficult. The difference is one of degree, and it may need an expert to define this.

Heartrending newspaper stories about childhood suicide make the headlines regularly. Every year one in a hundred UK twelve- to sixteen-year-olds attempts suicide. Dr Peter Hardwick, Consultant Child and Adolescent Psychiatrist, has made a study of adolescent and childhood suicide and has written about his findings in *Young Minds* magazine. He noted certain pointers to a suicide risk.

Most of the victims had suffered known psychiatric problems, particularly depression – but the depression was very apt to be masked by antisocial behaviour or alcohol or drug abuse. About a third had a history of self-harm and others had communicated their suicidal intent. Many had been rendered vulnerable by bullying or other child abuse. Others had particular personality traits and were either over-impulsive and aggressive or too perfectionist and rigid. The adolescent suicide cases were often unemployed, socially isolated and were in open conflict with family and/or their contemporaries. The suicide was often triggered by a specific crisis – exam failure or loss of an important relationship, for instance – but in general their attitude showed the expected feelings of hopelessness together with those of humiliation and anger.

The upbringing provided to a child has the power to modify the pattern of any inherited psychiatric disease by influencing an emerging temperament. A good bridge player may still win, even if dealt a poor hand. One particularly poor hand for a child to receive is that which includes the loss of a mother early in childhood. The mother may not necessarily have died but may have left her family and husband, could perhaps have spent years in and out of hospital or even have been too with-drawn while at home, as a result of her own depression, to join in the family life. A child born with the genetic predisposition to be well-adjusted, easygoing, with an outwardly friendly and socially adept manner, may find that he or she is still able to play a winning hand although the ace of hearts, his mother, is elsewhere.

However, if he or she is dealt a few more low-quality cards – is deprived of other loving support, is not valued for him- or herself, or is expected to be consistently successful, a paragon of all virtues, without any allowance made for normal physical desires – then there may well be trouble. As the growing teenager fails to meet impossibly high standards, every little lapse, as they have been taught to see it, drops a few more points. They are losers in life's great game, for self-esteem is fragile, vulnerable to the person's own self-estimate, and to the real or imagined criticism of those around them.

Childhood depression may culminate in suicide but most suicides in children have a very obvious trigger. Children are not masters of their own fate, with the result that life is much more circumscribed, so that they do not have the options to escape from the predicaments which could be overcome by adults. An adult, bullied in a factory, has the option to leave, but a child bullied at school has the full parental, scholastic and state's administrative weight unwittingly forcing them to return to the site of their torment. They can see no way out. The situation has been made worse, rather than better, by modern, enlightened education. In my youth there were a few bullies at school – but they were usually the masters. So savage was their bullying that no child dared to be one himself, and at least the magisterial violence had the advantage of uniting the class and, within one's own peer group, there was security. Sixty years later there should be a better solution.

The story of Jamie Evans, a fourteen-year-old Welsh schoolboy from Maesteg, who hanged himself with his belt after weeks of mental and physical harassment, made the headlines and is a typical case history. Jamie was rather small for his age, a treasured only child of elderly parents, who had given him an adoring home background. Unfortunately, this does not always fit a child for life in the jungle of the playground, or, even more frightening, the confrontation with the mob on the journey home. Small, intelligent and sensitive, Jamie would be easy prey for those who would derive sadistic pleasure, as well as being financially rewarded, by taking his money.

The lesson to be learnt from the deaths of Jamie and others like him is that the signs they show of emotional distress have to be followed up. Children do not like to admit that they cannot cope, and most of all they like to preserve their reputation with their parents as a success and one of the lads (or lasses). Parents, too, represent authority, and it is against the ethics of the playground culture to 'sneak' to authority. (Childline, the telephone service open to children so that they may report any mistreatment has, however, to some extent altered the secretive playground culture.) Parents must look for the signs of unhappiness in a child: a lack of high-spirited chatter and laughter, a withdrawn or unusually aggressive temperament, a sudden lack of interest in hobbies and in friends, and a reluctance to go out. A child's change in mood is always worth discussing with the school and the family doctor.

A change of school can sometimes help. Peter, the fourteen-year-old son of a Norfolk farmer, was a charming boy but, even though a good athlete, was remorselessly bullied at his private school. Peter's problem was that he was of below average academic ability. Investigation showed that he had been asphyxiated at birth, which had blunted what would otherwise probably have been a very normal intelligence.

I suggested that Peter should go into the state system, where he could benefit from a greater range of intellectual background and ability. He soon settled in and was as happy as the day is long. His first day had not been a great success as his clothes were too smart. It took his mother some time to realize that however often she bought him new jeans or jackets they always wore out quickly – until one day she spotted him rubbing his clothes on the rough stone of the doorstep. He was content so long as he belonged, and his clothes looked as worn as those of his contemporaries. Any child who is conspicuous for whatever reason is a likely candidate for bullying. Interestingly, Peter's mother suffered from depression as the result of an affective disorder and it is quite likely that his own reaction to bullying, together with his inability to withstand it, could, in part, be attributed to his genetic make-up.

Children who commit suicide are characteristically those who are escaping from what seems to them an impossible life without hope. They may also have an over-sensitive nature, and may suffer many of the symptoms of feelings of hopelessness, which could well be indicative of a depressive nature which may be with them all their lives. Jane is now in her fifties and has suffered all her life from recurrent bouts of depression with suicidal thoughts. She had a difficult home background, with authoritarian parents whose discipline would today be considered cruel. Jane remembers in great detail how as a child she planned to commit suicide to avoid the misery of yet another confrontation. She can clearly distinguish the year when she first made careful suicide plans because of other significant occurrences happening at the time. She was only four.

In childhood, as at other times of life, suicide is not only a reaction against an uncontrollable situation but it may also be used as revenge against a parent or other loved one, sometimes a sibling – the 'They will be sorry when I have gone' motivation. This same motivation particularly applies to the bullied child as they know the culprits will suffer terrible punishments after they have died, and that all their lives the culprits will feel remorse. Jane now admits that revenge, as well as unhappiness, lay at the back of her mind when she contemplated suicide.

The treatment of a depressed child or adolescent starts with the assessment of their environment, their home life as well as school or university, or place of work. Every effort must be made to boost the child's self-esteem and to do everything possible to ensure that he or she has an environment in which they may be happy and flourish. However good the child's background, some children will need medication for depression.

After any death, surviving relatives almost invariably ask themselves questions which start 'What if . . . ?' Others ruminate, and their regretful worries begin: 'If only I . . . ' If these are the standard emotions after a natural death, how much more unhappiness will be prompted by a death from suicide. The families and friends of people who have committed suicide have told me years later that neither they nor their relatives had ever recovered. This is a natural response but not always a logical one; often suicide has seemed an inevitable end, despite loving care and constant attention showered on the person by all around him or her.

Select Bibliography

Adamec, C., *How to Live with a Mentally Ill Person: A Handbook of Day-to-Day Strategies*, John Wiley & Sons, 1996

British National Formulary, British Medical Association and Royal Pharmaceutical Society of Great Britain, September 1998

Cayton, H., Graham, N. and Warner, J., *Alzheimer's at your Fingertips*, Class Publishing, 1997

Cutler, J. L. and Marcus, E. R., *Psychiatry*, W. B. Saunders Company, 1999

Davies, T. and Craig, T. K. J., *ABC of Mental Health*, BMJ Books, 1998

Fadem, B. and Simring, S., *Psychiatry Recall*, Williams & Wilkins, 1997

Feinman, J., *Surviving the Baby Blues: Recognizing, understanding and overcoming postnatal depression*, Ward Lock, 1997

Fuller Torrey, E., *Surviving Schizophrenia: A Family Manual*, Harper Colophon Books, 1985

Frangou, S. and Murray, R. M., *Schizophrenia*, Martin Dunitz, 1996

Gelder, M., Gath, D. and Mayou, R., *Concise Oxford Textbook of Psychiatry*, Oxford University Press, 1994

Gregory, I. and Smeltzer, D. J., *Psychiatry* (2nd edn), Little, Brown and Company, 1983

Grollman, E. A. and Kosick, K. S., *When Someone You Love has Alzheimer's: The Caregiver's Journey*, Souvenir Press, 1996

Halaris, A. (ed), *Sexual Dysfunction*, Bailliere Tindall, 1997

Halbreich, U. (ed), *Psychiatric Issues in Women*, Bailliere Tindall, 1996

Hamilton, M. (ed), *Fish's Schizophrenia*, John Wright & Sons Ltd, 1976

Levine, S., Loudon, J. B. and Soni, S. D., *Pocket Reference to Schizophrenia*, Science Press, 1993

Lintner, B., *Living with Schizophrenia: A Positive Guide for Sufferers and Carers* (2nd edn), Vermilion, 1989

The Merck Manual (16th edn), Merck Research Laboratories, 1992

The Merck Manual of Medical Information, Home Edition, Merck Research Laboratories, 1997

Mueser, K. T. and Gingerich, S., *Coping with Schizophrenia: A Guide for Families*, New Harbinger Publications, Inc., 1994

O'Mahoney, G. and Lucey, J. V. (eds), *Understanding Psychiatric Treatment*, John Wiley & Sons, 1998

Pitt, B., *Down with Gloom: or, How to Defeat Depression*, Royal College of Psychiatrists, 1993

Rowe, C. J. and Mink, W. D., *An Outline of Psychiatry* (10th edn), WCB Brown & Benchmark, 1993

Royal Pharmaceutical Company, *Martindale: The Extra Pharmacopoeia* (31st edn), 1883

Sainsbury, M. J., *Key to Psychiatry: A Textbook for Students* (3rd edn), H M + M Publishers, 1973

Scully, J. H., *Psychiatry* (3rd edn), Williams & Wilkins, 1998

Skrine, R., *Blocks and Freedoms in Sexual Life: A Handbook of Psychosexual Medicine*, Radcliffe Medical Press, 1997

Smith, C., Sell, L. and Sudbury, P., *Key Topics in Psychiatry*, Bios Scientific Publishers, 1996

Smith, T., *The British Medical Association Complete Family Health Encyclopaedia* (2nd edn), Dorling Kindersley, 1990/1995

Storr, A. *Sexual Deviation*, Penguin Books, 1964

Trethowan, W. H., *Psychiatry* (4th edn), Bailliere Tindall, 1979

Tyrer, P. and Stein, G., *Personality Disorder Reviewed*, Royal College of Psychiatrists, 1993

Waldinger, R. J., *Psychiatry for Medical Students*, American Psychiatric Press, Inc., 1997

Weatherall, D. J., Ledingham, J. G. G. and Warrell, D. A., *Oxford Textbook of Medicine* (2nd edn), Oxford University Press, 1987

Weinman, J., *An Outline of Psychology as Applied to Medicine* (2nd edn), Butterworth Heinemann, 1981

Woods, R. T., *Alzheimer's Disease, Coping with a Living Death*, Souvenir Press (Educational & Academic) Ltd, 1989

Youngson, R., *The Royal Society of Medicine Encyclopaedia of Family Health*, Bloomsbury, 1995

Glossary

Addiction A compulsive dependence on a drug to maintain the comfort of the body or mind, regardless of damage, whether physical or mental. *Physical addiction* indicates that the use of the drug has produced changes in the way the body functions so that its withdrawal induces physical symptoms. *Psychological dependence*, conversely, hasn't yet caused changes in the body's physiological functions but the sufferer's peace of mind is dependent upon the drug.

Agitation Physical and mental restlessness.

Affective disorders Disorders of mood, such as depression, hypomania and mania. *See* mood.

Agoraphobia Literally, a fear of open spaces, but in fact is more generally used as a fear of being in a place from which escape would be difficult, where help in the event of disaster would be unavailable or from where retreat, if possible, would be acutely embarrassing.

Alcoholism The term is usually used to imply that the person's drinking is compromising their social, domestic or professional lives.

Anorexia nervosa A refusal to maintain body weight over a minimal normal weight for age and height; an intense fear of gaining weight and becoming fat, even if underweight; a distorted body image so that sufferers visualize themselves as being fatter than they are. Absent periods in women.

Antisocial personality disorder The disorder previously known as *psychopathy*. Antisocial, irresponsible, impulsive behaviour maintained regardless of the damage it may cause to others, or even to the sufferer.

Anxiety and fear Anxiety is feelings of severe apprehension and uneasiness from a danger which may be indefinable and unidentifiable; when the source of the anxiety is known, and understandable, it can be described as *stress* (or normal anxiety). Fear,

In Your Right Mind

on the other hand, is the same severe feelings as anxiety but related to
a recognized cause, an understandable threat.

Avoidant personality disorder Feelings of unease or discomfort on
social occasions stemming from a dislike of being judged wanting. It
results in social withdrawal and extreme timidity.

Behaviour therapy Psychotherapy which relies upon being able to teach
someone to overcome their difficulties through learning.

Bipolar mood disorder Refers to either manic depressive disease or
mania. Previously known as manic depression. The patient's mood can
swing from apparent over-exuberance and irresponsibility to apathy
and depression.

Body dysmorphic disorder Also known as *dysmorphobia*. Preoccupation
with some aspect of appearance which the sufferer feels is a serious
defect, but which the rest of the world may consider totally normal.

Borderline personality disorder Difficulties with self image and, because
of that, with interpersonal relationships. There is a fear of
abandonment and hence a dislike of being alone. There may be wild
mood swings. Some doctors feel that the condition's multitude of
symptoms overlap so often with other more easily definable
personality disorders that it shouldn't be considered a single entity. It
has been known by a variety of different names.

Bulimia Recurrent binge eating followed by self-induced vomiting or
use of laxatives and diuretics, known as *purging bulimia*; or, conversely,
a period severe fasting followed by bingeing, known as *non-purging
bulimia*. Both types are also associated with excessive exercising
and there is a statistically increased risk of other personality
problems.

Compulsions A repetitive, ritualistic response to an obsession,
characteristic of obsessive-compulsive disorder and the obsessive-
compulsive personality disorder.

Computerised Axial Tomography (CT) Scans Designed to take
cross-sectional views of different parts of the body through X-rays.

Conscious Awareness of one's identity and surroundings, and the
presence of ideas, feelings, drives and urges.

Conversion disorder The disorders which used to be described as
hysterical. Apparently physical symptoms which are in fact the result
of psychological conflict or need.

Déjà vu The feeling experienced by someone that the situation which is in fact happening for the first time, has already happened.

Delirium An acute, and often transient, change in intellectual abilities which produces confusion, agitation, loss of memory and comprehension, as a result of some physical cause – such as fever, drugs or brain injury.

Delusion A fixed persistent untrue belief, often manifestly absurd, which is unaltered by reasoned explanation.

Dementia A slow, progressive decline in intellectual ability characterized by the loss of short- and long-term memory, judgement, command of language, physical and muscular co-ordination and an incapacity to make reasonable plans for everyday living.

Dependent personality disorder A disorder in which the sufferer shows a persistent pattern of behaviour which is submissive to others, and has a personality which is dependent on them.

Depersonalization A sense of being apart from oneself.

Depression Persistent sadness and unhappiness, characterizd by feelings of hopelessness, loss of self-esteem and a reduction in vitality. It is a symptom of many different psychiatric diseases and personality disorders.

Depot injections Long-acting injections given to control schizophrenia and allied conditions, particularly useful in treating uncooperative or withdrawn patients who would be unlikely to take their medication unless closely supervised. Enables many patients to be discharged into community care. Drugs used include Depixol (flupenthixol) and Piportil Depot (pipothiazine palmitate).

Diagnosis The assessment of a patient's symptoms, signs, history and background (domestic, professional and genetic) which the doctor undertakes so that the patient's trouble may be ascertained and appropriate treatment assigned. *Differential diagnosis*: when a single cause for the patient's troubles is not immediately apparent, a list of possible diagnoses may be made with the most likely heading the list.

Disorders of impulse control Irresistible, repetitious impulses which are resisted for only a certain length of time before being succumbed to. A temporary sense of pleasure and relief of tension is followed by remorse but the pattern is repeated.

Drug tolerance As the response to any particular drug decreases with repeated prescription, increasingly large doses are needed to achieve the same effect.

Dysthymia An unhappiness, not severe enough to be classified as depression, which is present more often than not for at least two years.

Empathy The ability to understand and to experience imaginatively other people's feelings. It is considered a sign of a well-balanced and adjusted person.

Exhibitionism A recurrent intense desire to expose genital organs to strangers. The symptom must be present for at least six months.

Factitious disorder The condition in which a person assumes fictitious symptoms which would lead a doctor to think that the person was suffering from some specific mental disorder. The sufferer wishes to assume the role of a patient.

Factitious symptoms Fictitious symptoms which have no foundations in physical or mental disease, designed to enable someone to assume the role of a patient.

Fantasy Daydreaming: the imagining of a series of events which may, for instance, be pleasurable or frightening.

Fetishism The use of inanimate objects in order to heighten or achieve sexual satisfaction. The fetishism must be present for at least six months before the diagnosis is made.

Free-floating anxiety Severe anxiety, not related to a particular cause but persistent and generalized. The patient may ascribe the anxiety to some specific reason, but if this is removed the anxiety will either become generalized again or transferred to another worry.

Frotteurism The stimulation of sexual excitement by touching or rubbing against a non-consenting person.

Generalized anxiety disorder (GAD) Excessive anxiety about at least two different aspects of the person's life, e.g. health or finances.

Grief The normal feelings of sadness, producing depression, which follow loss. The loss doesn't have to be related to death.

Histrionic personality disorder A group of symptoms which are essentially attention-seeking, and are often associated with an excessive display of emotion.

Huntington's disease A dementia related to a degenerative condition affecting the basal ganglia and cortex. It is inherited as a dominant gene and produces muscle weakness as well as cognitive loss.

Hypnagogic dreams Very realistic hallucinations which occur just before going to sleep or on waking up. The basis of many ghost stories.

Hypnopompic dreams A dream which doesn't fade on waking but persists for a short time.

Hypochondriasis A preoccupation with illness, particularly a groundless fear that symptoms, usually no more than everyday sensations, are harbingers of an illness.

Hypomania An abnormally elated and expansive character which may be associated with irritability and an over-emphatic manner.

Idealization According someone else qualities they do not have, or, if they have them, over-estimating their value.

Insight The ability, or otherwise, of a patient to understand their illness.

Kleptomania An impulse control disorder in which a person is intermittently unable to resist the increasing desire to steal. The actual theft produces a great relief of tension, this is often followed by remorse before the gradual slow increase in the desire to repeat the theft.

Mania An alteration in a patient's mood so that they are persistently over-euphoric, expansive and very often irritable.

Manic depression Also known as bipolar affective, or mood, disorder. In this condition a patient's mood may vary from the abnormally and severely depressed to the over-euphoric, expansive and irritable.

Melancholia The old term for severe depression.

Mood disorders Also known as 'affective disorders'. A persistent alteration in mood so that patients are abnormally depressed, manic or hypomanic.

MRI Magnetic resonance imaging. A scan, more advanced than the CAT scan, which gives high-definition images of the central nervous system and other bodily tissues. The MRI scanner does not expose the patient to radiation.

Munchhausen syndrome The adoption by someone of fictitious symptoms which is likely to lead to their admission to hospital.

Narcissistic personality disorder An over-estimate of one's own ability and own personality which can lead to grandiosity, coupled simultaneously with a very thin skin so that other people's opinions matter. People with this personality disorder find it hard to make close human relationships.

Neurones The nerve cells of the central nervous system. The neurone consists of a cell body with processes, like tendrils, projecting from it, bringing messages into the body (the dendrites), and an axon, a process which carries messages away from the cell.

Obsessions Persistent troublesome worries and impulses that are intrusive and take up an inordinate amount of someone's time.

Obsessive-compulsive disorder Recurrent and long-lasting obsessions and compulsions which take up so much of the person's time that they interfere with their life and disrupt their social, professional and domestic existence.

Obsessive-compulsive personality disorder Extreme perfectionism and inflexibility. The type of temperament which is used unfairly to depict the stereotypical accountant or solicitor.

Panic Acute anxiety which causes severe distress with all its associated symptoms with mental confusion and a fear of death and disaster.

Panic disorder Recurrent panic attacks with crippling fear associated with dizziness, faintness, feelings of unsteadiness, inability to draw a breath and a sensation of being smothered.

Paranoid personality disorder The tendency to interpret, without good cause, other people's actions as being threatening or demeaning.

Paranoid schizophrenia A delusion or delusions that someone or some group is systematically determined to do you down, associated very often with hallucinations.

Paraphilia Finding sexual pleasure and satisfaction in situations, or by methods, which are not part of normal sexual behaviour, in terms either of the cultural norm or of the usual pattern of sexual response.

Passive aggression Dumb insolence in which a person only indirectly, even unobtrusively, expresses aggression towards somebody else, usually a person in authority.

Passive aggressive personality disorder A disorder in which a person regularly shows a resistance to perform tasks, despite the demands of authority. This is achieved in a passive way.

Paedophilia The desire to have sex with a child under the age of puberty. The law considers that any one act constitutes paedophilia;

medically, the sexual desire must have been present for at least six months.

Personality A person's distinctive character, encompassing the overall way, both internally and externally, in which someone adjusts to the changing scenes of life.

Physical dependence The phenomena by which a person has physical signs and symptoms if they discontinue taking a drug, or dramatically reduce its dose.

Post-traumatic stress disorder The psychological response to severe mental or physical trauma.

Precipitating factors Factors which lead to the onset of some disease or disorder.

Predisposing factors Factors which make someone vulnerable to some disorder.

Pseudo-dementia The loss of interest and apparently of cognitive ability which can occur in very depressed people and which appears to be similar to a dementia.

Psychoanalysis A form of therapy which involves investigating someone's past life in the hope of bringing repressed experiences and fears into their conscious mind.

Psychological dependence The use of a drug as a psychological crutch but without becoming physically dependent on it.

Psychotherapy A form of therapy in which a person, through the means of a relationship with their therapist or group, has their problems treated by psychological rather than physical means. More loosely, the term is used to describe any psychological method of treatment for mental or emotional disorders.

Residual schizophrenia Only a minority of patients who have had schizophrenia make a total recovery. Most are left with some symptoms, are therefore in partial remission, and are said to have residual schizophrenia.

Schizoaffective disorder A condition in which a patient becomes psychotic during an attack of depression or mania and continues to have psychotic symptoms for at least two weeks after their mood has recovered. The persistence of the psychotic symptoms after the mood returns to normal is what characterizes the condition.

Schizoid personality disorder A detached indifference to normal social

and emotional relationships which can leave the sufferer appearing to
be distant and uncaring.

Schizophrenia A group of psychotic disorders which affects not less than
one in a hundred people. Of worldwide distribution, it is characterized
by delusions, hallucinations, disorganized thinking and, as in all
psychotic diseases, a loss of contact with reality.

Schizophreniform disorder The essential features of this condition are
exactly the same as for schizophrenia with the difference that all its
stages are over within six months.

Schizotypal personality disorder Unusual, even bizarre patterns of
behaviour, appearance and philosophy which lead to difficulties in
interpersonal relationships.

Seasonal affective disorder (SAD) The onset of a major depressive
episode during the winter months when there is little exposure to
daylight. Sometimes followed by a period of hypomania.

Simple phobia A persistent fear of some particular situation or object.
Panic disorders, and social phobia in which there is a fear of
humiliation and embarrassment in a social situation, are excluded
from this definition.

Social phobia The essential feature is a fear of humiliation or
embarrassment, the two most common examples being fears of
blushing and of eating in public.

Somatization disorder Physical complaints for which, despite
investigation, no cause can be found. The problem tends to last for
many years.

Somatoform disorder The patient complains of symptoms which
suggest some recognized condition but no evidence of this condition
can be found. Likewise in *somatoform pain disorder*: the presenting
symptom is one of pain which remains unexplained.

Tardive dyskinesia Involuntary movements of the face and mouth
(grimacing) coupled sometimes with movements of the limbs,
occurring as a side-effect of the older antipsychotic drugs.

Tension A manifestation of anxiety. Technically, the tautness of
muscles which is a manifestation of it – hence *tension headaches*, very
often associated with restlessness and a sense of foreboding, used
usually in idiomatic terminology as being 'wound up' or
overwrought.

Transference A patient's unconscious transfer to their therapist of the feelings they have, or had, for parents, grandparents, siblings or others who have been important in their early life.

Transsexualism Someone's overwhelming feeling that they have been ascribed the wrong gender, and that they would be much more at home and happier if they were redesignated to the opposite sex.

Transvestism The urge to cross-dress. In men this has a sexual significance but not, so it seems, in women.

Unconscious The ideas, feelings and urges which may help to determine someone's actions but of which they are unaware.

Unipolar mood disorder A mood of sustained depression so that the outlook is dominated by feelings of hopelessness and despair.

Voyeurism The intense desire to watch people, who are usually unknown, dressing or undressing or while they are involved in more intimate actions.

Wernicke's disease An acute and very dangerous rare dementia found in alcoholism, it is associated with thiamine deficiency.

Glossary of Drugs

5HT-reuptake inhibitors (or selective serotonin reuptake inhibitors): drugs which prolong the action of the neurotransmitter serotonin (5-hydroxytryptamine), thus relieving depression. While they have fewer unpleasant side-effects than other antidepressant drugs, and are safer in accidental or deliberate overdose, they lack their sedative effects.

amphetamines: stimulant drugs which give a sense of mental alertness. They are subject to abuse and have well-publicized serious side-effects involving a danger of dependency.

Anafranil: trade name for clomipramine.

antipsychotics: drugs treating psychotic disease where a sense of reality is lost. 'Atypical antipsychotics' were the first major advance of drugs for twenty years after the introduction of the first generation of antipsychotics, the phenothiazines. Atypical antipsychotics have fewer side-effects than the original antipsychotics and therefore encourage greater compliance from patients.

Aricept: trade name for donepezil.

barbiturates: drugs used as sedatives, now largely replaced by drugs less likely to cause addiction.

benzodiazepines: a large group of tranquillizers which contain such well known drugs as Librium, Frisium and Valium, and many of the sleeping pills.

bromides: a group of drugs formerly widely used as sedatives.

Buspar: trade name for buspirone.

buspirone: a non-benzodiazepine anti-anxiety drug. Trade name Buspar.

chlordiazepoxide: a benzodiazepine. Trade name Librium.

chlorpromazine: one of the earliest antipsychotics. Trade name Largactil.

clobazam: a benzodiazepine tranquillizing drug. Trade name Frisium.

clomipramine: a tricyclic antidepressant drug. Trade name Anafranil.

depot drugs: these are long-acting injections given for schizophrenia and other psychoses, particularly useful in withdrawn and uncooperative patients who would otherwise be deprived of treatment. They include such drugs as Depixol (flupenthixol) and Piportil Depot (pipothiazine palmitate).

diazepam: a benzodiazepine tranquillizing drug. Trade name Valium.

donepezil: an acetycholinesterase inhibitor drug used in the treatment of Alzheimer's disease. Trade name Aricept.

dothiepin: a tricyclic antidepressant drug. Trade name Prothiaden.

Exelon: trade name for rivastigmine.

fluoxetine: a 5HT-reuptake inhibitor (or SSRI) antidepressant drug.

Frisium: trade name for clobazam.

haloperidol: an older, much prescribed antipsychotic. Trade name Serenace.

imipramine: a tricyclic antidepressant drug. Trade name Tofranil.

Largactil: trade name for chlorpromazine.

Librium: trade name for chlordiazepoxide.

Manerix: trade name for moclobemide.

MAOIs: *see* monoamine oxidase inhibitors.

methylphenidate: one of the amphetamines used in the treatment of ADHD. Trade name Ritalin.

moclobemide: a reversible inhibitor of monoamine oxide (RIMA), a later development of the MAOI antidepressant drugs, with fewer side-effects. Trade name Manerix.

monoamine oxidase inhibitors (MOAIs): antidepressant drugs that work by inhibiting the action of the enzyme monoamine oxidase, which is involved in the breakdown of the neurotransmitters serotonin (5HT) and noradrenaline which elevate mood.

Nardil: trade name for phenelzine.

neuroleptics: antipsychotic drugs previously known as 'atypical neuroleptics'. Literally translated, 'neuroleptic' implies that the drugs may cause stiffness, but since this more rarely happens with atypical neuroleptics, they are better named atypical antipsychotics.

olanzapine: an atypical antipsychotic drug used in the treatment of schizophrenia and allied conditions. Trade name Zyprexa.

paraldehyde: a hypnotic drug, used to control mania, delirium, convulsions.

Parnate: trade name for tranylcypromine.

paroxetine: a 5HT-reuptake inhibitor antidepressant drug also licensed to treat obsessive-compulsive disorders. Trade name Seroxat.

Parstelin: trade name for a combination drug which includes both the monoamine oxidase inhibitor antidepressant tranylcypromine and the antipsychotic trifluoperazine.

phenelzine: a monoamine oxidase inhibitor antidepressant drug. Trade name Nardil.

phenothiazine: an early group of antipsychotics, including Stelazine and Largactil.

Prothiaden: trade name for dothiepin.

Prozac: trade name for fluoxetine.

reserpine: a drug used to treat high blood pressure which also has a sedative and tranquillizing action.

risperidone: a benzisoxazole derivative drug used as an atypical antipsychotic in the treatment of schizophrenia and allied conditions.

Risperdal: trade name for risperidone.

Ritalin: trade name for the amphetamine methylphenidate.

rivastigmine: an acetycholinesterase inhibitor drug used in the treatment of Alzheimer's disease. Trade name Exelon.

selective serotonin reuptake inhibitors: *see* 5HT-reuptake inhibitors.

Serenace: trade name for haloperidol.

Seroxat: trade name for paroxetine.

sildenafil: a drug used in the treatment of impotence, better known by the trade name Viagra.

spironolactone: a long established potassium-sparing diuretic drug with a variety of trade names.

SSRIs: *see* 5HT-reuptake inhibitors.

Stelazine: trade name for the phenothiazine antipsychotic drug trifluoperazine.

tacrine hydrochloride: an acetycholinesterase inhibitor drug used in the treatment of Alzheimer's disease; the first to be used, it had undesirable side-effects and was of limited efficiency. Trade name Tacrine.

Tacrine: trade name for tacrine hydrochloride.

Tofranil: trade name for imipramine.

tranylcypromine: a monoamine oxidase inhibitor antidepressant drug. Trade name Parnate. Also included in Parstelin.

tricyclics: the original antidepressants introduced in the 1950s which revolutionized the treatment of depression. They have more side-effects than later antidepressants and are dangerous if taken in overdose. However, some side-effects, in particular their sedative

action, may be useful. A group of drugs which also has uses in
neurology.

trifluoperazine: one of the oldest phenothiazine antipsychotics. Trade
name Stelazine. It is also incorporated into Parstelin.

Tryptizol: trade name for amitriptyline.

Valium: trade name for diazepam.

Viagra: trade name for sildenafil.

Zyprexa: trade name for olanzapine.

Resources

1 Depression

Asian Family Counselling Service
74 The Avenue, West Ealing, London w13 8LB
0181 997 5749

The Association for Postnatal Illness
25 Jerdan Place, Fulham, London sw6 1BE
0171 386 0868

Black Mental Health Resource Centre
Jamaica House, 227 Chapeltown Road, Leeds LS7 3HA
0113 237 4229

British Association for Counselling
1 Regent Place, Rugby, cv21 2PJ
01788 578328

British Association of Psychotherapists
37 Mapesbury Road, London NW2 4HJ
0181 452 9823

Careline (confidential counselling on any issue)
0181 514 1177

Cruse Bereavement Care
126 Sheen Road, Richmond, Surrey, TW9 1UR
0181 940 4818

Depression Alliance
35 Westminster Bridge Road, London SE1 7JB
0171 633 9929
Scotland: 0131 467 3050
Wales: 01222 521 774

Depressives Anonymous
57 Moira Court, Trinity Crescent, London sw17 7AQ
0181 519 1920

Health Education Authority
Trevelyan House, 30 Great Peter Street, London sw1P 2HW
0171 413 1991

MACA (Mental After-Care Association)
25 Bedford Square, London wc1B 3HW
0171 436 5194

Manic Depression Fellowship
8–10 High Street, Kingston-upon-
Thames, KT1 1EY
National advice line: 0181 974 6550
Scotland advice line: 0141 331 0344
Wales advice line: 0163 430 430

The Mental Health Foundation
20–21 Cornwall Terrace,
London NW1 4QL
0171 535 7400

Mental Health Helpline
0345 660606

*MIND (National Association for
Mental Health)*
15–19 Broadway, London E15 4BQ
Mindinfoline: 0181 522 1728
Outside London: 0345 660 163

*National Association of Bereavement
Services*
20 Norton Folgate,
London E1 6DB
0171 247 1080

The Royal College of Psychiatrists
17 Belgrave Square,
London SW1X 8PG
0171 235 2351

*SADA (Seasonal Affective Disorder
Association)*
PO Box 989, Steyning,
West Sussex BN44 3HG
01903 814942

SANE (see under Schizophrenia)

The Samaritans
(see under Suicide)
0345 909090

2 Anxiety Disorders and Phobias

Agoraphobic Advisory Service
22 Herbert Street, Barry,
Glamorgan CF6 7EA
01446 735 225

*HOPE (Help Overcome Panic
Effects)*
Martello House,
Martello Street,
London E8 3PE
0171 739 0059

No Panic
93 Brands Farm Way, Randlay,
Telford TF3 2JQ
Helpline: 01952 590 545

PAX
4 Manorbank, Blackheath,
London SE3 9AW
0181 318 5026

The Phobics' Society
Cheltenham Road, Chorlton-cum-
Hardy, Manchester M21 9QN
0161 881 1937

TACT (Trauma After-Care Trust)
Buttfields, The Farthing, Withing-
ton, Gloucestershire GL54 4DF
01242 890306

Triumph over Phobia (TOP UK)
PO Box 1831, Bath BA1 3XX
01225 330 353

3 Personality Disorders

Mental Health Helpline
0345 660606

Obsessive Action
P O Box 6097,

London W2 1WZ
0171 226 4000

SANE (see under Schizophrenia)

4 Schizophrenia

National Campaign for Homeless People
88 Old Street, London EC1V 9HU
0171 505 2000

The National Schizophrenia Fellowship
28 Castle Street, Kingston-upon-Thames, KT1 1SS
0181 547 3937
Advice: 0181 547 3937

SANE
1st Floor, Cityside House, 40 Adler Street, London E1 1EE
0171 375 1002
Saneline: 0345 678000

The Schizophrenia Association of Great Britain
International Schizophrenia Centre,
Bryn Hyfryd, The Crescent, Bangor, Gwynedd,
Wales LL57 2AG
01248 354 048

Schizophrenia Association of Ireland
4 Fitzwilliam Place, Dublin 2, Eire
003531 676 1988

The Zito Trust
PO Box 265, London WC2H 9JD
0171 240 8422

5 Alzheimer's Disease

Age Concern England
Astral House, 1268 London Road, London SW16 4ER
0181 679 8000

Alzheimer's Disease Society
Gordon House,
10 Greencoat Place,
London SW1P 1PH
0171 306 0606

Alzheimer's Research Trust
G. J. Livanos House,
Granhams Road,
Cambridge CB2 5LQ
01223 843899

Carers' National Association
20–25 Glasshouse Yard,
London EC1A 4JS
0171 490 8818

Resources

The Dementia Relief Trust
Pegasus House, 37–43 Sackville
Street, London W1X 2DL
0171 333 8115

Help the Aged
St James's Walk,
London EC1R OBE
0171 253 0253

6 Eating Disorders

Eating Disorders Association
1st Floor, Wensum House,
103 Prince of Wales Road,
Norwich, Norfolk NR1 1PW
01603 619 090
Helpline: 01603 621414
Youth helpline: 01603 765050

*National Centre for Eating
Disorders*
54 New Road, Esher,
Surrey KT10 9NU
01372 469 493

8 and 9 Orgasmic Disorders and Paraphilia

The Amarant Trust
(menopause and HRT)
Sycamore House, 5 Sycamore
Street, London E1Y 0SR
Adviceline: 0891 660620
Helpline 01293 413000

Beaumont Trust Helpline
(gender)
07000 287878

*British Association of Sexual and
Marital Therapy*
PO Box 13686, London SW20 9ZH

Brook Advisory Centres
(sexual help)
165 Gray's Inn Road,
London WC1X 8UD
0171 708 1537

Young People's Information Line:
0171 713 9000; phone numbers of
local centres

FPA (Family Planning Association)
(sexual health)
2–12 Pentonville Road,
London N1 9FP
0171 837 4044

Gender Trust Information Line
07000 790347

The Impotence Association
(male and female problems)
PO Box 10296, London SW17 9WH
Helpline: 0181 767 7791

National Relate
Herbert Grey College, Little
Church Street, Rugby, CV21 3AP
01788 573241
Helpline: 0870 601 2121

343

Terence Higgins Trust
(support for HIV and AIDS)
52–54 Grays Inn Road,
London WC1X 8JU
0171 831 0330
Helpline: 0171 242 1010

10 Drugs

ADDACTION
67–69 Cowcross Street,
London EC1M 6BU
0171 251 5860

Adfam National
Waterbridge House,
32–36 London Street, Southwark,
London SE1 0EE
Helpline for families and friends
of drug users: 0171 928 8900
Also houses:
Institute for the Study of Drug
Dependence (ISDD)
0171 928 1211
The Standing Conference on Drug
Abuse (SCODA)
0171 928 9500

Al-Anon Family Groups,
UK and Eire
61 Great Dover Street,
London SE1 4YS
Helpline: 0171 833 0022

Alcoholics Anonymous
The General Service Office, Box 1,
Stonebow House, Stonebow,
York YO1 7NJ
01904 644026
Helpline: 0171 833 0022

Drinkline
0345 320202

Families Anonymous
The Doddington & Rollo
Community Centre, Charlotte
Despard Avenue, Battersea,
London SW11 5JE
0171 498 4680

Lifeline
101–103 Oldham Street,
Manchester M4 1LW
0800 716 701

Narcotics Anonymous
PO Box 417, London SW10 0RP
0171 351 6794

National Children's Bureau Solvent
Misuse Project
8 Wakley Street,
London EC1V 7QE
0171 843 6038

The National Drugs Helpline
0800 77 66 00

RELEASE
388 Old Street, Islington,
London EC1V 9LT
0171 729 5255
Advice line: 0171 729 9904
Drugs in Schools Helpline:
0345 36 66 66

Re-Solv
30A High Street, Stone,
Staffordshire ST15 8AW
0171 729 9904

The Scottish Drugs Forum
5th Floor, Shaftesbury House,
5 Waterloo Street,

Glasgow G2 6AY
0141 221 1175

Turning Point
New Loom House,
101 Blackchurch Lane,
Whitechapel, London E1 1LU
0171 702 2300

11 Children's Disorders

*ADD/ADHD Family Support
Group*
1a The High Street, Dilton Marsh,
Nr Westbury, Wiltshire, BA13 4DL
01373 826045 or 01380 726710

ADHD Information Services
PO Box 340, Edgware,
Middlesex HA8 9HL
0181 905 2013

*Association of Child
Psychotherapists*
Burg House, New End Square,
London NW3 1LT
0171 794 8881

Childline
Royal Mail Building, Studd Street,
London N1 0QW
Freepost 1111, London N1 0BR
0171 239 1000
Helpline: 0800 1111

*ERIC (Enuresis Resource &
Information Centre)*
34 Old School House, Britannia
House, Kingswood,

Bristol BS15 2DB
0117 960 3060

*Hyperactive Children's Support
Group*
71 Whyke Lane, Chichester,
Sussex PO19 2LD
01903 725182

LADDER (Parents' support group
for ADD)
142 Mortyn Road, Merton Park,
London SW19 3LR
0181 543 2800

*National Association for Gifted
Children*
Elder House, Milton Keynes,
MK9 1LR
Helpline: 01908 673677
Youthline: 01908 692660

National Autistic Society
(also Asperger's)
393 City Road, London EC1V 1NE
0171 833 2299
Helpline: 0171 903 3555
Information Centre: 0171 903 3599

The National Light & Sound Therapy Centre (Autism, ADD, Hyperactivity)
90 Queen Elizabeth's Walk,
London N16 5UQ
0181 880 1269

NCB (National Children's Bureau)
8 Wakley Street, London
EC1V 7QE
0171 843 6000
Information line: 0171 843 6008

OAASIS (Office for Advice, Assistance, Support and Information on Special Needs)
Brock House, Grigg Lane,
Brockenhurst,
Hampshire SO42 7RE
01590 624484
Helpline: 09068 633201
(60p a minute)

Young Minds
102–108 Clerkenwell Road,
Camden, London EC1M 55A
0171 336 8445
Parents Information Service:
0345 626376

12 Suicide

Kidscape (Advice to parents about bullying)
2 Grosvenor Gardens,
London SW1W 0DH
0171 730 2999

Living with Suicide
West Arundel,
Sussex: 01903 885 963
Support line: 01903 744 851

NSPCC Anti Bullying Campaign (ABC)
0171 378 1446

PAPYRUS (Parents Association for the Prevention of Young Suicide)
Rossendale GH, Union Road,
Rawtenstall, Rossendale,
Lancashire BB4 6NE
01706 214 449

The Samaritans
10 The Grove, Slough SL1 1QP
01753 216 500
Helpline: 0345 909090

Complementary Medicine

*The British Homeopathic
Association*
27a Devonshire Street,
London W1N 1RJ
0171 935 2163

*British Medical Acupuncture
Society*
Newton House, Newton Lane,
Whitley, Warrington,
Cheshire WA4 4JA
01925 730727

*National Register of
Hypnotherapists and
Psychotherapists*
12 Cross Street, Nelson,
Lancashire
01282 699378

*Society of Teachers of the Alexander
Technique*
Suite 20, 10 London House, 266
Fulham Road, London SW10 9EL
0171 351 0828

Index

acetylcholine 198, 199
acetylcholinesterase 198
  inhibitors 198, 199
ADD *see* attention deficit disorder
Addison's disease 8
ADHD *see* attention deficit
  hyperactive disorder
adrenal glands 54, 205
affective disorders
  bipolar 11–14, 15, 22, 23
  and borderline personality 107
  and bulimia 211
  cyclothymia 6–7
  and depression 6, 8, 9, 11–12, 22, 38,
    323
  dysthymia 7
  and exhibitionism 252
  and family 37
  hypomania xvii, 6, 7, 9, 22
  mania xvii, 6, 7, 9, 11–12, 22
  SAD 40–42, 44
  unipolar 12, 15
aggression
  and antisocial personality 99, 100,
    101, 103
  and borderline personality 109
  and child suicide 321, 323
  and Lewy body dementia 190
  and paranoia 280
  and passive-aggressive personality
    disorder 116
  and PMS 119
  and schizophrenia 160, 178
agitation 57
  and Alzheimer's disease 183–4, 185
  and depression 13

agoraphobia 65–6
air travel, and phobias 66, 72
akathisia 177
alcohol
  and Alzheimer's disease 194, 195
  and antisocial personality disorder
    99, 100
  benefits of 192
  and borderline personality 108
  and delirium 189
  and depression 320
  and drug abuse 108
  and hyperactivity 294
  loss of appetite for 219
  and loss of libido 235
  and MAOIs 46
  and organic psychoses 131
  and paedophilia 258, 260
  and panic disorders 64–5
  and paranoia 88
  and social phobia 70
alcoholism 8, 124–5, 277
  and bulimia 211
  and depression 21, 26
  and eating disorders 205
  and heavy social drinking 273
  and suicide 318, 319
Alexander the Great 104
aluminium 192
Alzheimer's disease 3, 8, 28, 34, 131,
    180–201
  causes 185
  deficiency in neurotransmitters 198,
    199
  and depression 181, 187–8, 196
  diagnostic features 182

and environment 191
and family 181–2, 185, 195
and genetics 191
inflammation 200, 201
and Lewy body dementia 167, 182
and lifestyle 194
medication 195, 197–201
and memory loss 180–81, 182–6, 193, 195, 199, 200
pre-senile 185
prophylactic measures 194–5
and pseudo-dementia 187
statistics 182, 185
amenorrhoea 205, 206, 210, 212, 215
American Civil War 77
American Psychiatric Press 11
amisulpride *see* Solian
amitriptyline *see* Tryptizol
amphetamines xi, 64, 88, 287, 297
anaemia 214, 221
anaesthetics 192, 193
Anafranil (clomipramine) 76–7
anal incontinence *see* soiling
Andrey, Dr Robert 103
anhedonia 149
animals
  and appetite control 212
  and bestiality 268–9
  bezoars 203
  cruelty to 99, 121
  and drug addiction 278
  fear of 66–7
  and personality 10
anorexia nervosa 104, 202–19
  and amenorrhoea 205, 206, 212, 215
  and depression 26, 218
  and the endocrine system 207
  and family 205–6, 208, 212, 215–17
  food faddists 206–7
  incidence of 205
  obsession with physical activity 209, 214
  physical effects 205, 214
  statistics 208, 214–15
  symptoms and signs 205
  treatment 214, 215, 217–19

antacids 192
anti-anxiety preparations 59, 71, 226, 229
anti-inflammatory drugs 192
anti-prostaglandin effect 192
antidepressants, ix, xi, xvii, 3–4, 9, 13, 19, 34, 38, 39, 41–9, 291, 310, 317
  and anxiety disorders 72
  and borderline personality 109
  and dysmorphobia 232
  and hyperactivity 295, 297
  and paranoia 87
  and schizophrenia 167–8
  side-effects 34, 45
  and somatoform pain disorder 229
  tricyclics, xiii, 22, 43, 45, 47, 48, 77, 81
antipsychotic drugs ix, xi, 37, 102, 129, 130, 167, 168–9, 176–7, 201, 226, 232
  atypical 123, 140, 147, 150, 152, 171, 173–4, 178–9, 201
  depot injections 177
  see also neuroleptics
antirheumatic drugs 200
antisocial personality disorders 52–3, 84, 94, 96, 98–104, 106, 121, 122, 227, 260, 270, 274, 309
anxiety disorders and phobias 52–81
  acute 55–6, 62, 66, 67
  and ADHD 293–4
  and an avoidant personality 111
  and borderline personality 108
  and bulimia 211
  children and 52, 305
  chronic 56–7, 63, 77
  and cognitive therapy 71, 77, 80
  and complementary medicine 81
  defined 63
  and dependent personality disorder 113–14
  and depression 2, 13, 15, 19, 27, 31, 46, 57, 188
  and drug abuse 274
  and dysmorphobia 230–31, 232
  and exhibitionism 250
  and fear 52–3, 61
  free-floating 57–60, 62, 81

and hypochondriasis 225
and loss of libido 235
medication 48, 71–2
and physical symptoms 54
and PMS 119
and schizophrenia 57, 132
and somatization disorder 227
and suicide 64
women and 53–4
see also panic attacks
anxiety neurosis 57
appetite
and anorexia nervosa 202, 205
and bulimia 212
and depression 12–13, 19, 26, 31, 188,
314
and drug abuse 280
and physical disease 213, 218
apprehension 53, 54, 55, 63
arachnophobia 67, 71
Aretaeus 1
Aricept (donepezil) 197, 198, 199, 200
arson 124
arterial disease, and impotence 235
Asperger, Dr Hans 301, 303
Asperger's disorder 300–303
aspirin 192
associations 165
attention deficit disorder (ADD) 284,
285
attention deficit hyperactive disorder
(ADHD) 284–97
and diet 288, 295–6
hyperactivity 284, 285, 286, 289, 290,
292
impulsiveness 284, 285, 289, 290
inattentiveness 284, 285–6, 289
origins 288–9, 295
and schizophrenia 293, 294
treatment 287, 294, 296–7
types 286
autism 298–303
autonomic nervous system 56, 61, 203
avoidant personality 84, 110–12, 113

baby blues 35

back pain, and somatoform disorder
222
barbiturates xi, 39
basal ganglia 191
Bayley, John xv
Beauchamp, Lord 308
bedwetting 303–4
behavioural therapy 102, 112, 114, 240,
296–7, 299, 303
Bell, Martin 80–81
'la belle indifférence' 95
benzodiazepines 71–2, 229, 294
bestiality (zoophilia) 268–9
beta-amyloid protein plaques 186–7
beta-blockers 71, 81
bezoars 203
Bhugra, Dr Dinesh, and Dr Alistair
Munro: *Troublesome Disguises*
xv–xvi
bipolar affective disorder 12, 15, 23, 49
birds, fear of 67
bisexuality
and paedophilia 257
and transvestites 265
Blair, Tony 310
Bleuler, Eugen 172
blood count 49, 177, 178
blood pressure 3, 32, 46
and anxiety 61
and Tacrine 198
body dysmorphic disorder *see*
dysmorphobia
borderline ambulatory schizophrenia
106
borderline personality disorder 84,
93–4, 96, 104–10, 113, 270
Borrow, Peter 165–6
brain
and Alzheimer's disease 186–7, 189,
198
blood flow 179
hypothalamic-pituitary axis 207
Lewy bodies 189–90
physical disease 2, 3
tumour 8, 9, 86, 130, 251, 260
and vascular dementia 182

brain damage
  and ADHD 288–9
  and anaesthesia 192, 193
  and autism 299
  and delirium 189
  and interleukin production 201
breathing
  and anxiety disorders 53, 54, 63
  and phobias 67, 68
  and somatization disorder 227, 233
bridges, fear of 66
Brighton bombing 78
Briquet, Paul 226, 227
Briquet's syndrome *see* somatization
  disorder
British Medical Journal 34, 35, 186
bromides xi, 39, 88
Browning, Angela 300
Browning, Robin 300, 301
bulimia nervosa 104, 203, 209–14, 218
  and amenorrhoea 210, 212
  causes 211–12
  and depression 26
  and family 211–12
  non-purging 210
  obsession with physical activity 214
  physical effects 213–14
  purging 210
bulimic behaviour 210
bullying 52, 120–21, 262, 282, 303, 305,
  321–4
burglary, aggravated, and indecent
  exposure 252
Burton, Robert: *The Anatomy of
  Melancholy* 1
Buspar (buspirone) 72
buspirone *see* Buspar
butane gas sniffing 281

calcium deficiency 214
cancer
  and anxiety 60
  and depression 7–8, 10, 32
  and the immune system 61
  and loss of appetite 218–19
  of the prostate 244

cannabis 273, 274, 276, 278, 279, 280
cantharides 263
carbamazepine *see* Tegretol
carbohydrate metabolism 214
cardiovascular disease
  and anxiety 61
  and psychotropic drugs 171
CART peptide 212
castration complexes 250, 258
Caverject 234, 244
central nervous system
  and antipsychotic drugs 177
  diseases 8
  reliance on neurotransmitters 4
cerebral arteries 200
cerebral cortex 187
cerebral tumours 8, 9, 196, 260
cerebrospinal fluid 196
chemicals, toxic 131
chest disease, and anxiety 60
chest pain
  and anxiety disorders 53, 54
  and depression 14
  in a panic attack 54, 66
  and phobias 67
  and somatoform disorder 222
Chevalier, Maurice 185
Child Guidance Clinics 289, 305
Childline 322
children
  ADHD 284–97, 297
  and anorexia nervosa 205
  and antisocial personality disorder
    99
  and anxiety 52
  and Asperger's disorder 301, 302,
    303
  autism 298–303
  bedwetting 303–4
  and borderline personality 109
  and bulimia 211
  and bullying 52, 121
  and cross-dressing 265–6
  and depression 32–3, 320, 321, 324
  and drug abuse 272, 281–2
  and exhibitionism 250, 252

and fear 50, 55
growth 297
highly intelligent 292–3
loss in childhood 50
and masochism 262–3
obsessive-compulsive disorder 73–4, 75, 114
and paedophilia 257, 258, 259, 260
and passive-aggressive personality disorder 117
physical/sexual abuse 260–61, 321
and pica 203–4
and post-traumatic stress disorder 79
and rumination 204
and sadism 263–4
and schizophrenia 137–9, 173
school refusal 303, 305, 306
soiling 303, 304–5
suicide in 320–24
truancy 303, 305–6
chlordiazepoxide see Librium
chloride 213
chloroform 281
cholinesterase 198, 199
chronic fatigue syndrome see ME
Clare, Professor Anthony xvi, 81
classification of mental diseases 2
claustrophobia 66
Cleopatra 94
climatic phobias 68
clobazam see Frisium
clomipramine see Anafranil
Clorazil (clozapine) 178, 179
clozapine see Clorazil
Coates, Tony 311–12
Coca-Cola 287
cocaine 64, 65, 88, 271, 278, 280
cognitive behavioural therapy 77
cognitive therapy 3–4, 19, 43, 44, 47, 49–50, 71, 77, 80, 81, 114, 123, 218
Coleridge, Samuel Taylor 271
community care workers ix–x
complementary medicine xiv, 31, 81
compulsions, see obsessive-compulsive disorder
concentration, lack of

and ADHD 285
and depression 21, 27
in post-traumatic stress disorder 80
The Concise Oxford Textbook of Psychiatry 172
constipation 202
and depression 32, 34, 45, 47
and soiling 305
conversion disorder 223–4, 226
coprophilia 269
coronary thrombosis
and an obsessive nature 115
and a Type A personality 115
cortisol levels 207
counselling, and depression 44, 50
COX-1 200
COX-2 200
COX-2 inhibitors 200
crime
antisocial personality disorder 98
crimes of violence 252
schizophrenia and 153
cross-dressing see transvestic fetishism
CT scan 10, 196
Cushing's syndrome 205
cyclothymia 7
cysteine 194

Dad's Army (television programme) 28, 56, 114
Dalí, Salvador 123
Dante Alighieri: Inferno 307
daycare centres 195, 197
De Quincey, Thomas: Confessions of an English Opium Eater 271
death
and depression 10, 21, 50
drug abuse and 280, 281
and grief 18
of a loved one, and suicide 313, 314
and panic attacks 63, 64
and post-traumatic stress disorder 78, 80
sudden cardiac 65
debt
and antisocial personality 101

and anxiety disorders 63
and depression 21
and suicide 313, 314
delirium 131, 181, 189
delusions
  of control 163, 165
  and dementias 185, 201
  and depression 17–18
  and drug abuse 275, 280
  grandiose 163
  paranoid 85, 87, 163
  and paraphrenia 168
  post-natal 37
  of reference 163–4
  and schizophrenia 127, 128, 131, 132,
    140, 146–9, 156, 160–61, 163, 164,
    170, 171, 176
  and schizotypal personality 144
  shared paranoid disorder 86
  and suicide 319
dementias 8, 34, 131
  Alzheimer's disease 3, 8, 27, 28, 33–4,
    131, 181, 193
  and delirium 189
  diagnosis 182
  and family 185, 197
  and folic acid 194
  and Huntington's chorea 190, 191
  Lewy body dementia 131, 167, 182,
    189–90
  and paedophilia 260
  and Parkinson's disease 182, 189
  pseudo- 34, 187
  vascular (multi-infarct) 182
  and vasodilators 200
dependent personality disorder 84,
  112–14, 224
depersonalization 81
depersonalization disorder 81
depression 1–51
  and ADHD 293
  adolescent 33
  age groups 32–4
  and Alzheimer's disease 181, 187–8,
    196
  and anorexia 26, 218

and anxiety 2, 13, 15, 19, 27, 32, 45,
  57, 188
and appetite 12–13, 19, 26, 31, 188,
  314
atypical 19–20, 22, 27, 40, 45–6, 48
and an avoidant personality 111
and bestiality 268, 269
bipolar affective disorder 11–14, 22
and borderline personality 106, 107,
  109
and bulimia 211
in carers 197
children and 32–3, 320, 321, 324
clinical 6, 8, 9, 175
and dependent personality disorder
  113–14
diagnosis 28–9
and drug abuse 274
and dysmorphobia 230
endogenous 20–21, 22
and environment 176
and exhibitionism 250
exogenous 22
and family 21, 29, 30, 36, 37, 318
and GAD 53
and genes 10–11, 21
grief 18–19
history of treatment 2–3
and hyperactivity 297
hypochondria 14, 48, 224, 226
and irritability 13, 16, 29, 33, 35, 188
and libido 41, 235
and loss 50
masked 31
and ME 228
medication 2, 16, 19, 38–40, 42–9, 62,
  315, 324
  see also antidepressants
in men 34–5
mild 16, 28, 29–30, 36, 47
moderate 16, 36
mood 1, 2, 6, 29, 35, 175
and narcissism 96–7
need for regular treatment xiii–xiv
neurotic 19
and obsessive-compulsive

personality 115
and paedophilia 260
and panic disorder 64
and paranoia 85–6, 87, 188
and Parkinson's disease 189
as part of another condition 7–8, 10
and passive-aggressive personality
117–18
physical origin 3
and PMS 119
predisposing factors 9–11
psychomotor retardation 13–14
and psychotic symptoms 17–18,
50–51
reactive 22
and schizophrenia 7, 9, 127–32, 138,
140, 148, 149, 150, 156, 167, 171,
172, 175, 177
and school refusal 305
and self-defeating personality
disorder 122
senile 33–4
severe (profound) 16–17, 28, 37, 38,
44, 49, 53, 107
sleeping pattern 12–13, 26–7, 314
'smiling' 314
and somatization disorder 227
and somatoform pain disorder 229
statistics ix, 1, 4
and suicide 14, 17, 21, 30, 33, 37, 47,
62, 312, 317, 318–19, 323
symptoms 1, 4, 7, 13–15, 19, 26, 29,
30–32
use of the term 5, 6, 7
in women 12, 33, 34–7
desensitization 69, 70
Desmopressin 304
Desmospray 304
Desmotabs 304
diabetes 4, 5, 43, 304
and anxiety 61
and impotence 235, 239, 245
Diagnostic and Statistical Manual of
Mental Disorders (DSM) 11, 16, 18,
19, 40, 42, 53, 62–3, 75–6, 77, 78, 84,
89–90, 92–3, 96, 97, 103, 108–9,

111–12, 113, 117, 118, 124, 131,
146–7, 222–3, 229, 234–5, 238,
248, 257, 267, 276–7, 286
Diana, Princess of Wales xvii, 84, 104–5,
123, 202, 209, 210
diarrhoea
and bulimia 213
and depression 32
diazepam see Valium
Dickens, Charles 56
diet
and ADHD 288, 295–6
and Alzheimer's disease 191, 194–5
and anorexia nervosa 207
irritable bowel syndrome 204
and MAOIs 46
diuretics 120, 210
divorce
and anxiety disorders 63
and depression 21, 50
and suicide 313
dizziness
and panic attacks 53
and phobias 68
dogs, fear of 67–8
donepezil see Aricept
dopamine 61
dothiepin see Prothiaden
dreams
and panic attacks 62
and post-traumatic stress disorder
78, 79
drug abuse 8, 271–83
after-effects 276
and antisocial personality disorder
99
the 'bad trip' 279
and borderline personality 108
and bulimia 211
causes 283
and delirium 189
and depression 320
the drug ritual 279
early symptoms 280
and family 274
giving up drugs 282–3

and loss of libido 235
and panic disorders 64–5
and paranoia 88
signs and symptoms of addiction
    276–7
and social phobia 70
and suicide 280, 319
drug advice service 282
drug toxicity 86
Dryden, John 144
DSM *see Diagnostic and Statistical
    Manual of Mental Disorders*
dysmorphobia (body dysmorphic
    disorder) 223, 230–33
dyspareunia 237
dysthymia 7

E numbers 288
'early morning waking' 13, 19, 27, 33,
    188
eating disorders 124–5, 202–19
    and depression 26
    and families 204–5, 219
    and fashion 213
    see also anorexia nervosa; bulimia
        nervosa; pica; rumination
echopraxia 168
Ecstasy 64, 88, 273, 277, 278, 280
Edronax *see* reboxetine
'EE' *see* 'expressed emotion'
Efexor (venlafaxine) 49
elderly people, and depression 33–4
electroconvulsive therapy (ECT) x, 3,
    47
emotionally unstable personality
    disorder 106
encephalitis 299
endocrine system 207
    disorders 8
enuresis *see* bedwetting
epilepsy
    and amphetamines 297
    and mania 49
    and SSRIs 47
erectile dysfunction *see* impotence
erogenous zones 243

ESN (educationally sub-normal) 292
ether 20
euthanasia 310, 317
evening primrose, oil of 120
Exelon (rivastigmine) 197, 198, 199, 200
exhibitionism 249–52, 256, 258
'expressed emotion' ('EE') 141–2, 174
eyesight, and antipsychotic drugs 177

faecal incontinence, *see* soiling
failure, sense of 13, 14
faintness
    and anxiety 61
    and tricyclics 47
false memory syndrome 259
family
    and ADHD 288, 290, 293, 296
    and Alzheimer's disease 181–2, 185,
        195, 196–7
    and anorexia 205–6, 208, 212, 215–17
    and antisocial personality disorder
        100, 101, 103
    and anxiety disorders 54
    and Asperger's disease 303
    and autism 298
    and bedwetting 303
    and borderline personality 109–10
    and bulimia 211–12
    and child suicide 321, 322–4
    and dementias 185
    and depression 21, 29, 30, 36, 37, 318
    and drug abuse 274, 281–2
    and eating disorders 204–5, 219
    and an obsessive-compulsive
        personality 115
    and paedophilia 259
    and paranoia 86
    and phobias 70–71
    and sadistic personality disorder 121
    and schizoid personality 90
    and schizophrenia 129–30, 132,
        134–5, 138, 140–42, 151, 152, 153,
        157, 173, 174–5
    and school refusal 305, 306
    of a suicide 308–9, 321, 323–4
    and transvestic fetishism 265

and truancy 305, 306
and voyeurism 267
family therapy 109, 218
Faverin (fluvoxamine) 48, 77, 78
fear 52–3, 54, 55, 62, 63, 66–7, 68, 70, 71,
    78, 111, 113, 128, 149, 256–7
    paranoid 87, 89, 131–2
female orgasmic disorder 236
female sexual arousal disorder 235
fetishism 249, 252–6
    transvestic 249, 264–6
fever 131
First World War 2, 78
5HT-reuptake inhibitors 19, 22, 34, 43,
    47, 49, 72, 77, 81, 109, 116, 123
flagellation 261
flashbacks 77–8, 79, 81
flashers see exhibitionism
flooding 71
fluoxetine see Prozac
fluvoxamine see Faverin
flying, fear of 66, 72
folic acid 194
folie à deux 86
food faddism 206–7, 214
food sensitivity 287, 288, 295
foreplay 243, 245
Freeman, P. S. and Gunderson, J. G.:
    'The Treatment of Personality
    Disorders' 89
Freud, Sigmund 2, 50, 89, 248
frigidity 249
Frisium (clobazam) 59, 72
frotteurism 249, 256
functional magnetic resonance
    imaging (fMRI) 179

GAD see generalized anxiety disorder
galactorrhoea 177
galantamine 199–200
gambling 124
gastric reflux 214
gastrointestinal changes, and anxiety
    63
gastrointestinal upsets
    and SSRIs 48

and Tacrine 198
Gauguin, Paul 123
gender identity disorders 248
General Practitioner 311
generalized anxiety disorder (GAD)
    53–4
genes
    and ADHD 288–9
    and Alzheimer's disease 191
    and antisocial personality disorder
        99
    and anxiety disorders 64
    and Asperger's disease 302
    and autism 298
    and character flaws 11
    and depression 10–11, 21
    and Huntington's chorea 191
    and schizophrenia 128, 134–5, 136,
        137
George V, King 308
gephyrophobia 66
glue-sniffing 281
Glueck, Dr B. C. 257
grandiosity 147, 153, 161–3
Gray, Dr John: Men are from Mars,
    Women are from Venus 58–9
Gregory, Ian and Smeltzer, Donald:
    Psychiatry 261
grief 18–19, 63
group therapy 89, 97, 102, 114
growth, and amphetamines 297
growth hormone 207
guilt
    and depression 13, 14, 18, 26
    and exhibitionism 249
    and frotteurism 256
    and paedophilia 259
    and schizophrenia 151
    and self-defeating personality
        disorder 122
    and voyeurism 267
Gunderson, J. G. 89

hallucinations
    auditory see voices, hearing
    and dementia 201

and depression 17–18
and drug abuse 275
hypnagogic 167
and Lewy body dementia 190
olfactory 167
and post-traumatic stress disorder 79
and schizophrenia 131, 132, 140, 148,
    149, 156, 170, 176
visual 167–8
Hardwick, Dr Peter 320
head banging/shaking 159
head injury, and Alzheimer's disease
    192
headaches
    and anxiety 56
    and depression 14, 31, 32
Health Education Authority 280, 282
Health of the Nation targets 310
heart
    heart rate/rhythm 53, 54, 60, 63
    sudden cardiac death 63
    and tricyclics 34, 45, 47
heart attacks
    and anxiety 61
    and drug abuse 273
    fear of 66
heart disease
    and anxiety 60, 61
    and homocysteine levels 194
    psychosomatic element 204
    and smoking 171
    and SSRIs 48
'heartsink patients' 81, 122, 220, 227,
    233
heights, fear of 66
hepatitis 196–7
hepatitis B 273
Hergé: *Tintin* 92
heroin 271, 273, 278, 281
heterosexual paedophiles 257–8
hippocampus 187
Hippocrates 223, 224
histrionic personality disorder 84, 93–6,
    105, 106, 113, 123, 224, 227
HIV infection 273
homocysteine 194

homosexuality 248, 308
    and impotence 246
    paedophiles 257
    and sexual masochism 262
    and transvestic fetishism 266
hopelessness 1, 4, 13, 14, 19, 26, 314,
    318, 321, 323
hormone therapy 240
hospital closure ix
Howard, George 55
HRT 191, 246–7
Hughes, Thomas: *Tom Brown's
    Schooldays* 120
Huntington's chorea 134, 135, 190–91
Huxley, Aldous
    The Doors of Perception 271–2
    Heaven and Hell 272
hyper-arousal 77
hyperactivity 213, 284–90, 292, 294–5,
    299
hyperexcitability 148, 289
hyperkinesis 284
hyperkinetic brain disorder 285
hyperkinetic reaction 284
hyperkinetic syndrome 284
hypersomnia 40
hypertension, and anxiety 61
hyperventilation 54, 68
hypnagogic states 62
hypnotic drugs 316
hypoactive sexual desire disorder *see*
    libido, loss of
hypochondria *see* hypochondriasis
hypochondriacal neurosis 223
hypochondriasis 14, 31, 33, 46, 48, 115,
    223, 224–6
    and schizophrenia 164, 225
    and suicide 319
hypochondrium 224
hypomania xvii, 6, 7, 9, 12, 22, 23, 48,
    106, 132, 211
    and bulimia 211
    characteristics of 25, 28
    and drug abuse 274
    and exhibitionism 252
    and mania 26

and schizophrenia 156
hypothyroidism 8, 220
hysteria *see* conversion disorder
hysterical neurosis *see* conversion
    disorder

imipramine *see* Tofranil
immune system
    and anxiety 61–2
    and eating disorders 214
impotence (erectile dysfunction) 177,
    213, 217, 235–6, 239–45, 247, 249,
    250, 255, 258, 267
impulse-control deficit 210
impulse-control disorders 124–5, 211
inappropriate social behaviour 153–6
incontinence, and anxiety 55, 63
indecent exposure *see* exhibitionism;
    frotteurism
indigestion
    and anxiety 56
    and depression 14, 32
Institute of Psychiatry 179
insulin coma 2–3
insulin production 207
interleukin 1, 201
introversion 89–90
iproniazid 3
IQ
    and ADHD 292
    and autism 300
irritability
    and antisocial personality 101, 103
    and anxiety 57, 77
    and borderline personality 108
    in children 320
    and depression 13, 16, 30, 33, 35, 188
    and drug abuse 280
    and hypomania 25
    and mania 24
    in post-traumatic stress disorder 77,
        80
irritable bowel syndrome 204

Janssen-Cilag 198, 199
jaundice 177

Jerry, M. B. 258
Jones, Dr Kingsley 17
Jones, Maxwell 103
junk foods 288

Kanner, Dr L. 298, 301
Kennedy Onassis, Jackie 95
kidney disease, and SSRIs 48
Kinsey, Alfred 253
Kipling, Rudyard 18
kleptomania 124
klismaphilia 269
'knight's move thinking' 165
Kraepelin, Emil 2

The Lancet 137
Larkin, Philip 212
late luteal phase dysphoric disorder
    118
laudanum 2
laxatives 210, 305
learning difficulties 292
Lewis, C. S.: *Surprised by Joy* 73–4
Lewy bodies 189–90
Lewy body dementia 131, 167, 182,
    189–90
libido
    loss of 13, 41, 48, 151–2, 168–9, 207,
        212–13, 217, 235, 239
    and Viagra 234
Librium (chlordiazepoxide) 71
limited symptom attack 63
'liquid coshes' 201
lithium 26, 49
liver disease, and SSRIs 48
liver failure 273
lobotomy 2, 3
LSD (acid) 272, 274, 279, 280

malingering 221, 223, 224
Manerix (moclobemide) 46, 49, 72
mania xvii, 6, 7, 9, 10, 12, 22, 23, 172
    and borderline personality 106, 107
    and bulimia 211
    characteristics of 23–5, 28
    and drug abuse 274

and exhibitionism 252
and hypomania 26
medication 49
and psychotic symptoms 17
and schizophrenia 131, 132, 148, 175
manic-depressive illness 2, 11–12, 49,
  51, 84, 131, 175, 308
MAOIs *see* monoamine oxidase
  inhibitors
masochism 121, 249, 259, 261–3
Masters and Johnson technique 240
Maxwell, Robert 82, 102–3
ME (chronic fatigue syndrome) 8, 228
melancholia 1
  senile 188
melancholic facies 1–2
memory
  autism and 300
  false memory syndrome 259
  repressed 259
memory loss
  and Alzheimer's disease 180–81,
    182–6, 193, 195, 199, 200
  benign 180–81, 182
  and depression 27–8, 34, 188
  and diagnosis of dementia 182
  and passive-aggressive personality
    disorder 117
  and somatization disorder 227
men
  anorexia 208, 213, 217
  antisocial personality disorder 93–4,
    98
  dependent personality 113
  depression 34–5
  exhibitionism 249
  fetishism 253
  frotteurism 256
  homosexual 246
  hypochondria 223
  obsessive-compulsive disorder 115
  over-enthusiasm for exercise 217
  paedophiles 258
  paranoid personality disorder 83
  schizophrenia 132
  solvent abuse 281

and suicide 316–17
  transvestic fetishism 264
  and Viagra 234
  voyeurism 266–7
meningitis 299
menopause 119, 132, 191, 247
menstruation
  and animal protein 206
  and antipsychotic drugs 177
  and appetite 202
  lack of 205, 206, 210, 212
  and somatization disorder 227
mental retardation 181
  and exhibitionism 250
  and hyperactivity 290, 294
  and paedophilia 260
  and psychotherapy 51
mercury amalgam 192
moclobemide *see* Manerix
Mohr, J. W. et al: *Paedophilia and
    Exhibitionism* 258
monoamine oxidase inhibitors
  (MAOIs) 46, 48–9, 72, 81
Monroe, Marilyn 94, 95
mood
  and autism 299
  baby blues 35
  and borderline personality 108
  change of mood in a child 323
  cyclothymia 6–7
  depression 1, 2, 6, 29, 35, 49, 175
  diurnal variation 13, 19, 29, 188
  drugs and 3, 280
  dysthymia 7
  hypomania xvii, 6, 7
  and psychotic symptoms 18
  and receptors 61
  and schizophrenia 129, 131, 132, 138,
    145, 149, 150, 156, 160, 171, 319
  standard 6
  swings 6, 7, 13, 41
Moran, Lord 15, 80
morphia 38
Morton, Andrew 105
MRI scan 196
multiple sclerosis 8, 10

Munro, Dr Alistair xv
murder
    and indecent exposure 252
    and paedophilia 261
    and PMS 119
    schizophrenia and 170, 171
Murdoch, Iris xv
MUSE 234, 244, 245, 247
myxoedema 221

Napoleon Bonaparte 104
narcissistic personality disorder 84,
    96–7, 106, 113, 121, 123, 259
narcolepsy 167
Nardil (phenelzine) 45, 46, 49
National Health Service (NHS) xviii,
    272
natural selection 10
necrophilia 261, 268
neologism 165
neurofibrillary tangles 186, 187, 190
neuroleptic drugs 93, 174, 201
    atypical xvii, 37, 88, 91, 177–8
    see also antipsychotic medication
neurological diseases 48
neurones 5, 186, 212
neuropharmacology 243
neurophysiology 243
neurosis
    anxiety 55
    hypochondriacal see
        hypochondriasis
    hysterical see conversion disorder
neurotic disorders, and cluster C
    personality disorders 84
neurotransmitters 4, 5, 61, 187, 198, 199,
    200, 212
nicotine see smoking
nicotinic receptors 199
Nightingale, Florence 123
nightmares 77–8
noradrenaline 5, 49, 54, 61
normal arousal activity patterns 248

obesity 205, 209
'obligate running' 217

obscene telephone calls 267–8
obsessional behaviour 38, 139, 157, 169,
    230, 254
obsessive-compulsive disorder (OCD)
    48, 51, 72–7, 84, 114–16, 205
oestrogen supplements 200
oestrogenic hormones 214
oestrogens 132
olanzapine see Zyprexa
Onassis, Aristotle 95
opium 38
organic food enthusiasts 207
orgasmic disorders (sexual
    dysfunction) 234–47, 248
Osler, Sir William 23, 29
osteoporosis 214
Oxford Textbook of Medicine 210,
    217–18

paedophilia 249, 256–61
Pagett, Nicola 84–5
painkillers 229, 230
palpitations
    and panic attacks 64
    and phobias 66, 67, 71
Pan 62
panic attacks 63–4
    and agoraphobia 63
    and air travel 66
    and atypical depression 19
    characteristics of 54
panic disorders 62–5
paraldehyde xi
paranoia
    and alcohol/drug abuse 88
    and antisocial personality 102
    and depression 85–6, 87, 188
    paranoid personality 84–9, 105, 106
    post-natal 37
    Princess Diana and 84
    and schizophrenia 85, 131–2, 144–9,
        152, 160, 161, 163, 164–5, 170
    and schizotypal personality 143–4
    shared paranoid disorder 86
paraphilia 124–5, 248–70
    defined 248–9

paraphilias not otherwise specified 249, 267–70
paraphrenia 85, 146, 168
parasuicide 312
parietal lobe 187
Parker, Dorothy 316
Parkinson's disease 8, 10, 177, 182, 187, 189, 190
Parnate (tranylcypromine) 45
paroxetine *see* Seroxat
Parstelin (tranylcypromine) 45
partialism 253–4
passive-aggressive personality 84, 116–18
passivity phenomena 157
pathological crying/laughing 48
pelvic surgery 245
perception impairment 17
personality 10–11, 82
   changes 186, 191, 196, 276
   Type A 115
personality disorders 48, 82–125, 225, 309
   and anorexia nervosa 205, 218
   characteristics 82
   cluster A 83
   cluster B 83–4
   cluster C 84
   and depression 8, 9, 21
   and drug abuse 274
   and exhibitionism 249
   and GAD 53
   and paedophilia 260–61
   and PMS 35
   and somatization disorder 227
   and suicide 318
Pert, Dr Candace: *Molecules of Emotion* 61
phenelzine *see* Nardil
phobias 53, 65–72
   and atypical depression 19
   and an avoidant personality 111
   cognitive therapy 69
   desensitization 69
   medication 69
   social phobia 66–8, 69, 70

physical peculiarities 231
pica 203–4
pituitary gland 207, 217, 304
plastic surgery 231, 233
Plato 223, 224
PMS *see* premenstrual syndrome
pop music movement 272
porn films 268
post-natal depression 35–6
post-traumatic stress disorder 77–81
potassium 213
The Practitioner 127
pregnancy 35, 36, 136, 137, 204
premature ejaculation 238, 249, 267
premenstrual syndrome (PMS) 118–20
   and suicide 35, 119
'primary gain' 224
progesterone 118, 120
promiscuity 99, 108
prostaglandins 200
prostate
   cancer 244
   enlargement 61
Prothiaden (dothiepin) 228
Prozac (fluoxetine) 34, 43, 45, 47, 48, 72, 77, 119
pseudo-dementia 34, 187
psyche 2, 20, 159, 168, 204, 207, 244, 279, 287
psychiatry
   and medical students 30
   and science 3
   view of psychiatrists xi
psychoanalysis 2, 3, 50, 68–9, 71
psychomotor agitation 27
psychomotor retardation 13–14, 27
psychoneurotics 106
'psychopath' 98, 102
psychopathy
   creative psychopaths 96
   early-warning signs 52
   pseudo-psychopathic 106
   see also antisocial personality disorder
psychosexual problems 205

psychosis
  organic 131
  and suicide 319
  toxic 8, 17
psychosomatic diseases 60–61, 203,
  204, 207
psychotherapy xiv, 3, 21, 47, 50–51, 71,
  75, 80, 81, 89, 91, 97, 109, 112, 123,
  125, 218, 232, 233, 252, 256, 270
psychotic behaviour
  and bestiality 268
  and depression 17–18
  and exhibitionism 250
  Freud and 2
  and a histrionic personality 96
  and paedophilia 257
  and paranoia 87
  and psychoneurotics 106
  and sadism 264
  and schizoid personality 91
  and schizophrenia 17, 129, 131, 153,
    172
  and schizotypal personality 93
  and suicide 316, 319
psychotic breakdown 153
  and drug abuse 274–5, 276, 279
  post-natal 37
psychotropic drugs 167, 171
pupils, dilated 63
purple hearts 287

quetiapine see Seroquel

Rantzen, Esther 8
rape
  and indecent exposure 252
  and voyeurism 266
Reagan, Nancy xv
Reagan, Ronald xv, 180, 183
reboxetine see Edronax
receptors 61, 200, 212
recovery phase, and suicide xii
renal failure 214
renal function 49
repressed memory 259
reserpine 3

resilience 15
respite care 195
reversible inhibitor of monoamine
  oxidase (RIMA) 46, 72
Risperdal (risperidone) xvii, 178
Ritalin (methylphenidate) 287, 297
rivastigmine see Exelon
Rothwell, Professor Nancy 200–201
Royal London Hospital 213
Royal Society 46
rumination 204

Sacher-Masoch, Leopold von
  261
SAD (Seasonal Affective Disorder)
  40–42, 44
Sade, Marquis de 263
sadism 249, 261
sadistic paraphiliac 121, 260
sadistic personality disorder 121
sadness 4, 7, 16
sado-masochism 261, 263
SANE 126, 151
Saunders, Ernest 34, 187–8
schizoaffective disorder 131, 175
schizoid personality 84, 89–91, 111, 123,
  302
schizophrenia 126–79
  abortive 106
  acute 172
  and ADHD 293, 294
  ambulant 109
  and anxiety 57, 132
  and Asperger's disease 302–3
  attitudes to 129–30
  borderline ambulatory 106
  and borderline personality disorder
    106–7
  catatonic 146, 147, 156–7
  children and 137–9
  chronic 172
  and class 128, 142–3, 176
  coping with 126
  and delusions 127, 128, 131, 132, 140,
    146–9, 156, 160–61, 163, 164, 170,
    171, 176

and depression 7, 9, 127–30, 132, 138, 140, 148, 149, 150, 156, 167, 171, 172, 175, 177
diagnosis 126–8, 138, 140, 175
disorganized 147
and dysmorphobia 230, 232
and environment 136, 137, 175–6
and exhibitionism 252
family 129–30, 132, 134, 140–42, 151, 152, 153, 157, 173, 174–5
features of 131–2
Freud and 2
and GAD 53
and guilt 17–18
and hallucinations 131, 132, 140, 148, 149, 156, 170, 176
hebephrenic 146
and hospital beds 126
and hypochondriasis 164, 225
in an immigrant population 133
inappropriate social behaviour 153–6
in inner cities 133–4
inter-personal relationships 132, 148, 174–5
introversion 89–90
latent 106, 109
life expectancy 171
living on the streets xiv, 153, 176
loss of libido 168–9, 235
and mania 131, 132, 148
medication xvii, 126, 140, 147, 150, 167–9, 172, 173–4, 176–9
and murder 170, 171
and paedophilia 260
and paranoia 82, 85, 131–2, 144–9, 152, 160, 161, 163, 164–5, 170
physical origin 3
pre- 106, 137, 294
prodromal symptoms 131
prognosis and treatment 170–79
pseudo-neurotic 106, 109
and psychotherapy 50–51
and psychotic symptoms 17, 129, 131, 153, 172
residual 147
risk of developing 132, 135–6

and schizoid personality 91
and schizotypal personality 91, 107, 143–4
simple 146
statistics ix, 126, 135–6, 172, 178–9
stigma of 127, 128, 130, 138, 150
and suicide 127, 140, 148, 168, 170–71, 318, 319
symptoms 144–70, 173
undifferentiated 147
schizophreniform disorders 130
schizotypal personality disorders 57, 84, 91–3, 106, 107, 113, 123, 130, 131, 133, 141, 143–4, 151, 169–70, 173–6, 225, 319
schools
expulsion 99
school refusal 303, 305, 306
Seasonal Affective Disorder (SAD) 40–42, 43, 315
Second World War 116
'secondary gain' 224
sedatives 201, 297
selective serotonin reuptake inhibitors (SSRIs) 43, 45, 47–8, 72, 77, 81, 238, 270
self-defeating personality disorder 121–2
self-esteem
boosting 69, 117, 252, 267, 317, 324
fragility of 321
loss/lack of 13, 15, 26, 44, 64, 70, 112, 215, 228, 229, 250, 259, 289, 290, 304, 305, 318
self-mutilation 108
Sell, L. 249, 309
senile dementias 86, 182
Serdolect (sertindole) 171
Seroquel (quetiapine) 178
serotonin 5, 61, 119
Seroxat (paroxetine) 48, 72, 77, 119, 238
sexual aversion disorder 235
sexual dysfunction *see* orgasmic disorders
sexual masochism 249, 261–3
sexual sadism 249, 263–4

sexually transmitted diseases, and
    anxiety 60
Shakespeare, William 94
    Hamlet 155
shared paranoid disorder 86
Shaw, George Bernard 117
    Pygmalion 91
Shaw, Professor Robert et al, eds:
    Gynaecology 35, 119
shell shock 2
Shire Pharmaceuticals 199
shopaholics 124
sildenafil *see* Viagra
SLE (systemic lupus erythematosus)
    220
sleep deprivation 86
sleeping patterns
    Alzheimer's disease 197
    in anxiety disorders 62
    depression 13, 27, 28, 31, 32, 33, 314
    in post-traumatic stress disorder 77,
        80, 81
    and schizophrenia 128, 149
Smith, C., et al, *Key Topics in Psychiatry*
    249, 309
smoking
    and Alzheimer's disease 191, 194,
        199–200
    and anorexia 212, 213
    and schizophrenia 171
Soames, Nicholas 84
social phobia 49, 68–70, 71, 72
'sociopath' 98
soiling 303, 304–5
Solian (amisulpride) 178
solvent abuse 281
somatization disorder 223, 226–8
somatoform disorders 220–33, 235
somatoform pain disorder 223, 229–30
sore throat
    and bulimia 214
    and depression 31
Soutter, Patrick 35, 119
Spanish fly 263
speech therapy 300
speed 287

Spencer Churchill family 205
Spencer-Paterson, Dr Arthur x, xi, 315
spinal cord damage 235, 239
Spironolactone 120
SSRIs *see* selective serotonin reuptake
    inhibitors
Stanton, Professor Stuart 35, 119
Stelazine 168
stereotyping 168
Stevenson, Robert Louis 123
Stone, Michael xvi
Storr, Anthony: *Sexual Deviation* 262
Straw, Jack 271
stress
    and free-floating anxieties 81
    and paedophilia 260
    and paranoia 88
    and psychoneurotics 106
    and schizophrenia 133, 140
strokes 196, 200
    and an obsessive-compulsive
        personality 115
    and anxiety 61
    and delirium 189
    and drug abuse 273
    and homocysteine levels 194
    and Type A personality 115
    and vasodilators 200
subconscious 2
substance abuse 281
substance use disorder 74
Sudbury, P. 249, 309
suicide/suicide attempts 104, 157,
    307–24
    and alcoholism 318, 319
    and anxiety 64
    and borderline personality 104, 105,
        106, 108
    in children 320–24
    and the Church 307, 309
    and depression 14, 17, 21, 30, 33, 47,
        64, 312, 317, 318–19, 323
    and drug abuse 280, 319
    and families 308–9, 321
    gender differences 315–16
    in history 307–9

holiday 314–15
and hypochondria 319
motivation for 313–14, 317, 318–19
myths about 311–12
and panic disorder 64
and personality disorders 318
and PMS 35, 119
psychiatric background of victims
    309
and psychotic behaviour 316
and the recovery phase xii
the risks 310, 311–13, 314, 318, 320–22
and schizophrenia 127, 140, 148, 168,
    170–71, 319
seasonal 315
and social phobia 69–70
statistics 312, 313, 317, 319
a taboo subject xvii, 309
systematic lupus erythematosus 220

Tacrine 197–8, 199
tardive dyskinesia 177
TCAs *see* tricyclic antidepressants
Tegretol (carbamazepine) 49
telephone chatlines 268
telephone scatologia 267–8
television, and hyperactivity 287
temporal lobe 187
tension 52, 57, 58, 73, 97, 111, 124, 142,
    145, 171, 176, 237, 249, 260, 261, 320
testosterone 61, 207, 240, 244
Thatcher, Margaret (later Baroness) 78
theft
    and antisocial personality 99
    and bulimia 211
thought block 165
thought disorders
    and depression 17, 44
    and drug abuse 275
    and schizoid personality 91
    and schizophrenia 130, 131, 132, 148,
        155–9, 165, 166, 173, 176
thought reading 148
thought withdrawal 158, 159
thought-broadcasting 157, 159
thought-insertion 158, 159

thyroid 49
thyroid disease 8, 9, 43
thyroid hormones 207, 210, 220, 221
thyroxine 210
tiredness, and depression 14, 19, 26, 28,
    31, 32
Tofranil (imipramine) xiii, xvii, 45, 77
toxic psychoses 8
tranquillizers 39, 71, 112, 294, 295, 299
transvestic fetishism 249, 264–6
tranylcypromine *see* Parnate; Parstelin
tricyclic antidepressants (TCAs) xiii,
    22, 43, 45, 47, 48, 77, 81, 229
truancy 303, 305–6
Tryptizol (amitriptyline) xvii, 45, 47, 77
tuberculosis x, 3, 60, 202
tumours 9, 10
    brain 8, 9, 86, 130, 196, 251
    and olfactory hallucinations 167
Turner, R. E. 258

unconscious 50
undifferentiated somatoform disorder
    223
unipolar affective disorder 12, 15
urophilia 269

vaginismus 236–7
valerian 2
Valium (diazepam) 71, 294, 295, 297
vasculitis 8
vasocongestion 20, 243
vasodilators 200
vasopressin 304
vegans 207
venlafaxine *see* Efexor
venous leak 20, 242, 245
vertigo
    and anxiety disorders 53
    and fear of heights 68
Viagra (sildenafil) 234, 241, 243–5,
    247
Victoria, Queen 50
Viridal Duo 234
Vitamin B6 120
vitamin deficiency 214

voices, hearing 129, 131–2, 160, 163,
166–7
  running-commentary voice 167
  second-person voice 166
  and suicide 140, 148, 319
  third-person voices 166–7
  thought echo 167
voyeurism 249, 266–7

Waugh, Evelyn: *The Ordeal of Gilbert
    Pinfold* 88
'waxy flexibility' 157
weakness
  and anxiety disorders 63
  and conversion disorder 224
  and depression 14
  and phobias 67
weight loss
  and anorexia nervosa 202–3, 205,
      213, 217
  and bulimia 210
  and depression 12, 13, 26, 31, 32
  and rumination 204
Wernicke's encephalopathy 3
Wilde, Oscar 83
Wilson, Harold 192–3
women
  Alzheimer's disease 185
  anorexia 208, 213, 215–17, 218

anorgasmic 240
and anxiety disorders 54
borderline personality disorder 93,
    106
bulimia 210
comfort eating 210
conversion disorder 223
dependent personality 112–13
depression 12, 33, 34–7
and exhibitionism 249, 252
GAD 53–4
histrionic personality disorder 93, 94,
    95
parasuicide 312
and sado-masochism 261
schizophrenia 132
self-defeating personality disorder
    121
somatization disorder 227
and suicide 313, 316
Thai 240–41, 242
and Viagra 234
Woolf, Virginia 176

Young Minds magazine 320

Zito Trust 126
zoophilia *see* bestiality
Zyprexa (olanzapine) xvii, 178